General Studies Series

MAINTENANCE MANAGEMENT MANUAL

WITH SPECIAL REFERENCE TO DEVELOPING COUNTRIES

UNITED NATIONS
INDUSTRIAL DEVELOPMENT ORGANIZATION

INTERNATIONAL
LABOUR ORGANISATION

Vienna, 1994

The designations employed and the presentation of the material in this publication do not imply the expression of any opinion whatsoever on the part of the Secretariat of the United Nations Industrial Development Organization (UNIDO) concerning the legal status of any country, territory, city or area, or of its authorities, or concerning the delimitation of its frontiers or boundaries.

Mention of the names of firms and commercial products does not imply endorsement by UNIDO.

The views expressed in this paper are those of the authors and do not necessarily reflect the views of UNIDO.

This publication has not been formally edited.

ID/SER.O/15

UNIDO PUBLICATION
UNIDO 94.1.E
ISBN 92-1-106292-6

LIST OF PRINCIPAL ABBREVIATIONS

AFNOR	Association Française de Normalisation (French Standards Institute)
AI	Artificial intelligence
AW	Aid welder
BC	Bin card
BMI	Building and infrastructure maintenance
BSI	British Standards Institution
CA	Acquisition cost
CIV	Civil works
CMMS	Computerized maintenance management system
CMPO	Central maintenance planning office
CORR	Corrective maintenance
CMWS	Central maintenance workshops
DC	Developing countries
DCD	Designation card
DIN	Deutsche Industrie Normen (German industrial standards)
DOC	Technical documentation
EDP	Electronic data processing
EFNMS	European Federation of Maintenance Societies
ELEC	Electricity
ENG	Engineering
ES	Electrical service
EWS	Electrical workshop
FM	Foreman
FMECA	Failure mode effects and criticality analysis
FTA	Fault tree analysis
GAR	Garage
GM	General maintenance service
HAZOP	Hazard and operability study
HRD	Human resources development
ICC	Inventory check card
ILO	International Labour Organisation
INS	Instrumentation service
INSTR	Instrumentists

INT	Interventions
IS	Issuing sheet
JO	Job order
JR	Job request
LAB	Laboratory for instrumentation
LO	Lathe operator
MA	Average monthly spare parts consumption
MAS	Mason
MEC	Mechanic
MET	Methods
MHAN	Material handling
MIS	Management information system
MISC	Miscellaneous
MM	Maintenance management
MMIS	Maintenance management information system
MO	Milling machine operator
MRS	Maintenance of rolling stock
MS	Mechanical service
MT	Machine tools
MTBF	Mean time between failure
MTTF	Mean time to failure
MTTM	Mean time to maintain
MTTR	Mean time to repair
MU	Management unit
MW	Metalworking
MWS	Mechanical workshop
N	Normal timetable
NT	New technologies
PC	Personal computer
PERT	Programme Evaluation and Review Technique
PL	Planning
PLC	Programmable logic controller
PO	Purchase order
PR	Purchase request
PREV	Preventive maintenance
PU	Purchase unit
QW	Qualified worker
R & D	Research and development
REP	Repair
S	Shift
SC	Store catalogue

SCC	Stock control card
SECR	Secretariat
SM	Stock management
SME	Small- and medium-scale enterprises
SMW	Sheet metalworking
SOAP	Spectrometric oil analysis program
SPMS	Spare parts management and stores
ST	Stores
STP	Standard spare parts
SUV	Standard unit value
SW	Specialized worker
T	Technician
TOR	Terms of reference
TPM	Total productive maintenance
TRIB	Tribology
TST	Toolstore
TWI	Training within industry
UNDP	United Nations Development Programme
UNIDO	United Nations Industrial Development Organization
UTIL	Utilities
W	Welder
WS	Workshop

TABLE OF CONTENTS

PREFACE

Developing countries have, in the last 10 years, been subject to profound economical, political and social changes. These changes, taken together with the increased pace of technological development, have forced developing countries into a process of adjustment of their production mechanisms which is without precedent.

Part of these mechanisms is the production equipment, for which increased demands for better performance are being made on a technical, human and management level.

It has been noted in developing countries that the equipment, in general, has not lived up to expectations because of poor reliability or total non-functioning.

One of the principal reasons for this is the very little emphasis that is put on the maintenance function and its management.

UNIDO and the International Labour Organisation have become increasingly aware of the importance of maintenance in social and economical development. This has caused them to undertake various programmes to improve the situation.

Drawing on their far-reaching knowledge and experience, the two organizations have established the need for a reference manual with a special focus upon problems of maintenance management in developing countries, aimed at executives as well as maintenance managers.

The aims of the manual are :

(a)   To make top management aware of the importance and benefits of good maintenance, and conversely of the problems and costs of neglecting the maintenance function;

(b)   To provide a professional guide for maintenance managers in medium-scale enterprises in developing countries to help them organize their maintenance departments and to implement efficient maintenance management systems.

The manual does not refer to any specific branch of industry : the object is to provide an overall approach to the maintenance management problems of the various process industries (continuous, batch, seasonal etc.).

As to the target group of readers, the manual can be especially helpful to general managers and maintenance managers by emphasizing the benefits which accrue out of well-organized maintenance systems, e.g. reduction in cost of spare parts stocks, increase in productivity, better energy and environment management, longer life cycles for machinery, lower failure rates, especially in continuous process industries etc.

Patrick De Groote (1945) is the author of the present manual. He graduated in 1971 from the State University of Ghent, Belgium, where he obtained a Master of Science in mechanical engineering. He worked as a maintenance engineer and maintenance manager in Algeria for many years and has carried out frequent missions as senior consultant in over 50 developing countries worldwide. As such, he has become a well-known figure on the international maintenance scene.

Special thanks are due to the following experts for their highly appreciated contributions to the manual : Professor Robert Leenaerts (Université catholique de Louvain, Belgium), who wrote a major part of section 1.2 of chapter I, entitled "Economic importance of maintenance"; Dirk Deceuninck (SQL Systems, Belgium), who wrote section 3.6 of chapter III, entitled "Computer-aided maintenance"; Claude Georges (DGS International, Belgium), who contributed to section 6.2.2 of chapter IV, entitled "Maintenance and new technologies"; and Maurits Depraetere (DGS International, Belgium), who wrote section 6.3 of chapter VI, entitled "Maintaining excellent maintenance".

INTRODUCTION

ABOUT THIS MANUAL

Is the introduction of a planned maintenance system worth the investment, and, if so, where should it begin in order to make it profitable as soon as possible ?

The objective of the maintenance function is to ensure the most efficient availability of production equipment, utilities and related facilities at optimal cost and under satisfactory conditions of quality, safety and protection for the environment.

To write a book on maintenance management in general and in developing countries in particular is a multi-faceted challenge.

First of all the subject is very wide-ranging, if the public that would be interested in it is considered : maintenance people and technical managers of equipment owners, decision-making centres of companies or economic sectors, professional federations, training organizations, financing and development aid organizations, consultants etc. It would be an illusion to think that this theme could be discussed thoroughly in the limited framework of this book, and be relevant to each one of the interested parties.

Then the subject is complex. It concerns many different fields : technique, organization, management, training, computerization, finance, personnel, economy etc. It would be an impossible task to deal, in depth, with each of these topics in one book.

Moreover, the subject concerns equipment of a very diverse nature : various sectors of industry, mining, energy, agriculture, earth-moving equipment, rail transport, road and water transport, hospital equipment, equipment for laboratories and training centres etc., in short all technical equipment as well as the related infrastructures.

Finally the subject deals with a difficult environment : that of developing countries. This alone is a subject for multiple studies.

This book is, of necessity, incomplete.

In addition, the authors wish to reply, though only partially, to the above question, asked so often by entrepreneurs of enterprises of various sizes in developing countries.

Just as there is no simple solution to a complex problem in mathematics, there is no miracle answer to the problems of maintenance.

It is on the basis of over 20 years of experience in the field of maintenance in developing countries, that several approaches of a practical and feasible nature are presented in this Manual.

By way of introduction, the executive summary is devoted to the problems of maintenance in developing countries, as they are being experienced today.

Then, since the intention is to address, primarily, the decision-making centres of the companies concerned, the case for maintenance is presented and its importance emphasized.

Chapter I highlights the challenge of maintenance and its close link with quality, productivity, safety and the protection of the environment. A second topic concerns microeconomic and macroeconomic considerations, including some relevant statistics.

Chapter II is devoted to the definition of the maintenance function, its activities, its levels and the different aspects of terminology.

Chapter III is especially intended for maintenance managers who are looking for a satisfactory method of introducing a planned maintenance system. Maintenance strategies, organization charts, personnel, data processing, maintenance planning, and computer-assisted maintenance management systems are the main topics. The chapter concludes with practical considerations on management tools for maintenance.

Preconditions for implementing the plan are dealt with in chapter IV. This chapter includes some practical advice for the introduction of a maintenance system in a new factory and for the restructuring of maintenance services in an existing one. It also gives ideas for a permanent maintenance promotion and awareness-raising campaign. How to execute a maintenance audit is explained in detail. The important topic of technical documentation is introduced, as well as the problem of spare parts.

Chapter V deals with the development of human resources in maintenance. It includes some considerations about personnel administration in relation to recruitment and salaries and incentives policies. Furthermore, an enterprise policy for human resources development for maintenance is described, including recommendations for practical actions.

Chapter VI is in fact a conclusion of the whole book. It offers reflections on how maintenance can face the constant technological evolution in terms of methods, techniques, training, control devices etc., and how an excellent level of maintenance can be kept up when a satisfactory performance has been reached.

At the end of each chapter there is a selection of related literature. A detailed bibliography for those wishing to pursue the subject further has been added to this Manual, as well as a glossary of over 400 current terms in the profession, including their French translation.

The appendices provide examples and illustrations to complete the text.

The Manual is not aimed at any economic sector in particular. A "horizontal approach" has been chosen, and it can be used as basic reading for all users of technical equipment. The industrial atmosphere which pervades the book is intentional. The notion "industrial maintenance", as presented here, should be understood as "maintenance as it is practised with professionalism in industry", and not solely as "maintenance of industrial equipment".

The authors hope that this work will contribute to the economic and social development of developing countries.

EXECUTIVE SUMMARY

1.   The present state of maintenance in developing countries

To date, the process of industrialization of developing countries has not been very successful, and maintenance of production equipment in particular has suffered.

Many industrial plants now stand idle, or are badly run, and cannibalizing of equipment often occurs. In addition, the finished products generally do not meet the standards of quality for which the plants were designed. Safety is in many cases insufficient, and the protection of the environment non-existant. The consumption of spare parts is far too high, the morale of personnel far too low. Overgeneralization should certainly be avoided (some plants clearly work better than others, and not all countries suffer from identical problems), but the trend, the overall pattern, is the same in the majority of developing countries. From over 500 maintenance audits in which the author was involved in about 40 developing countries, it was found that the technical availability of industrial equipment in the countries concerned did not average more than 30 to 40 percent. It was estimated that 80 percent of the unavailability was due to problems in the maintenance of the production equipment at all stages, that is, pre-investment studies, equipment design, construction, commissioning and operation.

When reviewing the facts which affect the maintenance of industrial plants in developing countries, five major problem areas can be distinguished :

(a)   The plant and its operation;

(b)   Maintenance organization and its management;

(c)   Material resources with special emphasis on technical documentation and spare parts administration ;

(d)   Human resources for maintenance ;

(c)   Financial constraints and problems which originate from the local infrastructure and logistics.

Each of these problem areas will be discussed in the following sections.

1.1.   The plant and its operation

The origin of many maintenance problems can be found at the design stage long before the start-up of installations.

These problems concern essentially the correct adaptation of the equipment to local conditions, the timely supply of all operation and maintenance documentation, the supply and installation of machines, spare parts, training of personnel, technical assistance and after-sales service.

In pre-investment studies, the maintenance factor (budgets, human and material resources) is rarely considered.

The terms of reference and technical specifications deal particularly with the production machines and related infrastructures. They never deal in detail with factors such as standardization, maintainability, technical documentation, spare parts, training of maintenance personnel and maintenance organization.

During contractual negotiations, maintenance specialists are usually absent. The requirements of maintenance are rarely taken into consideration, on the one hand because of the lack of consciousness of this problem and on the other for reasons of increase in costs. The extra cost that maintenance requirements entail is in no relation to the benefit - both financial and moral - gained from a well-running plant.

Regarding the design of the factory, too little attention is paid to the factors which determine its success, such as location, size, availability of energy and water, adaptation of the equipment to the environment (human and climatic). This is often due to the fact that the designer is not a plant operator himself.

Regarding the choice of adequate technology for developing countries, this does not imply the use of outdated technology. Not enough attention is paid to the following factors which have a direct influence upon maintenance : distance between the plant and the suppliers, communication deficiencies, severe climatic conditions, lack of a suitably qualified workforce, operational errors occuring more frequently than in the traditional industrial context, etc.

Regarding the strategy of construction of a plant it has been found that the auxiliary services (workshop, stores, offices etc.) are built after the installation of the production machines. Precious time is therefore lost in training and organizing maintenance.

From the organizational point of view, the various maintenance sections are planned too late (in many cases just before start-up), leading to insurmountable problems during the start-up period.

The supervision of plant construction by the customer concentrates almost only on the erection, commissioning and start-up of the production machines and buildings. The control of services rendered by the supplier in the field of technical documentation, spare parts or training for maintenance is for instance usually neglected.

Finally, the construction planning rarely being respected, the contractor tries to make up for the delay by accelerating the remaining work at the end of the construction. This concerns mainly electricity, instrumentation and automation. It has been found that these measures lead to points of neglect and error in vulnerable installations, where maintenance will have to face most of the problems after start-up.

1.2.   Maintenance organization and management

The lack of organization and management of maintenance particularly concerns the following topics :

(a)   maintenance is generally underestimated and its productive function is not recognized :

(i)   Insufficient attention is paid to the requirements of maintenance in the pre-investment and engineering phases, as well as during the purchase of equipment;

(ii)   There is a belated preparation of the maintenance function when implementing new projects (human, material and financial resources);

(iii)   The maintenance department is placed in a minor position in the organization chart;

(iv)   Insufficient financial means are allocated to maintenance;

(v)   Not enough qualified personnel are assigned to the maintenance department;

(b)   The maintenance organization chart is unclear or ill-defined and the job descriptions are non-existent;

(c)   The following functions are non-existent or underestimated : methods, programming, job preparation, scheduling, maintenance management and stock administration;

(d)   Data collection is insufficient, information flow is not defined, and there is no feedback nor evaluation of data;

(e)   The internal organization is neither established nor formalized

(f)   The aspect "maintenance management" is practically non-existent :

(i)   Definition of a maintenance concept;
(ii)   Establishment of a management steering-chart;
(iii) Selection of maintenance ratios;
(iv)   Establishment of failure and reliability statistics concerning the production machines;
(v)   Analysis of breakdowns (nature, frequency, direct or indirect effect);
(vi)   Assessment of maintenance costs and life-cycle costs;
(vii) Dosage of periodic, condition-based and corrective maintenance in maintenance planning;

(g)   Maintenance methods are underdeveloped and the consequence is :

(i)   No maintenance planning;
(ii)   Incomplete lubrication planning;
(iii) No job preparation and no work analysis;
(iv)   No machine history files;
(v)   Poor selection of parts or raw material to be stocked;
(vi)   Impossibility of indicating or respecting a delay;
(vi)   Training in maintenance organization, methods and management intended for engineers and foremen is not covered in detail, and often does not correspond to the real needs.

1.3.   Material resources

The material resources which are necessary for maintenance practice are the technical documentation, spare parts, tools, measuring and control instruments, machine tools and workshop equipment. The lack of technical documentation and spare parts is especially serious and is explained below.

(a) Technical documentation

Experience has shown that the lack of adequate technical documentation is one of the most serious handicaps which developing countries are faced with in maintenance practice, in particular : no detailed drawings, poor operation and maintenance instructions, unclear instructions for removal, no adequate spare-parts lists and insufficient failure diagnosis check lists. Drawings - if presented at all - are general assembly drawings instead of manufacturing drawings or exploded views. These are just a few of the most common problems. Incomplete or inadequate technical documentation (in a language which is not commonly used in the country, bad translation, unclear descriptions, fuzzy figures etc.) jeopardizes fault diagnosis and repair. In addition, the safety of the plant environment and personnel is in danger. Poor documentation makes the training of the personnel impossible, and it causes serious problems in the reordering of spare parts in a situation where the local manufacturing of parts is often barely possible.

(b) Spare parts administration

The shortage of spare parts is a permanent nightmare for those responsible for the operation and maintenance of an industrial plant in a developing country. First, the installations are more vulnerable, if compared to the operating conditions in the industrialized countries for which the plant was designed. Extreme differences in climate and other physical aspects of the region, human shortcomings, lack of technical support from the local dealers and, very often, the selection of unsuitable equipment cause the consumption of spare parts to be much higher than in industrialized countries. In addition to this, the purchasing of spare parts creates enormous problems: the identification and codification of the parts is an almost impossible job due to language or information barriers and the technical documentation is generally incomplete, unclear and inadequate. Other dilemmas exist in finding a supplier for one or another spare part. It is a fact that parts which cost only a few cents can cause the shut-down of a complete plant, whilst the supplier may not be interested in selling such a small part. Then, the problems of international currency transfer; customs clearance procedures and the sometimes unbelievable bureaucracy slow down a commercial transaction up to a point where the whole business grinds to a halt. When the parts finally do arrive, they are often stocked under unsatisfactory conditions, and maintenance stores are very poorly organized, so that there is a risk that parts may be lost forever.

1.4. Human resources for maintenance

Apart from the lack of motivation and attitude towards the job, the technical qualifications and experience of the local workforce are generally very low, particularly amongst the craftsmen and foremen. A lack of technical training and, above all, the absence of an industrial tradition and experience mean that maintenance practice becomes problematic.

The magic word "training" does appear in capitals on each and every construction contract. However, this training is often reduced to some totally inadequate study tours all over the world. Training is given to the higher-level personnel of the future plant or is only limited to operating personnel, while the foreman who has to maintain and repair the equipment later on is neglected.

Employment conditions for the few technically educated people are generally very poor. Most of the time the organization in which they have to function is inadequate and there is a high turnover of personnel. An extremely difficult and delicate problem is the mental attitude of the workers (personnel) towards the requirements of a modern, industrial society. People who have demonstrated technical capability in a rural environment are not necessarily able to master the additional collective disciplines required in every industrial pattern of society. There is little motivation, originating from the lack of accepted industrial traditions or incentives policies. Many of the workers do not even understand the importance of their jobs in the framework of the company. How could discipline be expected from a greaser (a very important function) when he does not have any understanding of the need for lubrication? The personnel problems can sometimes be solved by so-called "technical assistance". However, it is very difficult and expensive to bring in experts from developed countries. This cannot be considered as a permanent solution, but only as a possible palliative for the time being.

1.5. Financial constraints and other problems

Generally, maintenance budgets are set too low, or they do not exist at all. There is hardly any cost control, and cost data, as far as they can be obtained from the manufacturer, are not appropriate for a developing country. The scarcity of hard currency makes the reordering of necessary spare parts in sufficient quantities nearly impossible. The other problems - i.e. infrastructure and logistic support problems - may be summed up briefly. Housing and supply problems, power cuts, telecommunication problems, bureaucracy, inefficiency : all these are elements which make maintenance of technical equipment in developing countries extremely difficult and frustrating.

2. Improving industrial development by adequate maintenance

The question now is to establish what can be done to alleviate this situation. Can the specialized personnel needed be found? Can the spare parts be acquired in alternative ways? Can these, and the other problems discussed here, be solved satisfactorily? If so, how? Experience has shown that if the necessary action is taken in a correct and suitable way at different levels, the conditions of industrial development in developing countries can be improved considerably. This, however, requires an individual approach for each project, in which the specific local maintenance and operating conditions are examined very closely indeed. The people involved in this kind of work must operate together as a disciplined team, which in turn requires them to have ample experience concerning the operating and maintaining of industrial plants in situations typical for developing countries.

2.1. Design and acquisition of equipment

Plants which are built in developing countries often have not been designed to be run in a developing country environment. They have been designed for quite different operating and maintenance conditions, for different levels of personnel, for substantially different climates, assuming the unhampered availability of spare parts, in short, for a completely different set of requirements. This dominant reason shows where to find the key to the solution of the problems of industrial development. People who thoroughly know what it is to run and maintain a plant in a developing country have to be involved. They also must take part in the specification of requirements, in the design and in the setting-up of the plant.

As long as the construction of copies of plants from developed countries in developing countries continues with, in addition, a very small amount of complementary training, and with inadequate technical documentation, the problem will never be solved; it will only become worse. A completely new strategy has to be adopted, the aim of which must be to ensure a total transfer of technology, which would not only allow the production of the products in the quality and volume required, but which would also include the measures needed to ensure that the plant be maintained in such a way that it can continue to operate for an acceptable period of time.

Though adequate technology is only a part of the new strategy, it is an important one. It is this technology which enables the equipment to be operated and maintained correctly under the local human and physical circumstances. Great care must be taken with highly sophisticated machines, because it is extremely hard to maintain them under the particular conditions generally prevailing in these countries. This requirement does not mean a need for old technology but rather for a strong, modern, proper technology adapted to the environment. In this respect there is also a need for the setting-up and strict application of national and in-plant standards.

It cannot be too strongly emphasized that attention must be paid to maintainability at the time of design of the equipment, to accessibility and to easy repair, in other words, to the action measures needed in order to prevent the plant from being a total failure.

Detailed specific technical specifications concerning maintenance should be part of the general specifications, in particular : for the technical documentation; for spare parts delivery; and for training of maintenance personnel.

2.2. Maintenance organization and its management

Adequate organization can relieve the substantial personnel problems which exist. Detailed elaboration of job descriptions is necessary down to the lowest level. A simple but strict organization should be applied and a clear maintenance concept should be defined.

Concerning the maintenance organization at plant level, centralized maintenance systems have proven to be the most effective at least for small- and medium-scale enterprises. Nevertheless centralization or decentralization remains a difficult question in organization techniques, which will be dealt with in a separate chapter (3.2.3). Clearly defined organization charts should be flexible enough in order to follow the growth of the plant. Separation into different services of the different trades involved reduces the problem of lack of highly qualified multi-skilled personnel. However, great care must be taken with European-oriented pre-established organization charts. It has been seen in the past that these generally are unsuitable in a difficult industrial environment. A tailor-made chart should be compiled for each individual plant.

Regarding the paperwork, it should be done in mind that data collection and information systems are an absolute necessity if the maintenance department is to be managed correctly. However, they should be as simple as possible with routings well defined.

Finally, because of the importance of the maintenance function in the production process, the maintenance manager should be on the same hierarchical level as the production manager. A maintenance strategy should be defined and should result into a corporate maintenance management master plan. This should include policies concerning subcontracting of maintenance work and renewal of equipment. A sound maintenance planning system should be introduced, based on regular inspections. Condition monitoring and preventive maintenance programmes should be established, including a rigorous lubrication programme.

Appropriate maintenance management systems should be introduced and the full commitment of the general management is an absolute precondition for the success of maintenance.

2.3.   Material resources

(a) Technical documentation

It is imperative that clear and complete technical documentation in the correct language suitable for inexperienced people is provided. In this respect the following requirements must be covered :

(a)   Detailed machine drawings with comprehensive description of all components;

(b)   Complete manufacturing drawings for parts subject to wear and also for important parts, thus enabling their local manufacture;

(c)   Detailed operation and maintenance instructions;

(d)   All electrical, hydraulical, pneumaticetc. drawings and diagrams with a list of components;

(e)   Detailed spare parts lists, together with exploded views, in which all standard parts are designated according to an international standard, and in which the manufacturer's parts code number is taken up for all specific parts;

(f)   Fault-finding check-lists, with necessary instructions for corrective action;

(g)   Detailed removal and reassembling instructions;

(h)   Complete information about preventive maintenance to be carried out, including lubrication instructions.

Moreover, close attention should be paid to important topics such as storage and conservation techniques for documentation, its uniform presentation, its internal management in terms of filing, dispatching, updating etc.

(b) Spare parts

When new equipment is acquired it is absolutely necessary to insist upon the provision of a realistic supply of spare parts. Not only of the expensive and bigger parts which hardly or never break down, but also of the small vital parts which cost next to nothing, but without which the plant comes to a standstill. As has been said before, detailed technical specifications concerning the delivery of spare parts should be included in the contract with the equipment suppliers. At plant level, a sound spare parts control system should be established. All spare parts should be given a code number according to an in-plant coding system, based on systematic identification and designation of the parts.

Special attention should be paid to the adequacy of the storage facilities and to the collection of concrete data concerning the consumption of the parts.

Finally, the possibility of local manufacturing of spare parts should be promoted. To this end the approach must anticipate the necessary equipment and facilities.

2.4. Development of human resources

The training of maintenance personnel is not easy, especially at the level of foremen. When new equipment is ordered, the supplier should be involved very closely in the training of maintenance personnel. This should be detailed in the technical specifications in the contract. Special attention should be paid to the possibility of "on-the-job" training during the erection phase (especially for the qualified workers and the foremen).

The engineers should also be trained during the erection phase, particularly in maintenance management methods used abroad. Study tours to equipment manufacturers can have very satisfactory results.

Regarding in-plant training, apprenticeship methods must be used in order to raise the workers to an acceptable level of qualification. Small nuclei should be established, composed of a foreman, a qualified worker and an apprentice. This formula has already produced very interesting results. In-plant training at foreman level is much more difficult. Here, well-selected technical assistance should be sought. A judicious selection of the foreman trainee, with on-the-job assistance by an expert has also led to very good results in the past. The same remarks are valid for the training of engineers. Special attention should be paid to training in maintenance management systems.

2.5. Maintenance cost control

The cost of plant operation, and especially the cost of maintenance, should be estimated realistically, a requirement which is very often neglected when evaluating industrial projects. The principle that local subcontracting is cheap is a fallacy. It should be made clear that for the slightest repair or modification, an extremely expensive expert may have to be called in from abroad.

Control of the cost of maintenance requires the setting-up of an appropriate cost control system. The first thing to do is to install a data collection system, which shows the exact origin of the costs. As was stated earlier, this necessitates the establishing of an adequate maintenance organization, including the procedures and forms for the information flow.

Only when this condition has been fulfilled can a correct maintenance budget be established. This gives the maintenance manager better ammunition with which he can support his arguments in discussions with the general management. Maintenance cost statistics are much more important in a developing country than in an industrialized country. They greatly support the argument when trying to obtain the necessary funding. Only too often it has been observed that general managers in developing countries look only at the direct costs of maintenance at the shop-floor level, completely ignoring the fact that other factors also have to be considered in the calculations, such as production and quality loss due to poor maintenance, or negative effects on safety and environment.

2.6. Setting-up of a national maintenance strategy for developing countries

To solve the maintenance problems in developing countries as mentioned above, coordinated and coherent actions far beyond plant level are necessary. A continuous dialogue between the economic actors and the authorities is indispensable. Decision makers should be made aware of the micro-economic, macroeconomic and social importance of maintenance. Moreover, a rapid exchange of information and experience between plants or countries is a necessity. This is the reason why a national maintenance strategy is recommended for each individual developing country. This must not be limited to the industrial sector only, but must concern other users of equipment, such as agriculture, public works, telecommunications, health and transport.

Existing experience in establishing such strategies in developing countries has proven that encouraging and satisfactory results can be obtained within a reasonably short term. A national maintenance strategy can be established through a support structure, such as a national maintenance institute whose objectives and tasks would be the following :

(a)   To promote maintenance at the national level;

(b)   To convince every level of the population of the importance of maintenance for the sake of the country's economy;

(c)   To coordinate maintenance improving activities in plants, ministries, institutions etc.;

(d)   To advise the ministries and planning departments;

(e)   To advise and provide technical assistance for new projects, which include an important equipment component;

(f)   To advise and provide technical assistance to equipment users (plants, workshops, transportation organizations, etc.);

(g)   To organize training and information sessions, seminars, workshops etc. for maintenance staff;

(h)   To exchange information and experience between equipment users in their own country and in other countries;

(i)   To promote local manufacture of spare parts;

(j)   To promote operational research in maintenance engineering and management;

(k)   To participate in international maintenance events.

Selected literature

AUTHOR	PUBLISHER	TITLE
SAKAKIBARA S.	UNIDO 1973	APPLICATION OF MODERN PRODUCTION MANAGEMENT TECHNIQUES TO MAINTENANCE FROM THE DEVELOPING COUNTRIES POINT OF VIEW
ILO	ILO 1987	IMPROVING MAINTENANCE IN DEVELOPING COUNTRIES : THE ILO APPROACH
UNIDO	UNITED NATIONS, NEW YORK 1976	INTRODUCTION TO MAINTENANCE PLANNING IN INDUSTRY UNITED NATIONS, NEW YORK, 1976
UNIDO	UNITED NATIONS 1971	MAINTENANCE AND REPAIR IN DEVELOPING COUNTRIES
UNIDO and VDMA	UNIDO DUISBURG (Federal Republic of Germany) - 1970	MAINTENANCE AND REPAIR IN DEVELOPING COUNTRIES

> # CHAPTER I
> # THE CASE FOR MAINTENANCE

1.1.   The challenge of maintenance

The profitability and efficiency of the investment in production equipment can only be guaranteed if the following components are ensured :

(a)   Productivity in terms of quantity, price and continuity;

(b)   Quality of final product or of service offered;

(c)   Safety of functioning and personnel;

(d)   Protection of the environment.

Well-run maintenance is a prerequisite for attaining these objectives. This is summarized in the chart below.

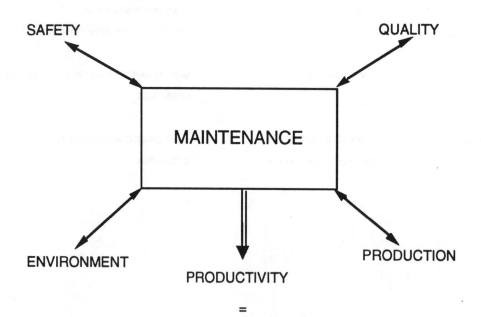

EFFICIENCY OF INVESTMENT

Maintenance is facing a colossal challenge as it must deal with complex influences which are often opposed on it, such as :

(a)   Physical : natural degradation, wear and tear of components, climatic influences;

(b)   Technical : in constant evolution, increasing introduction of new technologies;

(c)   Human : development of human resources, systems to motivate personnel, social and cultural evolution;

(d)   Organizational and managerial : new approach to management, development of computer aided systems;

(e)   Economic and financial : fluctuations in world economy, evolution of the national economy, speeding up of privatization and rapid disengagement from the public sector, uncertain availability of financial resources, in hard currencies as well as in local money;

(f)   The market : requirements of national and international markets which are in constant change.

Finally, because it has always been underestimated and often unaccepted as a major component of profitability, maintenance is placed on an inferior hierarchical level in many companies. This position is hardly favourable to dealing with the above-mentioned problems.

To sum up, the greatest challenge for maintenance, in particular in developing countries, is to a great extent a search for suitability and adaptability to a complex environment and vice versa.

1.2.   Economic importance of maintenance *

1.2.1. Introduction

The expenditure which a manufacturing plant, a company or a country has to make in order to ensure an "acceptable" level of maintenance of its production equipment is generally totally underestimated. Clear and objective data are hard to produce because a common terminology and standard accounting system do not exist. On the basis of several surveys which have been carried out in this field during the past 20 years and of the author's personal research and experience, it can nevertheless be concluded that this expenditure is tremendous.

---

*   By R. Leenaerts (Université catholique de Louvain, Belgium), except for the figures mentioned in
     sections 1.2.2 and 1.2.3 and the failure patterns in section 1.2.3.

1.2.2 Macroeconomic considerations

On the macroeconomic level in industrialized countries, the following figures highlight the importance of maintenance :

(a)   In France, maintenance of production equipment costs 15 percent of gross national product (GNP). On average, maintenance costs rank from 12 to 14 percent of GNP for European countries;

(b)   According to the European Federation of Maintenance Societies (EFNMS), every year 125 billion United States dollars (US$) are spent in the western part of Germany for the maintenance of production equipment;

(c)   An average of 5 percent of their turnover is spent annually by 165 of the most important industrial companies in the United States in order to maintain their production equipment;

(d)   In 1990 about 2 million people were employed in maintenance in approximately 350,000 industrial enterprises in Western Europe, according to EFNMS.

EFNMS has undertaken several surveys in selected European countries. Maintenance costs on a yearly basis have been compared to the turnover of enterprises, producing the figures listed below (1990) :

Country	Percentage of turnover	
- Ireland	5.1	
- Italy	5.1	
- Netherlands	5.0	
- Belgium	4.8	
- France	4.0	
- United Kingdom	3.7	
- Spain	3.6	(statistics of the author)

The economic development of many less industrialized countries has been hindered by the imbalance between the purchasing of appropriate technology, including modern technology and equipment, and its rapid premature deterioration. This imbalance is found at all levels (industry, transport, communications, infrastructure, roads, railways etc.), which indicates that it deals with a mechanism which has not been mastered, even partially, by political parties and Governments of the countries concerned. The result is, on a macroeconomic level, that the ratio of profit to investment is not only inferior to what it should be, but will become close to zero very soon.

The inevitable consequence of this state of affairs, which has aggravated the situation even more in the developing countries, is that over the last 20 years, developing countries have had recourse to huge loans with international financing organizations. They are now burdened by foreign debts of such importance that this has become one of the major headaches of the International Monetary Fund. It is therefore imperative to reduce investment drastically and, in the case of future borrowers, to demand a concrete proposition regarding objectives and profitability.

The problems involved in this situation include multiple axes of approach, among which maintenance can be a determining impetus towards a solution. By applying the principles of maintenance judiciously, systematically, rapidly and generally, it is possible to improve the use of production tools in the short and medium term. Over the longer term a better profitability of future investments can be assured in line with the required feasibility of projects.

Maintenance can be used at management level as a means to improve economic performance, thus helping to solve, if only partially, the problem of foreign debts. Undoubtedly this is a most optimistic conclusion if the gloomy prognostications that are made concerning the subject of development policy are taken into account.

1.2.3. Micro-economic considerations

The maintenance of production equipment obviously has an impact at the micro-economic level, as illustrated by the figures given below.

In a study published by "FACTORY" in the early 1970s, the maintenance costs of 687 United States industrial enterprises accounting for 53.8 percent of United States industrial production were analyzed. The following figures were obtained :

(a)   Yearly maintenance cost in relation to turnover : average of 4.12 percent, with a maximum of 17.5 percent;

(b)   Maintenance cost in relation to fixed assets : average ranging from 2.73 percent to 13.8 percent, with a maximum of 17.13 percent;

(c)   Maintenance cost in relation to production cost : average ranging from 1.38 percent to 12.15 percent, with a maximum of 15.86 percent.

Studies made in Japan in the mid 1970s gave 4 to 6 percent for the ratio of maintenance cost to fixed assets.

As to the maintenance cost compared to the production cost, most surveys gave a range of between 6 and 12 percent.

A survey made in 50 industrial enterprises in the metalworking, food, chemicals, textiles and paper industries, by the Centre for Inter-enterprise Comparison in the United Kingdom in 1977 resulted in the following interesting figures :

Ratio	Percentage range
Maintenance costs/fixed assets	5.3 to 26.7
Maintenance costs/turnover	2.5 to 9.8
Maintenance costs/added value	3.8 to 16.2
Maintenance staff/total plant workforce	4.7 to 16.9

In 1979 W.J. Marcelis carried out several surveys in various European industries. He compared maintenance costs with replacement cost of production equipment and obtained 7 percent on average. For buildings he obtained 1.5 percent.

A survey made by DGS INTERNATIONAL in 1987 in three industries in Europe (cement, mechanical construction, petrochemicals) resulted in the following figures:

Ratio	Percentage range
Maintenance cost/fixed assets	7.98 to 16.4
Maintenance cost/added value	10.44 to 12.9
Maintenance manpower cost/	
total maintenance cost	41.75 to 58.35
Cost for spare parts/	
total maintenance cost	17.02 to 44.64
Maintenance staff/	
total plant workforce	5.6 to 65.7

To be able to understand the place maintenance occupies in management, reference should be made to the life cycle and investment curve in relation to the equipment.

(a) Life cycle of equipment

For each item there is the phase of design followed by manufacturing or construction. Then comes the period of use which is limited because of progressive deterioration, and finally, after a certain time, total breakdown and scrapping.

Of equal importance is its economic evaluation. So whatever the equipment, the same life cycle as represented in figure I is used as a base. It clearly shows the quantity of goods or services produced annually.

The two areas in the diagram can be explained as follows: AC corresponds with the design (AB) and manufacturing (BC) phase of equipment, and CF represents the operation phase (exploitation).

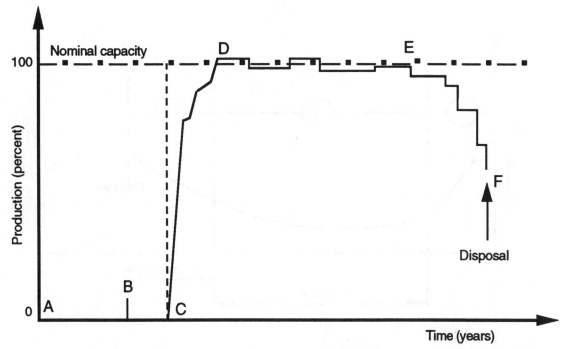

Figure I. Life cycle of production equipment (goods or services)

AC corresponds to zero production, whereas CF starts with a section CD (which corresponds to the start-up of the equipment), DE represents the operation phase and EF descends in relation to gradual obsolescence. Disposal (scrapping) is at point F.

It is essential for the manager to understand that an equipment life cycle generally follows the same pattern. To ease understanding, the failure rate λ has been introduced. This shows the number of breakdowns that occur during a certain period of time, e.g. weekly or monthly.

This failure rate obviously depends on the age of the equipment. This can be seen in figure II , shawing the "bath-tub curve", which is one of the existing patterns of failure.

Classically, curves of this sort can be divided into three zones. In zone 1, during the start-up, a decreasing number of hidden construction failures, errors of assembly and running-in problems cause breakdowns. In zone 2, exploitation, the failure rate is stabilized by controlling wear and tear, but this inevitably will increase. Zone 3 is characterized by an accelerated failure rate due to age followed by obsolescence of the equipment.

Any curve of that type will obviously stop suddenly if the equipment is discarded (disposal or scrapping) or rebuilt.

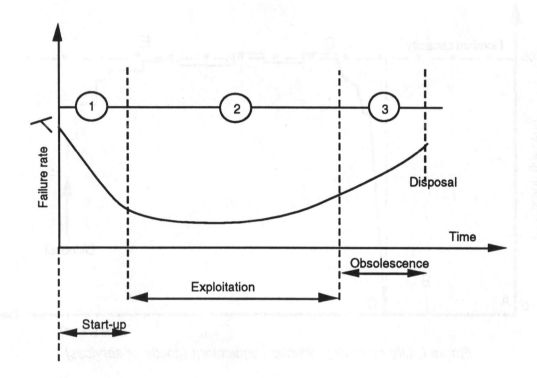

Figure II. Failure rate in relation to age of equipment.

Other failure patterns exist, as shown below :

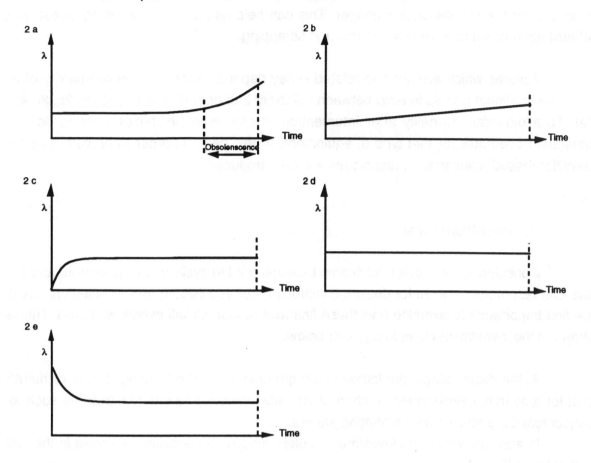

Pattern 2a shows a constant evolution which ends in an accelerated rate as in pattern 2.

Pattern 2b shows a steadily increasing failure rate with some acceleration (no identifiable wear-out age).

Pattern 2c shows a low failure rate when the item is new, and the failure rate increases suddenly to a constant level.

Pattern 2d shows a constant level of failure during the whole life cycle.

Pattern 2e starts with a high infant mortality (burn-in period) which drops to a constant level.

The pattern of figure II (bath-tub curve) is characteristic for electromechanical (classical) equipment. The more complex the equipment becomes the more the pattern evolves towards 2d and 2e (electronic, hydraulic and pneumatic equipment).

Knowledge of the age-related patterns of an item (e.g. figures II, 2a and 2b) is important for the maintenance manager. This can help him decide whether to invest in a rehabilitation or whether to proceed towards scrapping.

Failures which are not age-related - they depend usually on the complexity of an item - have almost no relationship between reliability and operating age (pattern 2c, 2d and 2e). To avoid infant mortality after intervention, it can even be decided not to do any scheduled overhauls for that type of equipment. In this case, in order to prevent failures, condition-based maintenance techniques will be introduced.

(b) Investment curve

Considering the close relationship between the life cycle of the equipment and the financial resources involved for design, construction (or acquisition) and exploitation, it is of the first importance to examine how these financial resources will evolve with time. This is shown in the investment curve in figure III below.

At the design stage, the following are grouped under the heading "pre-investment": cost for research, development, in short all activities involved before construction, such as project feasibility studies and marketing studies.

In absolute value, pre-investment is often modest; its evolution is shown in the first part of figure III.

As to the actual investment, this is the capital needed to acquire not only the equipment, but also all the resources necessary for its exploitation.

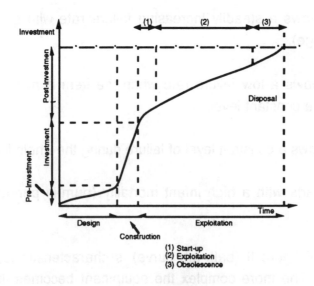

Figure III. Investment curve for production equipment (for goods or services)

Compared to pre-investment, the investment is of a completely different nature: it is much bigger. Because of this, once the decision to invest has been taken, it is in the interest of everyone to start up the equipment as soon as possible. This is the part close to the vertical as shown in figure III.

A logical consequence of this approach is to define post-investment as the invested amount during exploitation, which is necessary to ensure correct running of the equipment.

Post-investment obviously includes not only all maintenance costs, but also those incurred for improvements or modifications (small engineering and construction work) carried out on the equipment in order to assure technological updating. In figure III the post-investment occupies a place stretching over a normally long period. The curve shows, at first, a rapid increase in relation to the start-up of the equipment. This increase then attains a more or less constant rate, which means an efficient use of the equipment in practice. The final increase of the curve is due to the obsolescence of the equipment, thus resulting finally in the stoppage of exploitation and post-investment.

It should be noted that, because of the long period post-investment covers in total, a considerable financial value is represented, sometimes exceeding that of the actual investment.

1.2.4. Analysis of maintenance costs

Given that the results obtained from the exploitation of equipment are evaluated on the basis of the criteria of economic profitability, these same criteria must be used to evaluate the performance of maintenance. The analysis of maintenance costs is consequently a priority.

There are two sorts of costs : direct and indirect. The indirect costs are also called failure or non-efficiency or breakdown costs. The former are those which determine the actual maintenance practice and are all quantifiable. The latter correspond to production losses (and their harmful consequences) resulting in the unavailability of equipment due to insufficient maintenance. This explains why they are called failure costs. Certain of them can be quantified, others not.

(a) Direct maintenance costs

An overview of current direct maintenance costs is given below.

Regular maintenance costs. These are the first to be taken into consideration because without them the equipment could not even be put into service. An example is the technical inspection of a vehicle or a pressure resistance test for a boiler.

Labour costs. Their existence is obvious, but it is a good idea to remember that the relation between maintenance workforce / production workforce is in constant growth and the same applies for the related costs. Workforce in this sense signifies personnel at all levels : qualified workers, supervisors, cadres (engineers), management.

Equipment costs. The initial supply of equipment and tools is considered as part of the investment. Nevertheless, it is often necessary to acquire supplementary machines, tools or instruments after start-up. These must be charged to post-investment.

Consumables, spare parts and stock management costs. It is evident that maintenance work and the use of spare parts and consumables go together; their costs must be included in the list of direct maintenance costs. Moreover, storage costs and stock management costs are important and should also be noted.

Training costs. However satisfactory the qualifications of the workforce are, technological developments make it necessary to carry out training and upgrading on a regular basis. The costs of these training programmes are direct maintenance costs.

Subcontracting costs. These costs occur when, for technical or economic reasons (and if justified by correct equipment management), it is decided to partially subcontract maintenance work, as is happening more and more : the total amount of these costs (contract price increased by costs for internal preparation and follow-up) must be included in the direct costs.

Costs for technological updating. Although strict administration, accountancy and fiscal regulations cannot provide a clear picture, it is customary that costs of technological updating (for instance through minor engineering work executed by the maintenance department) are part of the direct maintenance costs. It is wise to verify the legality of each case, especially when taking into account the geographical location of the equipment.

These are the major elements which make up the inventory of direct maintenance costs. Each of them are quantifiable and, in a well-run business, are quantified. They are the basis for an erroneous and widespread presumption that maintenance is cost-making, unprofitable and in the end, a luxury.

(b) Indirect costs (failure costs)

Indirect or failure costs are caused by a deficiency or lack of maintenance and are a financial loss sustained by the company. A complete analysis of them is almost impossible to do with great precision because the majority are not directly measurable. This is not a reason though to ignore them. The following nomenclature does not pretend to be exhaustive. It merely brings to light the most important causes of failure costs and illustrates the way they should be approached.

Reduction of production or service. Here, financial loss immediately comes to mind. When equipment breaks down or is out of order due to failure, nothing is produced, thus profit is lost. When calculating the hours of breakdown, there is a way to evaluate the corresponding loss rigorously and, in nearly every case, to establish that it represents a much higher failure cost than could have been imagined in the first place, certainly far higher when compared to other costs.

Alteration in the quality of production or service. Insufficient maintenance does not only cause sudden breakdowns; it can have more insidious consequences such as a slowing-down of activity (thus a reduction in production), and an alteration in the quality of the goods produced or the services rendered. Sooner or later this will be felt commercially, either in a reduction of prices - hence profit - or in dissatisfied customers resulting in loss of part of the market.

Delivery delays. The corollary of the two preceding situations is temporary disorganization and consequently a delay in delivery time. Normal contracts will provide penalties for delivery delay which represent a supplementary failure cost.

Depreciation costs. It is well known that the depreciation of equipment is calculated on the basis of its lifetime. If this time is abnormally reduced because of breakdown the financial burden of depreciation will augment. The difference compared with that of the original depreciation plan has to be added to the list of failure costs.

Work accidents. Maintenance has the responsibility of ensuring not only the well running of the equipment, but also the safety of functioning, in particular the safety and protection of personnel. It is not surprising to note that statistics have proven that there is a direct link between quality of maintenance and the number of work accidents. Purely from the economic point of view, this link is covered by an insurance policy whose premiums will be much higher if safety is poor : thus a failure cost, less obvious, but which nevertheless should be considered.

Alteration in the work place and environment. What has been said about personnel is the same for the workplace and even to a certain extent the environment. There can be serious consequences caused by maintenance deficiencies if the workplace is alterated (buildings, useful surfaces), and if problems occur related to environment (i.e. increased pollution). Experience has shown that no comparison exists between the modesty of direct maintenance costs, which should have been consented to in order to prevent these situations, and the seriousness of damage done. The corresponding failure costs are thus comparatively high.

Demotivation of personnel. Unreliable equipment is caused by insufficient maintenance which in turn is the cause of incidents and repeated problems. This will demotivate the personnel. Obviously demotivated personnel will become completely disinterested in the production equipment and maintenance, so that a vicious circle ensues which does not end in measurable failure costs, but which can nevertheless cause a total work stoppage.

Company Image. The preceding factors concerning deficiencies of maintenance culminate in a negative image for the company. The cost of reducing this image has to be added to the preceding failure costs.

These are the principal indirect maintenance costs. They are not all of equal importance nor measurable, but must all be given close attention by management. Some (e.g. loss of production) are perfectly measurable, whereas others can only be evaluated by estimated imprecise factors. Whatever the case, the evaluation of failure costs (however approximate) is highly recommended and should always be part of management thinking.

1.2.5. Setting economic objectives for maintenance

Maintenance management involves establishing the objectives and determining and controlling the resources to carry them out. There are two principal aspects relevant to the economy :

(a)   One would involve combining direct and failure costs in order to obtain the best financial result possible - it is, in fact, a minimalization problem, as shown below;

(b)   Another would involve integrating direct and failure costs in the economic calculation of depreciation so that the life-cycle cost of the equipment also produces the best possible financial result.

Concerning the resources to be foreseen, short- and long-term management should be considered separately. The former involves the setting-up of a maintenance policy, whereas the latter is concerned with actual strategy.

(a) Minimization of direct costs and failure costs

Maintenance activity could be imagined as being measured by a "rate of maintenance" indexed from 0 to 1, where 0 corresponds to no maintenance at all and 1 to a rate of maintenance which keeps the equipment in perfect working order with a perfect remedy always on hand to deal with eventual breakdowns. These extreme situations are utopian, but allow the problem to be placed in its economic context.

Concerning the direct costs, it is easy to see that an increasing "rate of maintenance" results in increasing costs. Figures which illustrate this function do not exist, but it has been established that the growth is more or less exponential.

In figure IV the evolution of direct costs is represented by a constant growth curve identified by index (1).

Likewise, the rate of maintenance has an effect on the failures, and thus on the indirect costs. Failure costs appear as high as the maintenance rate is weak, which means that they should be considered as a decreasing function of the rate. In figure IV this function is represented by the decreasing curve (2). The same applies for the physical depreciation cost (curve 3 in figure IV).

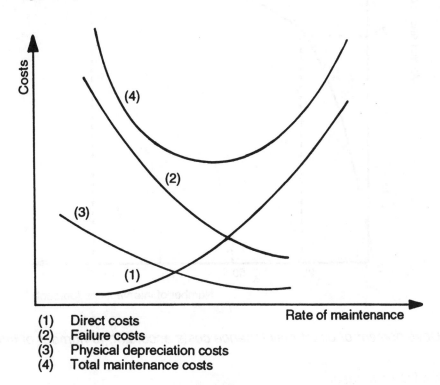

(1)   Direct costs
(2)   Failure costs
(3)   Physical depreciation costs
(4)   Total maintenance costs

Figure IV. Development of maintenance costs.

Considering direct costs together with indirect costs/failure and depreciation costs is a basic approach of management. It is obvious that a better financial result cannot be obtained by only reducing the direct costs to a minimum. Both costs must be dealt with together. The sum total of both costs can be easily determined by the combination of curves (1), (2) and (3) in figure IV. The result is shown in curve (4). The latter curve denotes that the management of maintenance and of post-investment is not a question of reduction but of minimalization, which is shown in the diagram as a minimum of total maintenance costs.

In other words, an optimal rate of maintenance exists which suggests fundamentally a new approach. Maintenance is no longer carried out to keep the equipment running at any cost, but so that the highest profit can be obtained at minimal cost.

As to the rate of maintenance, the important point is to be conscious of the existence of a minimal cost of maintenance and to manage accordingly. Pareto's law, well known by maintenance people, as reflected in figure V, shows that 75 percent of the maintenance budget is necessary for only 25 percent of the operations. This means also that 75 percent of direct costs of maintenance correspond to 25 percent of failures.

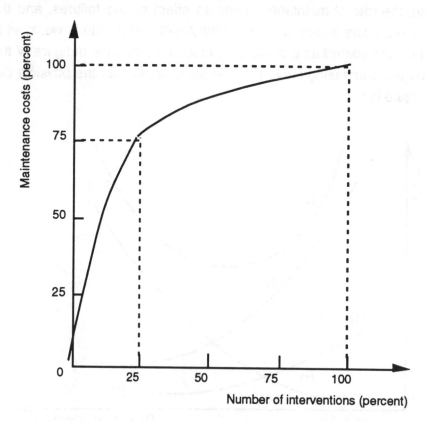

Figure V. Development of direct maintenance costs according to number of interventions

(b) Optimization of the equipment life cycle

Determining the lifetime of production equipment is a key question for management. In simple terms the question is : at which moment should the equipment be scrapped and replaced so that production can continue in the most economical way.

There are several methods of calculation, and probably the simplest is to make a yearly evaluation of the decrease (ΔI) in the inventory value of the equipment, and the total costs (C) of maintenance. By dividing the figure ($\Delta I + C$) by the cumulated running hours (H) a value is obtained which, after having decreased to a minimum over the first few years, will increase due to the progressive and rapid acceleration of maintenance costs (see figure VI).

In theory, the optimal lifetime is fixed by the value of the abscissa which is to the right of the minimum. This conclusion - rigorously theoretical - has to be judged with a certain flexibility because it is influenced by the more or less easy valuation of the inventory. Equally, it can be modified by the financial conditions governing the economic situation. In any case, the determination of the optimal lifetime must be obtained by calculating the financial costs taking into account rates of interest and inflation.

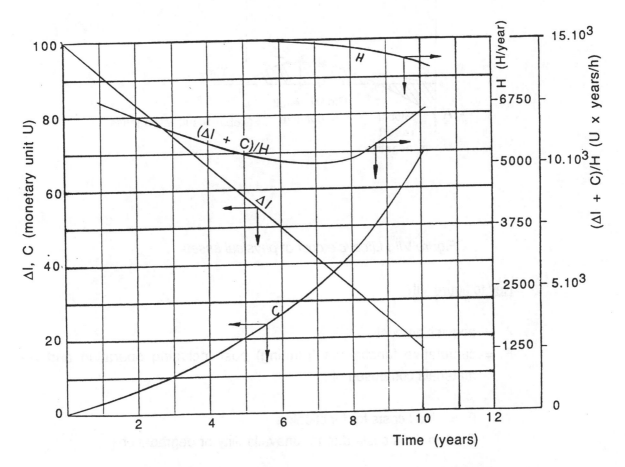

Figure VI. Graphical determination of the optimal lifetime of equipment

A second approach to the same topic by introducing management criteria in terms of the payback period and the optimal renewal time, comparing global costs of purchase, maintenance and running with the cumulative income during the lifetime, is given in the following figure VII (from F. Boucly and A. Ogus Le management de la maintenance; edited by the Association Française de Normalisation (AFNOR), 1987) :

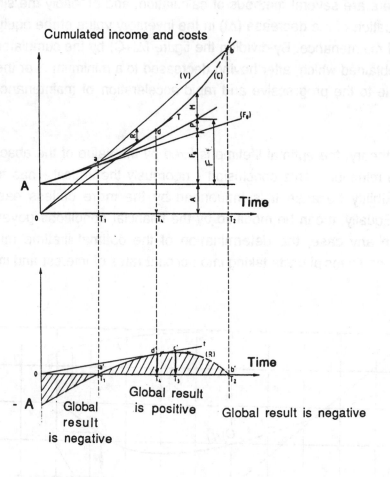

Figure VII . Lifecycle cost of physical assets

Key to figure VII

A = acquisition cost
F = cumulative functioning (running) cost including operation and raw materials composed of :

F = fixed costs for functioning
P = various costs due to unavailability or degradation

M = cumulative maintenance costs

C = total cost

V = sales (income)

Total exploitation result over the lifetime is (all cost/income considered in constant monetary value) :

$$R = V - (A + F + M)$$

T1 : global result is 0 - this is the payback period

T3 : global result is maximum

T4 : global result per time unit is maximum. This is the maximum efficiency of the investment.

The optimal age for replacement is T4 when the global cost per time unit is minimum. It should be mentioned that the above considerations still are influenced by the depreciation policy (long or short-term), the fiscal system of the country etc.

In chapter III this strategy is dealt with once again as part of an overall maintenance management master plan.

1.2.6. Evaluation of the efficiency of Maintenance

The methodology of evaluation of the efficiency of maintenance consists of two stages : first, a budgetary evaluation including budgetary control and the calculation of the differences stated. Second, efficiency is estimated through comparison of benefit and total production and post-investment cost.

(a) Budgeting

Budgetary evaluation is predictive, and is usually done on the basis of one of the previous situations of which the use has shown its validity.

(i)   Direct costs

Evaluation is done on the basis of the terminology proposed in section 1.2.4 (a) above.

Apart from some rare unexpected situations, direct cost budgeting can be done with high precision, and its forecast from year to year is repetitive.

All these costs are available based on the figures obtained from maintenance administration; their influence is conditioned by the exactitude of the unit prices, the quantities and the allocations, in other words, by the rigidity of this administration.

A rigorous and detailed procedure for budgeting is only necessary in relatively exceptional cases when direct maintenance costs represent an important part of the added value. In other cases, it is sufficient to evaluate the costs of the main operations by regrouping the smaller interventions under one separate and global budgetary position for each cost centre.

(ii) Failure costs

Referring to section 1.2.4 (b) above, failure costs are influenced by a number of parameters, some of which cannot be measured. Consequently, it is difficult to budget them. Fortunately, management principles allow a more general approach through a forecast of the following indirect costs : production loss (profit loss); salaries and wages of non-utilized production personnel; and depreciation cost of the equipment during the period of inactivity.

(b) Budgetary control

Budgetary control is done on the basis of accountancy of real post-investment expenses and the downstream calculation of profit losses. It measures the differences which exist between actual results and previous budgetary evaluations. This control highlights the necessity of forecasting maintenance work and allows for the improvement of future budgetary evaluation.

For easy comparison, the differences for each cost allocation which has been done to set up the forecast have to be measured. The resulting information is then linked to successive fixed deadlines (for instance every month) which represent a basis for the appreciation of the maintenance policy and of post-investment strategy.

(c) Economic ratios

Because of its importance, post-investment should be evaluated on a regular basis.

As maintenance is a logistic function integrated into a production process, its efficiency is hard to appreciate in absolute value. Consequently, appreciation parameters cannot be chosen amongst operational figures. They must be defined in relative values, i.e. through ratios.

Maintenance will be evaluated through some internal performance indicators which are discussed further in chapter III, section 3.7 (management tools for maintenance).

Selected literature

AUTHOR	PUBLISHER	TITLE
BLANCHARD B.	TEROTECHNICA ,1979	LIFE CYCLE COSTING : A REVIEW
FILE T.W.	BUTTERWORTH HEINEMANN , 1991	COST EFFECTIVE MAINTENANCE - DESIGN AND IMPLEMENTATION
HOLUB J.	UNIDO, 1970	CONSIDERATION OF PROBLEMS IN DESIGN OF INSTALLATIONS, MAINTENANCE AND REPAIR IN DEVELOPING COUNTRIES
MILLS P.	CONFERENCE COMMUNICATION - 13TH NATIONAL MAINTENANCE MANAGEMENT SHOW, LONDON ,1990	THE STRATEGIC LINK - MAINTENANCE COSTS VS RISKS
MOSS M.	MARCEL DEKKER INC., NEW YORK, 1985	DESIGNING FOR MINIMAL MAINTENANCE EXPENSE
MOUBRAY J.	BUTTERWORTH HEINEMANN, OXFORD,1991	RCM : RELIABILITY-CENTERED MAINTENANCE
PARKES D.	MAINTENANCE ENGINEERING ,1971	MAINTENANCE COST COMPARISONS

┌───┐
│   **CHAPTER II**   │
│   **WHAT MAINTENANCE REALLY IS**   │
└───┘

2.1.   Definition of maintenance function

2.1.1. Introduction

Maintenance is the function which should ensure the most efficient availability of production equipment, utilities and related facilities at optimal cost and under satisfactory conditions of quality, safety and protection of the environment.

AFNOR (Association française de normalisation [French Standards Institute]) defines the maintenance function as "everything that is necessary to enable equipment to be maintained, or restored to a specified condition or a fit state to perform a given service" (Standard X60 - 010). The DIN Standards Institute (Germany) defines maintenance as "the series of measures designed to maintain equipment or to restore it to the condition originally intended, and to ascertain and evaluate its present condition" (DIN 31051). The British Standards Institution (BSI) defines maintenance as follows (BS 3811) : "the combination of all technical and associated administrative actions intended to retain an item in, or restore it to, a state in which it can perform its required function."

Maintenance was long considered to be a subordinate function, entailing an inevitable waste of money. There was a tendency to lump it together with troubleshooting and repairing machinery that was subject to wear and obsolescence.

In actual fact, the maintenance function involves far more than that: it has become an unceasing effort to achieve a compromise between "technical-economic" and "technical-financial" considerations. Yet there is still a long way to go before its productive function is fully understood. For that to happen, people have to realize that maintenance has not merely the function of a "partner" of production : it is quite simply a _sine qua non_ of production.

Its relation with equipment performance is a matter of integrated strategy at the senior management level. As such, the maintenance function becomes a **total integrated physical assets management** function.

The whole cycle starts in fact long before start-up of the equipment. The stage of pre-investment studies for instance is of the utmost importance for the choice of the equipment both in terms of life-cycle cost as well as in terms of appropriate performance. The design stage however will have to take into account topics such as reliability, maintainability etc. If all this is underestimated from the very beginning by senior management, it could be said that future quality and production losses are in fact built in. Moreover, in the absence of an efficient maintenance management system, once the equipment is in operation, tremendous problems arise concerning productivity, quality, respect of production schedules, environment and safety.

To do its job successfully, maintenance calls for sizeable and correct human and material resources. It cannot become a dumping-ground for personnel who do not have, for instance, the necessary skills for manufacturing, and it must receive an operating budget so that it can perform as more than just an emergency repair service. Planning, organization, and a methodical work approach are essential for managing maintenance activities. Appropriate programmes are required in vocational training, as well as in research and development (R & D) in the field of maintenance, to enable the quality of work to be continually enhanced. Only then will the maintenance function be able to play its prime role fully in productivity, finished product quality insurance, personnel safety and environmental protection.

2.1.2. Objectives of maintenance

The main objectives of maintenance are as follows :

(a)   To optimize the reliability of equipment and infrastructure;

(b)   To see, on an on-going basis, that equipment and infrastructure are kept in good condition;

(c)   To ensure prompt emergency repair of equipment and infrastructure so as to secure the best possible availability for production;

(d)   To enhance, through the study of modifications, extensions, or new low-cost equipment, the productivity of existing equipment or production capacity ;

(e)   To ensure operation of equipment for production and for the distribution of energy and fluids;

(f)   To improve works safety;

(g)   To train personnel in specific maintenance skills;

(h)   To advise plant management as well as the production, purchasing, engineering and R&D departments in the fields of acquisition, installation and operation of machinery;

(i)   To play an ongoing role in guaranteeing finished product quality;

(j)   To ensure environmental protection.

2.1.3. Terminology

Maintenance is put into practice through 3 forms, namely :

(a)   Design-out maintenance;

(b)   Preventive maintenance, which includes systematic (periodic) maintenance and condition-based maintenance;

(c)   Corrective maintenance.

In chart form, the layout is as follows :

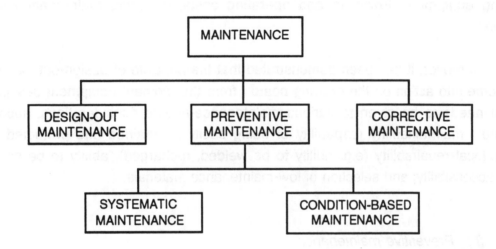

Maintenance can also be divided into planned and unplanned maintenance (or scheduled and unscheduled). The following chart highlights the relation to the previous chart :

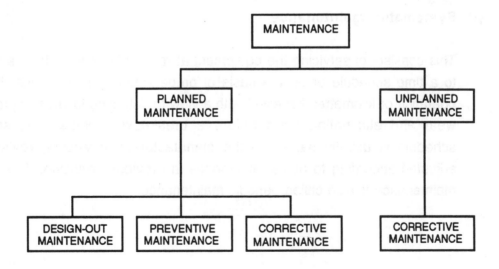

(a) Design-out maintenance

This is also known as plant improvement maintenance or as adaptive maintenance, and its object is to improve the operation, reliability or capacity of the equipment .

This sort of work usually involves studies, engineering, construction, installation, start-up and tuning.

The improvements which are brought about must always contribute towards reducing equipment downtime and operating costs, including maintenance costs in particular.

Moreover, it has been demonstrated that the principle of design-out maintenance must come into action on the drawing board: from the moment equipment design starts, thought needs to be given to various maintenance-related considerations, such as the following : maintainability (capability of being easily maintained and protected against failure); local repairability (e.g. ability to be welded, recharged); ability to be dismantled easily; accessibility; and selection of low-maintenance materials.

(b) Preventive maintenance

The principle of preventive maintenance is always based on thinking ahead. It is put into practice in two forms : systematic maintenance and condition-based maintenance.

(i) Systematic maintenance

This consists of servicing the equipment at regular intervals, either according to a time schedule or on the basis of predetermined units of use (hours in operation or kilometres travelled) with a view to detecting failures or premature wear and eliminating them before a breakdown occurs. The servicing schedule is usually based on the manufacturers' forecasts, revised and adjusted according to actual experience in previous servicing. This type of maintenance is also called periodic maintenance.

(ii) Condition-based maintenance

This type of maintenance, also called predictive or auscultative maintenance, is a breakdown prevention technique requiring no dismantling, and based on inspection by auscultation of the equipment involved.

It enables the state of wear of the equipment to be analysed while it is running. The advantage is that it makes it possible to get an idea of the condition of the equipment without down time and/or dismantling.

It calls, however, for rather sophisticated equipment and specialized personnel, and mainly makes use of techniques such as sound analysis, vibration analysis, thermography and thermoscopy, shock-wave analysis, ultrasound analysis, the frequency spectrum and spectrographic oil analysis programme (SOAP).

Failures are detected by comparing the measurements thus taken with the original data, and by analysing graphs that demonstrate the trend in the various measurements in relation to elapsed running time.

The failures observed, complemented by the findings of the programmed inspections and checks, are then dealt with through occasional corrective action, which enables breakdowns to be avoided.

The goals of a preventive maintenance programme are :

(a)   To inspect and improve the condition of the equipment before it interferes with production in terms of quality, quantity or price;

(b)   To take action before the repair costs become too high;

(c)   To eliminate or limit as far as possible the breakdown risks for equipment with heavy breakdown costs;

(d)   To enable repairs to be carried out under the best possible conditions;

(e)   To avoid the breakdown of important parts or excessive energy consumption;

(f)   To remove the causes of serious accidents;

(g)   To influence personnel attitudes : better-running equipment results generally in better-motivated personnel and a more accurate behaviour towards the upkeep of all physical assets ;

(h)   To reduce the overall maintenance burden through better work preparation and reduction of unforeseen production stoppages.

The implementation of a preventive maintenance programme requires a good maintenance department organization, with particular emphasis placed on the following areas :

(a)   Inspection of equipment in operation on the basis of a pre-established programme of periodic inspections so that working conditions can be checked;

(b)   Systematic servicing after inspection of the shut-down equipment and programmed parts replacement. The first step in devising this programme will be forecasting the lifetime of parts subject to wear and components (study of reliability, failure modes and effects, fault tree analysis etc.). The programme will subsequently be refined and adjusted according to the experience acquired from inspections, in order to optimize the replacement intervals. This activity emphasizes the capital importance of proper mastery of the statistics in the machine files and keeping the latter up to date. Indeed, too long a replacement interval increases the risk of a breakdown, while too short an interval results in the replacement of parts and components that have not completed their optimal lifetime;

(c)   Overhauls, which often require considerable work, can be carried out during programmed shut-downs or during low production periods (holidays or weekends);

(d)   Routine maintenance, such as greasing, tuning, cleaning, running in new or overhauled machines, painting etc.

Setting up a preventive maintenance programme, carefully researched and specially designed to deal with the problems specific to each item, continues to be one of the most effective ways of reducing breakdowns and keeping equipment in good condition. It is important to implement the preventive maintenance programme as soon as new equipment is put into service.

(c) Corrective maintenance

Also called breakdown maintenance, palliative or curative maintenance, this consists of :

(a)   Troubleshooting on machines whose poor condition results either in total or partial stoppage of the equipment, or in its operation under intolerable conditions;

(b)   Machine repairs.

Corrective maintenance can both be planned (e.g. scheduled repairs) as well as unplanned (e.g. troubleshooting).

It is therefore indispensable to work methodically to keep the time of repair as short as possible. Good work preparation and the gathering and processing of all the data relevant to the repairs will enable : down time to be avoided; mistakes in assembly or dismantling to be eliminated; and improvements to be made in the conditions under which the work has to be performed.

2.2. Activities of a maintenance department

The activities of a maintenance department embody the functions listed below according to a chronological order of occurrence in maintenance practice. The organizational structure and the related personnel which are necessary to implement these functions are described in chapter III.

2.2.1. Methods

The methods function consists in thinking through and making the best possible preparation for maintenance department work through the use of suitable techniques and appropriate resources.

This function can be applied either to a single well-defined job, in which case it involves "work preparation" as discussed below in section 2.2.3, or to a whole maintenance programme on a machine.

The way to proceed is to assemble as many factors as possible which can enable maintenance work to be properly carried out, by :

(a)   Coding machines according to where they are installed (itemization);
(b)   Establishing machine record cards and machine history cards;
(c)   Establishing machine files and keeping them up to date;
(d)   Defining work studies, among others for repetitive and important jobs;
(e)   Designing preventive maintenance programmes;
(f)   Enlisting the help of the engineering section in establishing the framework of design-out maintenance activities according to the equipment and tooling available - in particular with reference to shape, tolerances and materials;
(g)   Cooperating in the establishment of in-plant standards and standardization of equipment;

(h)   Taking part in shop-floor diagnostics in the event of critical breakdowns;

(i)   Analysing and evaluating on a continuous basis all the information gathered, with a view to improving methods for all the important jobs and updating and correcting the existing programmes and procedures;

(j)   Analysing repetitive failures and advising the engineering section of the resulting proposals for modifications;

(k)   Preparing for the annual shut-down;

(l)   Cooperating with the stock management department in selecting the spare parts, tools, and materials to be kept in stock and in deciding on the relevant management parameters;

(m)   Developing forms and documents for use by the various services of the maintenance department and determining their flow (management information system).

2.2.2. Engineering

The engineering function concerns the study and design of modifications or minor extensions to existing equipment and machinery, with a view to improving : capacity or output; quality of production; personnel safety; maintainability or accessibility; and environmental impact.

The work of the engineering section is thus characterized as much by the wide diversity of work studied as by the variety of techniques used to execute it.

The staff of this section therefore needs to be versatile and highly skilled, and should be very maintenance-minded and concerned about : speed of execution; avoidance of unnecessary petty details; the gravity of problems relating to spare parts and accessibility; and equipment maintainability.

The engineering section, as designer, will act as a monitoring body of the work executed by the relevant maintenance services. In this capacity, it will be responsible not only for the studies, but also for the erection, installation, start-up and fine tuning of the machinery concerned.

2.2.3. Job preparation

The job preparation function concerns the work study which determines operating procedures, job specifications, material resources, personnel requirements, time allocation and workload.

Job preparation results directly from the methods function, but centres on a given individual job.

Good job preparation involves studying and defining two facets : describing the job and breaking it down into separate operations. The description of the job is also a guide for the person responsible for monitoring safety, quality, and cost. Breakdown into separate operations provides the required time-lines for the job scheduling.

It is not necessary to prepare every maintenance job, because it is a good thing to let the foremen or the persons responsible take some initiative in carrying it out. Discernment must be used, therefore, in deciding which jobs do need preparation. In maintenance work, job analyses demonstrate that preparing for the work pays off in at least 25 percent of cases, even if for the sole reason that better use is made of personnel.

In addition, job preparation offers other advantages, such as :

(a)   An opportunity to draw up an estimate before the work is carried out;
(b)   An opportunity to request the customer's agreement before carrying out the work;
(c)   Setting realistic time-lines;
(d)   Greater accuracy in defining spare part and raw materials requirements;
(e)   An opportunity for making sure in good time that the spare parts and raw materials are available in stock;
(f)   The assurance of having a better balanced workload;
(g)   Greater freedom of action for the supervisory personnel, who thus have a chance to spend more time on organization tasks;
(h)   A better working atmosphere between the maintenance and production departments.

2.2.4. Programming - work scheduling - follow-up of work in progress

The programming function is responsible for assembling the required material and human resources, drawing up a programme and setting time limits. The function includes, in particular :

(a)   Planning the overall programme to be tackled by the department (long-term planning);
(b)   Assessing work request priorities;
(c)   Making sure that orders for subcontracting and supplies required for programmed work are followed through, in liaison with the work preparation staff;
(d)   Controlling the respect of instructions and time-lines

This function is therefore closely related to the work preparation task. Hence it is advisable to locate the programming function in the same office as the preparation function.

Work Scheduling is the function closest to job execution (short-term planning). It deals with workload planning in accordance with the plan laid down in relation to workers and machine workloads. In this context, it is a necessity if rational use is to be made of manpower.

Follow-up of work in progress is usually taken care of by the office in charge of work scheduling (also called planning-man). He is continually monitoring the workload of the personnel executing the work and of the machine tools, and correcting both underutilization and overutilization. The schedule must allow for contingency work time in which to deal with unexpected, emergency or delayed jobs. A special plan for preventive maintenance enables progress on jobs scheduled according to agreed time-lines to be monitored easily.

2.2.5. Job execution

Job execution is facilitated and optimized by good preparation and efficient planning, provided that those responsible for job execution keep strictly to doing quality work while also observing the agreed time-lines.

Without job preparation and planning, time will be wasted during execution, and that will result in a low rate of utilization of maintenance personnel, and consequently in :

    (a)   Poor synchronization in the timing of the work done by the various teams;
    (b)   A large number of unsolved problems emerging during execution;
    (c)   The use of tools that are unsuitable for the job;
    (d)   Poor use of skilled personnel.

Needless to say, wasted time raises both maintenance costs and equipment down time.

In other respects, with a new project, much time-wasting can be avoided by making the right choices of location, in designing the factory, for strategic maintenance points such as workshops, central stores, subsidiary stores and the maintenance planning office.

Generally speaking, decentralizing the various sections reduces trips between the stores, workshops and work sites, but on the other hand, centralizing often permits better organization, which leads to cost reduction.

2.2.6. Quality control of maintenance work

The quality control function for maintenance work is very important in that it guarantees quality of execution. The degree to which it is effective constitutes the hallmark of maintenance.

The essential nature of its role is full justification for the necessary investments, in both personnel, tools and measuring instruments. For manufacturing workshops, and in particular for machine-tooling, it is therefore worthwhile training some staff to specialize in quality control. On the shop-floor, the staff at the foreman level will often be made responsible for controlling the work of their own crews.

The instructions describing in detail both the inspection procedures and the tools needed for controlling on the job site, in the workshops and also for subcontracted work must be drawn up clearly in the course of job preparation.

2.2.7. Spare-parts management and maintenance stores

The function of the spare-parts management and maintenance stores should be fulfilled by the maintenance department rather than by the purchasing and reordering department. The tasks must be shared out between the two departments as follows :

(a)   Maintenance will be responsible for establishing the purchase or reordering request, concerning technical decisions, coding and description of the item;

(b)   The purchasing department will take care of commercial decisions, preparing the purchase orders and following up on them.

It stands to reason that harmonious cooperation between the two departments will ensure optimal selection in purchasing spare parts.

The prime task of stock management is to anticipate, at all times, the factory's needs as regards : consumables and current maintenance store items; standard parts; and spare parts specific to a machine.

Next, these parts must be administered and the quantities to be reordered must be determined. Moreover, stock levels and various other parameters, such as consumption, delivery delay, safety stock, the requirements peculiar to certain markets for products that need to be reordered, etc. should be defined.

This important function ought to involve everyone. But what actually happens is that conflicts frequently arise because the various users all see the stock situation from their own standpoint.

To avoid conflicts of this sort, it is indispensable to establish a sound stock management policy with coding and correct designation of all the parts. Coding and designation, applied at all levels of ordering, manufacturing, maintenance and industrial accounting, will avoid any ambiguity in the exchange of information.

2.2.8. Management of maintenance personnel

Personnel management is one of the essential aspects of running a maintenance department. The rational use, selection and motivation of personnel all depend heavily on it.

These criteria have a direct impact on the quality and quantity of work delivered by the department, hence on its efficiency and its cost-effectiveness.

In view of the above, managers should take particular note of the following points :

(a)   Personnel qualifications : maintenance jobs, which are often complex and varied, call for highly qualified staff;

(b)   Staff who have received training in a variety of fields will be much appreciated in view of the various disciplines with which they will be confronted;

(c)   Close attention should be paid to foreman-level personnel because they are often underestimated. In addition to their hierarchical role, they also have to take on a task of fundamental importance, namely personnel training;

(d)   Function and job descriptions must cover all maintenance positions;

(e)   Recruiting maintenance personnel calls for particular care;

(f)   Training and upgrading maintenance personnel;

(g)   Salary policy : care must be taken that average maintenance salary rates are the same as those for production, when qualifications are equal. Output-linked wage structures must be applied with caution; for instance, by judging the worth of personnel in money terms on the basis of efficiency and quality of service rather than on quantity.

2.2.9. Maintenance accountancy and cost control

By decreasing its own costs, any maintenance department enhances the profitability of an enterprise. To be able to control the costs, it is necessary to know what they are and to be able to interpret them.

For this purpose, a maintenance-oriented accountancy system should be set up in close cooperation with the company accounting department, with the objective of :

(a)   Supplying the maintenance department on a continuous basis with all the data relating to its own expenditures, and thus enabling it to react promptly to any discrepancy or error;

(b)   Ensuring better monitoring of allocations [to cost centres], and thus limiting the number of errors;

(c)   Facilitating the drawing-up of estimates;

(d)   Enabling the expenditures relative to a single job to be compiled more easily;

(e)   More closely defining and keeping track of the allocation of overheads.

2.2.10. Exploitation of utilities

The utilities, or facilities for the production and distribution of energy and fluids, include :

(a)   Electricity production and distribution;

(b)   Water treatment, distribution and sewerage;

(c)   Compressed air production and distribution;

(d)   The vacuum network;

(e)   Heating and steam production and distribution;

(f)   Refrigeration and cold network;

(g)   Storage and distribution of various gases;

(h)   Storage and distribution of fuels.

Exploitation of utilities includes not only the maintenance but also the operation of these facilities. Maintenance is the most suitable department for carrying out this task, since it requires qualified personnel who can act as operators and service technicians, rather than as operators only.

These facilities can be looked upon as ancillaries to production, the operation of which does not call for personnel with a one-machine speciality, but rather for good electromechanics trained in both fields. Especially since their job will consist, to a much greater extent, in routine inspections and maintenance than in operating a one-process machine.

2.2.11. Managing the maintenance department

All the above functions should be managed in a proper way. Apart from its technical aspect, maintenance is considered more and more as a top-management function on company level. Maintenance managers need to change their (often technical) language into a language which is understood by executives and decision makers (i.e. in terms of costs, return on investment, added value etc.)

The maintenance management function is involved at the following levels :

(a)   Shop-floor : technical management of maintenance work including methods, planning, quality control and analysis of operational statistics;

(b)   Maintenance department : strategical and economic management through the definition of maintenance policies, including a maintenance concept, the follow-up of economic performance indicators, personnel management , subcontracting policy etc.

(c)   Company-executive level : participation in the definition of corporate master plans concerning amongst others renewal policy, acquisition of new equipment, development of human resources etc.

In order to reach this objective, the maintenance manager must have quick access to both technical as well as economic data.

Moreover, as the maintenance function in many companies is now moving towards a "total integrated physical assets management" function, maintenance managers are becoming part of the corporate board of directors.

2.3.   Maintenance levels

In order to set up an efficient maintenance organization, and to take management decisions in matters such as the degree of subcontracting, the investment in maintenance workshops, the recruitment of appropriate personnel etc, maintenance activities have been analysed in relation to their complexity.

Five levels of maintenance can be discerned, according to the complexity of the work and the urgency of action to be taken. AFNOR Standard X60-011 gives the definitions presented below.

2.3.1. Level 1

Simple adjustments anticipated by the manufacturer, by means of accessible components, requiring no disassembling or opening of the equipment, or completely safe replacement of accessible consumable components, such as signal lights or some types of fuse.

Remarks : Servicing of this type can be performed by the equipment operator on site, without tools and by following the instructions for use. The stock of consumable parts required is very small.

2.3.2. Level 2

Troubleshooting by means of exchange units designed for this purpose, and minor preventive maintenance operations such as greasing or checking for proper functioning.

Remarks : Servicing of this type can be performed by an authorized technician with average qualifications, on site, with the portable tools specified in the maintenance instructions, with the help of the afore mentioned instructions. The transportable spare parts required can be easily procured without delay in the immediate area of the place of use.

Note : A technician is authorized when he has received training enabling him to work safely on a machine which could be potentially dangerous, and with full awareness of the problems.

2.3.3. Level 3

Identification and diagnosis of breakdowns, repairs by replacement of components or working parts, minor mechanical repairs, and all routine preventive maintenance operations, such as general adjustment or recalibration of measuring instruments.

Remarks : Servicing of this type can be carried out by a specialist technician, on site or in the maintenance shop. This is done with the aid of the tools specified in the maintenance instructions and measuring or calibration equipment, and if need be of test benches and machinery inspection benches, using all the documentation necessary for maintenance of the equipment, as well as store-supplied parts.

2.3.4. Level 4

All major corrective or preventive maintenance jobs except modernization and rebuilding. This level also includes gauging of the measuring equipment used for maintenance, and may also include calibration by specialized organizations.

Remarks : Services of this type can be carried out by a team which includes highly skilled technical specialists, in a specialized workshop fully equipped with tools (mechanical equipment, for cabling, cleaning, etc.) and if need be with measuring benches and the necessary callipers for the work, using all the general and specific documentation.

2.3.5. Level 5

Modernizing, rebuilding or execution of major repairs, entrusted to a central workshop or an outside workshop. Spare parts manufacturing.

Remarks : By definition, work of this type is thus carried out by the manufacturer or the rebuilder, with resources specified by the manufacturer and therefore very similar to those used in the original manufacturing. It may also be carried out by a fully equipped central workshop.

Selected literature

AUTHOR	PUBLISHER	TITLE
BSI	BSI, 1974	MAINTENANCE TERMS IN TEROTECHNOLOGY
BSI	BSI, 1969	GLOSSARY OF TERMS IN WORK STUDY
BOUCHE-PLANCHU-RETOUR	UNIVERSITE DES SCIENCES SOCIALES DE GRENOBLE 1988 - EUROMAINTENANCE 88, HELSINKI	"INDUSTRIAL MAINTENANCE AND TROUBLE SHOOTING EXPERT SYSTEM SOME HUMAN, MANAGERIAL AND ORGANIZATIONAL CONSIDERATIONS"
DGS	DGS INTERNATIONAL - SGS/LAGOS, 1991	SEMINAR ON MAINTENANCE MANAGEMENT
DUNLOT C.L.	BUTTERWORTHS, 1990	A PRACTICAL GUIDE TO MAINTENANCE ENGINEERING
KELLY A. and HARRIS M.	BUTTERWORTHS, 1978	THE MANAGEMENT OF INDUSTRIAL MAINTENANCE
PRIEL V.	MAC DONALDS AND EVIANS LTD, LONDON, 1974	MAINTENANCE

CHAPTER III
PLANNED MAINTENANCE SYSTEMS

3.1.   Maintenance strategies

Three major tendencies exist when setting-up a maintenance strategy which relates to the question of "ownership" of the equipment :

(a)   The "owner" is the maintenance department which makes the equipment available to the production department on the basis of a kind of "contract". The contract specifies the performance standards and operational criteria;

(b)   The "owner" is the production department which calls upon the services of a maintenance department to keep the equipment in good running order;

(c)   Both the maintenance and the production department render their service to an "owner" who specifies the expected output.

It is obvious that both technical as well as organizational decisions related to maintenance will depend on the choice of one of the three alternatives.

The most appropriate will depend upon the type of activity (industry, transport, etc.).

The explanation below is based on the third alternative, but can be used with small modifications for the two others.

Nevertheless, one thing should be clear whichever alternative is used : maintenance must play a leading role in maximizing the efficiency of the investment in terms of quantity, quality and cost, regardless of how it is organized.

The continuous evolution of the maintenance approach from the "oil is cheaper than steel" attitude towards that of the Life Cycle Cost/Profit (LCC/LCP) and Total Productive Maintenance concepts highlights the importance of defining integrated strategies on both the company as well as the maintenance-department level. This is set out in more detail in the chapter IV.

3.1.1. On the company level

The development of maintenance in a company must fit into a framework of a corporate strategy which should deal with the following topics : management of human resources; renewal of production equipment; acquisition of new equipment; introduction of computerized systems; financial management; marketing; maintenance; production processes; raw materials and the social, cultural and economic environment of the company.

An individual corporate management master plan should be developed for each of the above items.

3.1.2. On the maintenance department level

A maintenance management master plan should be drawn up and must deal with the following topics :

(a)   The hierarchical position of maintenance in the company organization chart;

(b)   The development of human resources in maintenance;

(c)   The introduction of an analytic accounting system which details maintenance expenditure per cost centre, per machine and per function;

(d)   The setting-up of a separate maintenance budget;

(e)   The acquisition and renewal of equipment (choice of technology, definition of reliability and maintainability specifications in the design, terms of reference, participation of maintenance specialists during negotiations, introduction of the life-cycle cost approach, taking into account the indirect costs);

(f)   The structure of maintenance : centralized, decentralized or mixed;

(g)   Computer-assisted maintenance (technical) and computerized maintenance management systems;

(h)   The subcontracting of maintenance work;

(i)   The definition of a maintenance concept;

(j)   Relations with the quality control department;

(k)   The safety of personnel and safety in general;

(l)   The protection of the environment.

Even though all the above fields are important, emphasis will only be put upon those which, in the author's opinion, are the most important.

The hierarchical position of maintenance in a company must be very high : at the same level as that of manufacturing/production, the commercial department, administration and finance. In other words the maintenance manager must be a member of the Board of Directors.

Various structures of the maintenance department exist : centralized, decentralized or mixed. The choice between centralization and decentralization depends on a multitude of factors such as geographic considerations, size of the plant, differences in process technology between the production areas, degree of requested availability, non-efficiency costs etc.

The structure that has given the best results in small- and medium-scale enterprises in developing countries is that of a centralized maintenance. Even for bigger companies a centralized structure produces excellent results. Chapter IV will deal with this theme in more detail.

In the development of human resources, there are two urgent priorities : motivation and training. One of the problems is to attract highly qualified personnel to a field which traditionally offers rather poor career prospects. This is certainly true in the case of engineers. It is the duty of the company to remedy this deficiency by setting up a career plan for the whole of the maintenance personnel.

Computerization of maintenance must not be looked upon as separate from the rest of the company computerization. The choice of computer programmes and hardware must match those which already exist in other departments such as accountancy, production and management of raw materials.

In the acquisition of equipment, either for reasons of renewal, or extension and modernization, maintenance must play an important role in the choice of the adequate technology, in the design of the equipment and infrastructures and in the setting up of specifications to ensure maintenance. This is the reason why it is imperative for maintenance specialists to take part in all contract negotiations.

A subcontracting policy is a factor which contributes greatly to the performance of the service. The inevitable question is : should the work be done by the company workforce or should it be done by outsiders ? In the latter case, which are the jobs that should be subcontracted and which ones should be kept within the maintenance department so that the loss of know-how can be avoided, even if an investment in specialized personnel is necessary ?

In the definition of the maintenance concept, a well-balanced dosage between the various forms of maintenance must be introduced (periodic, condition-based, corrective and design-out). This dosage must be decided on the basis of a thorough study of the importance of reliability and maintainability of components and systems in relation to safety, production, quality, cost of repairs and environment. The search for zero-defect is out-of-date : it has become more a question of mastering the breakdowns and learning to know where failures can be accepted or where they are absolutely unacceptable.

3.1.3. The maintenance concept

An important part of the Maintenance Management Master Plan is the definition of a maintenance concept, which in fact means a choice of a maintenance form for each machine depending on the priorities which are given by the company in terms of safety, production, quality, cost and protection of the environment.

The use of the following techniques can be considered :

(a)   Failure mode effects and criticality analysis (FMECA) deals with the study of failure mechanisms of components. Effects of possible failures are analyzed in relation to the function and performance of each component. They are divided into various criticality categories : catastrophic, complete or partial loss of function, no influence. A criticality index for each failure mode is obtained by calculating the product of the following ratings :

(i)   Probability of each failure mode occurring;
(ii) Criticality of the failure ;
(iii) Difficulty of detecting the failure in advance;

(b)   System reliability-analysis. This analysis is based, on the one hand, on FMECA for components and their influence on the system, and on maintainability considerations on the other;

(c)   Fault tree analysis is in fact a risk analysis based on the study of various failures or malfunctions influencing relations which can lead to a catastrophic failure. A risk rate of occurrence is given to each of these events, which finally gives, through a fault tree, the catastrophic failure risk;

(d)   Hazard and operability study is the study of possible failures and their effect on the operability of an item (component or system). This study is done during the design stage as well as continuously during operation;

(e)   ABC analysis (Pareto law) : production machines and utilities are grouped into three classes depending on the criticality of the effects which failures or malfunctions can cause. The criticality rate is given by an enterprise-specific priority rate in relation to safety, production, quality and protection of the environment. As a matter of fact, it can be stated that failures on, for example, 20 percent of the machines could be responsible for 80 percent of critical effects.

The above considerations will give an overview of the satisfaction rate of quantified requests in relation to reliability, maintainability and availability of the system. These requests will particularly be defined on the basis of their effects on safety, production, quality, cost and environment. This will allow the customer to formulate adequate specifications in the terms of reference as to the design of the equipment.

A maintenance concept (policy) can then be defined in terms of the dosage between the various maintenance forms (periodic, condition-based, corrective or design-out maintenance), which must be applied to each component or system.

Periodicities which will be fixed for components or subsystems based on the above approach must then be grouped to packages on the system level. This will lead to related maintenance programmes, which in turn should be linked to the maintenance levels (see chapter II). For each level, the maintenance tasks can then be defined in order to assess the necessary human and material resources needed.

Regular evaluation of the implementation of the above maintenance concept and the effect on the behaviour of the equipment must be carried out. This will allow a tuning of the maintenance programme and a feedback of information which can be helpful to adapt the design.

3.2.   Organizational structure of the maintenance department

3.2.1. Principles of maintenance organization

The most efficient organization is not the one which is perfect from the design point of view, but the one that is applied correctly. This often means a simple organization at the initial stage. Clear, concise explanations of the various mechanisms and information routings are necessary for the personnel to fully understand the interdependencies. After the introductory period, the chosen organization is adapted step by step so that it may be improved and completed.

The principles which the author would recommend as being fundamental for the organization of maintenance in enterprises in the developing countries can be summarized as follows :

(a)   Decide on the structure of the maintenance department. If possible, centralize all maintenance activity in one department under one head;

(b)   Place the maintenance department high on the factory organization chart;

(c)   Make sure that maintenance is not headed hierarchically by production. Ensure that both are on the same level;

(d)   Assign fully qualified personnel to the maintenance department;

(e)   Allocate sufficient financial resources;

(f)   Devise an organization which suits the particular needs of each factory and allow it to evolve accordingly;

(g)   Avoid trying to set up a perfect organization from the start. Find flexible structures and ensure that the personnel understand the system thoroughly before final implementation;

(h)   Avoid useless paperwork but fill in carefully any forms necessary to ensure an efficient flow of information.

3.2.2. Position of the maintenance department in the organizational structure of the plant

It is important to establish a direct link between the head of maintenance and the factory or company manager. The responsibilities of the former encompass every function explained in chapter II on "what maintenance really is".

The hierarchical position which should be assigned to the maintenance department is illustrated in the following general organization chart.

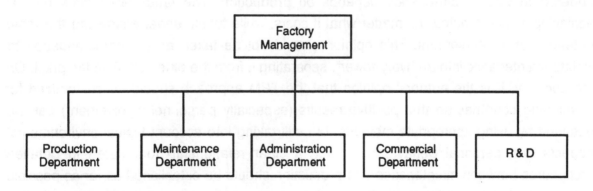

As the objective for the production and maintenance departments is the same, i.e. production at a minimum cost under good quality and safety conditions, it is indispensable that both departments are placed on the same hierarchical level in order to allow interrelations, based on an equivalent decision-making power.

Maintenance organizational structures have been subject to continuous modifications since the early 1950s. Until that time "breakdown maintenance" was the most common maintenance "system". With the development of continuous process industries (petroleum, electricity, steel etc.) preventive maintenance was introduced more and more and moved, in the late 1960s, towards the "productive maintenance" concept. This concept considered the maintenance function as a real "partner of production". This concept was extended in the late 1970s to the total productive maintenance (TPM) approach under the impulse of the Japanese Management Association. The three most important aspects which already existed in the various other maintenance models became the headlines of TPM, i.e. measurement, operator involvement and planned maintenance. In analogy with quality and production control techniques, the most typical characteristic of TPM is the involvement of all the actors concerned in the production process including upstream and downstream actors, independently of their hierarchical level. This "total" involvement of personnel in the TPM model was first developed in Japan (especially in the automobile industry) and produced good results. Obviously all kinds of motivation techniques and incentives were used (and were possible to use) to reach the objectives. In particular, involvement of machine-operating personnel in maintenance activities is one of the key issues of TPM. This led towards a kind of integration of production and maintenance.

Despite positive experience with the TPM approach in some industrialized countries, where both maintenance (up to certain activities of the third level) and operation are carried out by the same personnel, experience in developing countries suggests that - at least for the moment - maintenance should be to a certain extend independent and the company should be very careful with the transfer of maintenance tasks to operators. Moreover maintenance should not be placed hierarchically under production. A head of maintenance has to be able to use his or her authority in relation to operation (i.e. stop for urgent interventions), to renewal of equipment or to acquisition policy. This is not always understood when maintenance depends on production. The latter often aims only at achieving a record output no matter what it costs, while totally under-estimating the rapid deterioration of equipment. This opinion should not be taken as a recommendation to isolate maintenance into an "ivory tower", separating it from the other actors in the plant. On the contrary, it is the authors' opinion that the TPM approach should be customized for developing countries so that positive results (especially personnel involvement) can be obtained by using appropriate methods, but still taking into account typical environmental aspects and personal behaviour. In fact, a clear relationship formulated in detailed procedures between maintenance and production should be established as far as possible before actual start-up of a plant. This relationship should be the basis of yearly production plannings and should be reviewed during monthly or three-monthly meetings, in order to ensure a satisfactory system of consultation between the two departments

The role of maintenance during the acquisition of new equipment or plant extensions is of the utmost importance. During the preparation of a project or contract negotiations the purchaser must not only be represented by production or commercial people, but also by maintenance, whose opinion must be a deciding factor.

The centralization of maintenance has a number of advantages. The most important are :

(a)   Keeping the Board of Directors advised by means of one source of information;

(b)   Efficient use of personnel and sound job preparation;

(c)   Avoidance of non-respect of procedures due to personnel turnover, by means of written procedures and a central storage of information;

(d)   Better supervision and optimalization of maintenance costs through a clear separation between "clients" and "suppliers";

(e)   Better use of specialists, machine-tools and specific tools ;

(f)   Optimalization and better follow-up of sub-contracted work;

(g)   The possibility of reducing down time for yearly overhauls and major repairs through the concentration of all available resources;

(h)   The improvement of quality and efficiency of maintenance work through the centralization of experience gained in repair and trouble shooting for the whole plant;

(i)   An easier setting-up of adequate technical specifications for the purchase of new equipment, taking into account better maintainability and measures to ensure proper maintenance (such as technical documentation, training, spare parts etc.).

3.2.3. Maintenance organization chart

(a)   Introduction

A maintenance organization chart (organigram) which can be used as a discussion base for different types and sizes of factories signifies an approach in terms of the necessary functions which must be assured. For that purpose, it should be understood that a function on the chart can be carried out by one or several people, or conversely one person can assure several functions. It all depends on the size.

Given that this manual is aimed in particular at small and medium-scale enterprises in developing countries, in order to facilitate a better understanding of the organization charts, their compilation can be done in successive stages :

(a)   The first stage is a simple organization chart for a small factory showing the basic functions indispensable for an efficient maintenance operation;

(b)   The second stage concerns a bigger factory with one single production area and working 8 hours a day;

(c)   The third stage is for a new factory with several production areas and working on a continuous basis (24 hours a day);

(d)   Finally, the fourth stage concerns the evolution of the preceding organization chart towards alternatives depending on various particularities of plants.

The functions are explained step by step so that the reader can find all the elements needed to adapt the given advice to each particular situation.

(b)   About maintenance organization charts

Before dealing with the organization charts in detail, it is important that emphasis be put upon some principles.

In a maintenance department five groups of functions should be present in order to cover all the tasks as described in chapter II. They are :

(a)   A function of reflection : methods, job preparation, planning;
(b)   An execution function;
(c)   A control function;
(d)   A logistic function : workshops, laboratories, garage, stores;
(e)   An evaluation and management function.

These functions must always be part of an organization chart, however small.

Regarding maintenance trades, the organization chart should be established in such a way that the trades are separated as much as possible (mechanics in a mechanical section, the same for electricians etc.). Even though the current tendency in modern industry is to set up multi-skilled teams, the authors consider that this is not yet opportune for most developing countries. This subject will be dealt with further in chapter V.

Maintenance activities should be split up into preventive and corrective maintenance. Job descriptions should be defined accordingly. In medium or large-size factories, this results in one (or several) team(s) working a normal day and carrying out preventive tasks exclusively. As to the team(s) in shift, they should take care of breakdowns and minor repairs. The latter case is only relevant when the factory is working around the clock. For a factory which only works eight hours a day, the above teams in shift will do the normal timetable, but will still be in charge of corrective maintenance exclusively.

Logistic supports should be centralized : central workshop, spare parts store, planning office. Independent decentralization in the production areas should be avoided especially for small plants. For bigger plants, the setting-up of communication links between each of the above services in the main production area could be helpful, particularly for the planning office. Nevertheless workshops in this case should only be equipped with basic equipment, as it would not be efficient to have a double set of equipment from the central workshop located in the production area.

(c)   Basic organization charts

c.1. First stage

The simplest organization chart (first stage) for a maintenance department   is composed of five boxes which correspond to the five principal functions mentioned above. It is presented below.

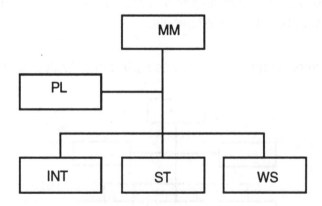

MM : Maintenance management
PL   : Planning
INT : Interventions
ST   : Stores for spare parts
WS : Workshop

This organization chart contains the following functions :

(a)   MM : maintenance management, responsible for technical and administrative management. This particularly concerns the supervision of various tasks, the establishing of a budget, the follow-up of expenditure, the interpretation of technical failures, the instructions for maintenance programmes, the recruitment of personnel, taking part in the board meetings and advice in the field of renewal and purchasing of equipment;

(b)   PL : planning, responsible for methods (preventive programmes, work preparation), work planning (programming - scheduling) as well as for the technical documentation. This function will also be in charge of the choice of parts to be stored and their administration;

(c)   INT : shop-floor interventions, responsible for all mechanical, electrical and other interventions, and for preventive as well as corrective maintenance;

(d)   ST : spare parts storing, responsible for stockkeeping of spare parts (registration, filing, conservation, storage) and issuing;

(e)   WS : mechanical and electrical repair, responsible for minor welding jobs, metalwork and small electrical repairs.

In fact, for very small factories these functions could actually be carried out by one person (e.g. a plant with a total workforce of 10) or by 4 or 5 people for larger ones (e.g. total workforce 20 to 30). For still larger factories (workforce 50 to 100) maintenance departments will have a staff of 10 to 20 people.

This organization chart could progress (for small factories) towards the following chart :

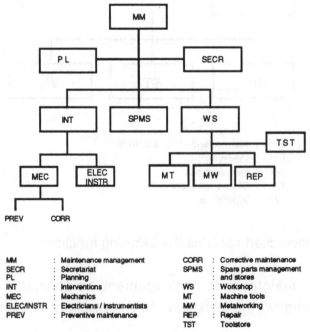

MM	: Maintenance management	CORR	: Corrective maintenance
SECR	: Secretariat	SPMS	: Spare parts management
PL	: Planning		and stores
INT	: Interventions	WS	: Workshop
MEC	: Mechanics	MT	: Machine tools
ELEC/INSTR	: Electricians / instrumentists	MW	: Metalworking
PREV	: Preventive maintenance	REP	: Repair
		TST	: Toolstore

The same functions as in the previous organization chart are found here, but with some developments, as follows :

(a)   INT has been split up into two subfunctions, one mechanic (MEC), the other electricity and instrumentation (ELEC/INSTR). Moreover, the mechanical function is composed of two : one for preventive work (PREV), the other for breakdowns and minor repairs (CORR);

(b)   the workshop (WS) has been reinforced by the following subfunctions : MT (machine-tools), REP (mechanical and electrical repairs) and a small store for raw material and tools (TST).

This case involves a factory workforce of 80 to 130 and a maintenance department staff of 20 to 25.

Examples of detailed manning tables for the above organization charts are given in section 3.3 below.

c.2. Second stage

A second stage in the design of organization charts concerns a larger factory with one production area working eight hours a day. The preceding organization charts could evolve as follows :

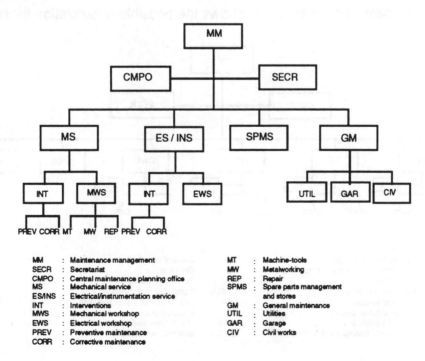

MM	:	Maintenance management
SECR	:	Secretariat
CMPO	:	Central maintenance planning office
MS	:	Mechanical service
ES/INS	:	Electrical/instrumentation service
INT	:	Interventions
MWS	:	Mechanical workshop
EWS	:	Electrical workshop
PREV	:	Preventive maintenance
CORR	:	Corrective maintenance

MT	:	Machine-tools
MW	:	Metalworking
REP	:	Repair
SPMS	:	Spare parts management and stores
GM	:	General maintenance
UTIL	:	Utilities
GAR	:	Garage
CIV	:	Civil works

The maintenance department is composed of the previous functions, resulting in four line services (MS - ES - SPMS - GM) and one staff section (CMPO). The various functions put forward in the preceding organization charts appear again, but for certain amongst them the implementing services have been adapted slightly.

This is the case with the mechanical and electrical functions which have now grouped together not only the interventions but their respective workshops (MWS : mechanical workshop/EWS : electrical workshop). In other words, the mechanical and electrical functions are big enough to host their own workshops. On the contrary, a central workshop would probably be too small to exist as a separate service.

A new service has been added : GM (General maintenance). This service is responsible for the exploitation of utilities (production and distribution of energy and fluids), maintenance of rolling stock (GAR : garage) and civil works (CW).

As can be seen in section 3.3 below, an organization chart of this size is applicable for a factory workforce approaching 200 and a maintenance workforce of approximately 40 to 50.

If a plant has a lot of control, regulation or automation equipment it is wise to create a separate service "Instrumentation"(INS). Moreover, in the case of a plant with mechanical and electrical equipment which necessitates a continuous follow-up (for instance, plants with a high breakdown cost such as a power plant), creating a heavy workload on the two services, then it would be wise to group the workshops MWS and EWS into a CWS (central workshop). The organization chart below shows the possible organization for such a case.

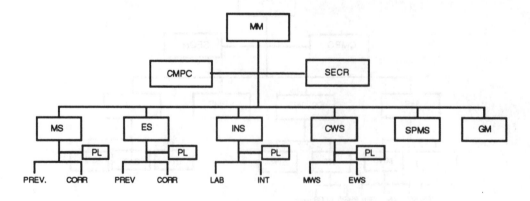

MM : Maintenance management	GM :	General maintenance
CMPO : Central maintenance planning office	PL :	Planning
SECR : Secretariat	PREV :	Preventive maintenance
MS : Mechanical service	CORR :	Corrective maintenance
ES : Electrical service	LAB :	Laboratory for instrumentation
INS : Instrumentation service	INT :	Interventions
CWS : Central workshop	MWS :	Mechanical workshop
SPMS : Spare parts management and stores	EWS :	Electrical workshop

The function PL (programming - preparation - scheduling) has been decentralized as a staff function in each of the services concerned. Taking into consideration the amount of work the mechanical, electrical and instrumentation services have to do, the centralization of PL within the central maintenance planning office would not give the necessary flexibility. The central maintenance planning office will then mainly focus on methods, technical documentation and minor engineering work.

The workforce and size of the factory for this organization chart are not so different from the preceding one. Above all, it is the nature of the work and urgency of the interventions which justifies a more extensive organization chart.

An example of a manning table for the above organization charts is given in section 3.3 below.

c.3. Third stage

A *third stage* in the design of maintenance organization charts applies to a factory with several production areas and working 24 hours a day. It is the most complete organization chart for a maintenance department. If considering the various services as functions, exactly the same ones are found as described above. Thus, even though this organization chart can be considered more or less as a standard one, it has to be adapted to each factory. Therefore, it can be used only as a guide, not as a master plan.

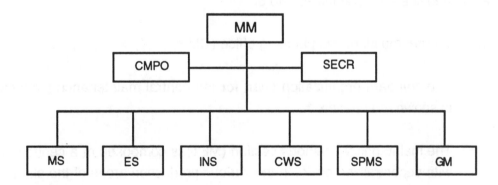

MM	:	Maintenance management
CMPO	:	Central maintenance planning office
MS	:	Mechanical service
ES	:	Electrical service
INS	:	Instrumentation service
CWS	:	Central workshop
SPMS	:	Spare parts management and stores service
GM	:	General maintenance service
SECR	:	Secretariat

The above organization chart may be useful when discussing the various problems and activities of the maintenance department. It shows the principles of an organizational structure for a maintenance department, but must not be considered as an all purpose organization chart, which may be applied in any plant.

The standard organization chart is composed of seven centralized services, each reporting to a service head : central maintenance planning office, mechanical service, electrical service, instrumentation service, the central workshops, spare parts management and stores, and general maintenance services.

All the heads of services report to the maintenance manager. In large plants, some of the services may be decentralized in each production area (assigned maintenance), under the authority of the maintenance manager. This is especially the case for CMPO, MS and ES.

Many alternatives of the standard organization chart are possible and may be justified in some cases. The chart represents a general organization for which the principles may be applied in any plant.

The various services of the maintenance department

For better understanding, the various services of a maintenance department are detailed hereafter, based on the last organization chart. For each service reference is made to a more detailed chart in appendices 1 to 6.

1.   Central maintenance planning office (CMPO)

The standard organization chart for the central maintenance planning office is shown in appendix 1.

The maintenance methods section (MET) is composed of a centralized office with decentralized desks in the various production areas of the plant.

The maintenance engineering and construction section (ENG) has a drawing office at its disposal and will deal with (apart from modifications and small extensions) updating drawings, the standardization of parts and machines in the plant and plant improvement studies.

The tribology section (TRIB) will mainly be involved in the planning of greasing and oiling, the organization and the inspection of lubrication work, and with the selection of lubricants. Lubricators (greasers) should be integrated into the preventive maintenance teams of the mechanical department.

The maintenance management (MM) section takes charge of analysis of data for management and control of the cost of maintenance and of various statistics and data such as frequency and origin of breakdown. This section will calculate performance ratios and compile them into a steering table for the maintenance manager.

The central documentation section will gather and administer all documents, drawings, instruction manuals, catalogues etc. regarding the plant and its equipment.

To ensure a correct flow of documents, a copying section, equipped with photostating and other copying equipment is a necessity. This service is generally underestimated and neglected.

2.   Mechanical and electrical services (MS-ES)

Appendix 2 shows the standard organization chart for the mechanical and electrical services (MS and ES).

The mechanical and electrical services deal, principally, with troubleshooting, on-the-spot repair, supervision of the equipment and the carrying-out of routine and preventive maintenance activities. They are responsible for the quality of work and for the activities of the craftsmen. To facilitate internal communications and to specialize the personnel in one or more production areas, the electrical and mechanical services can be decentralized by assigning maintenance teams to the different production areas of the plant. Each maintenance team would be composed of two parts : the planning section (PL) (maintenance programming - job preparation - scheduling) and the intervention teams (INT), which are split into a day crew for preventive work and three crews for corrective work working on eight-hour shift (SHIFT), thus giving a 24-hour cover.

As has been seen before, centralizing of PL at the level of the central maintenance planning office can be justified in small or medium-sized plants. The function of "inspecting" the installations, which is frequently carried out by the maintenance methods technicians, can as easily be carried out by the foremen. This function seeks out causes of possible breakdowns before they actually occur and draws up a list of unscheduled work. This is carried out by a programme of systematic inspection visits. Experience shows that 70 percent of breakdowns could be avoided if the visits were well organized.

3.   Instrumentation service (INS)

Appendix 3 shows the standard organization chart for the instrumentation service (INS).

The instrumentation service deals with the apparatus and equipment for control and regulation of the production process, as well as with all pneumatically and electronically controlled equipment including automation.

The principles of decentralization and organization, as described for the mechanical and electrical services, are equally applicable in this case.

Frequently the telecom-service, which deals with all telecommunication equipment of the plant, is part of the instrumentation service.
INS also has a specialized workshop (LAB).

4.   Central maintenance workshops (CMWS)

Appendix 4 shows the standard organization chart for the central maintenance workshops. This chart applies to a universal and completely integrated maintenance workshop. Small plants will have only some of the sections mentioned.

Heavy and light machine tools are part of the metalworking section (MW) of the mechanical workshop (MWS). In some cases, there may be a large number of these machines.

All work concerned with metallic construction is part of the sheet metalworking (SMW), piping, welding and cutting section. A team of specialized welders (high pressure welders, welders of non-ferrous metals, etc.) is not always warranted, but will depend on the frequency of work and of the possibility of subcontracting it.

The foundry and the forge are an essential element in the manufacturing of spareparts. Often subcontracting may replace such equipment, as it may also for other specialized shops such as gear-cutting, toolmaking, heat treatment, chrome-plating, metallization, diesel engines, pumps, vulcanizing, hydraulic equipment, overhead traversing bridges, refractories and maintenance section for machine tools.

The repair shops deal with important overhauling, as well as with repairs in the shop and on the spot. On-the-spot repair work should be avoided as much as possible. It is better to dismantle the machine or subassembly in question and repair it in the central workshops. If repairs on the spot cannot be avoided, the crews of the central workshops should deal with them.

The electrical workshop contains a rewinding section. In some cases a factory lighting section may be justified.

A planning section in each shop will deal with job planning and preparation.

Intermediate and final checks will allow the quality and the rate of output of jobs carried out by the craftsmen to be controlled, and testing-benches (electrical, hydraulic, pneumatic etc.) will confirm the reliability of the manufactured or repaired parts.

5.   Spare parts management and stores service (SPMS)

Appendix 5 shows the standard organization chart.

A "selection of spare parts" and "codification of specific parts" section will deal with the selection of all spare parts, which should be kept in stock to assure a normal operation of the plant. At the same time this section will deal with the codification of the safety parts (subassemblies or parts which are subject to very little wear, but which have a critical importance for the operation of the equipment) and of specific parts (parts for one well-specified machine or equipment, and thus of one well-specified manufacturer).

The "codification of standard parts" section will deal with the codification and the designation of standard parts and of all maintenance materials.

The "standardization" section deals with the standardization and interchangeability of parts with a high turnover. This is the basis for an economical management of these parts, since it will limit the number of stock items, eliminating equivalent or identical parts.

The "stock management" section deals with the proper administration of stock. The section has at its disposal a Stock Control Card on which all the information for sound management is written down. This will enable the purchase of parts or material according to one of the existing types of stock management.

Common parts and articles are stored in a central store, which may possibly have some decentralized buffer stores in different areas of the plant. It is the central store which will receive the parts, distribute them and keep the parts and articles in stock.

6.   General maintenance (GM)

Appendix 6 shows the standard organization chart.

General maintenance normally has its own teams for operating and maintaining the factory utilities (equipment for production and distribution of energy and fluids such as electricity, air, water, gas, steam etc.). In some large plants, utilities (UTIL) can be separated from the maintenance department due to their size.

The "maintenance of rolling stock" section (MRS) will have at its disposal its own maintenance infrastructure (garage, store etc.).
 The maintenance of the buildings and infrastructure (BM) is done by a special section, which has masons, electricians, plumbers, carpenters, painters, etc.

The "materials handling" section (MHAN) has crane drivers, drivers for light and heavy vehicles, drivers for lifting equipment etc.

Maintenance of tracks, roads and sewerages is done by a specialized section.

c.4. Fourth stage

Finally, *in a fourth stage* an application of the above organization chart for a medium-sized plant (actual workforce of 900) is given below. The organization chart is composed of four line services and one staff service. The mechanical workshop and the electrical workshop (EWS) - although geographically in one building - are from the organization point of view assigned to the mechanical and to the electrical service. The manning table for this example is given in chapter III, section 3.3.

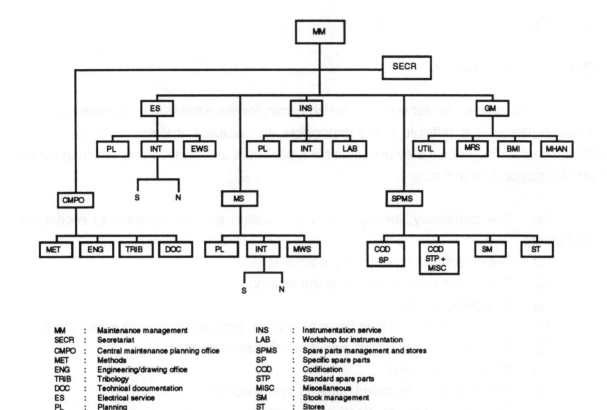

MM :	Maintenance management	INS :	Instrumentation service
SECR :	Secretariat	LAB :	Workshop for instrumentation
CMPO :	Central maintenance planning office	SPMS :	Spare parts management and stores
MET :	Methods	SP :	Specific spare parts
ENG :	Engineering/drawing office	COD :	Codification
TRIB :	Tribology	STP :	Standard spare parts
DOC :	Technical documentation	MISC :	Miscellaneous
ES :	Electrical service	SM :	Stock management
PL :	Planning	ST :	Stores
INT :	Interventions	GM :	General maintenance
S :	Shift (3 x 8 hours)	UTIL :	Utilities
N :	Normal timetable (8 hours/day)	MRS :	Maintenance of rolling stock
EWS :	Electrical workshop	MHAN :	Material handling
MS :	Mechanical service	BMI :	Building and infrastructure maintenance
MWS :	Mechanical workshop		

Remarks

The above organization charts concern a centralized maintenance department. The reasons for a centralized structure have been listed previously. Nevertheless, the organization charts of a decentralized structure and of a mixed structure have been included in appendices 7 and 8. In addition, and for reasons of comparison, two alternatives of a centralized structure for the same type of plant have been included in appendix 9.

As to the latter, the first alternative has assigned maintenance teams in the production area for each service (MS and ES); the INS is centralized but could - for bigger plants - be assigned to the production areas. The second alternative has maintenance heads for each production area dealing with MS, ES, INS and the related PL. These maintenance heads depend on the maintenance manager.

3.3.   Staffing

3.3.1. Manning tables

There is no particular standard which allows for the establishing of manning tables for maintenance. It is difficult, if not impossible, to compare maintenance services in different companies, even if they are similar in type. There are many factors which affect the basis for comparison including :

(a)   The complexity, the degree of automation and the diversity of production installations;

(b)   The diversity of production processes;

(c)   Age and physical condition of the factory;

(d)   Size of the factory;

(e)   The organization of maintenance service, work methods and crew output;

(f)   The degree of preventive and corrective maintenance;

(g)   Climatic influences;

(h)   The degree of computerization in maintenance;

(i)   The degree of subcontracting of maintenance work;

(j)   The qualifications of the workforce and the value of the supervisory personnel.

Thus great care must be exercised when comparing manning tables for maintenance. There are international statistics which indicate , in average figures, the maintenance workforce relative to the total workforce of a factory in each industry.

These figures have been substantiated in the table below by the results of approximately 500 audits in developing countries. They represent average figures which have been established according to stated needs. They cannot be considered as absolute objectives, and are given for purely indicative purposes. They can change in a very important way, depending on the above factors. Introduction of more automation, for instance, will increase the figures of the maintenance workforce compared to the total workforce.

The introduction of new technology will also increase the percentage of engineers, and in this case part of them will become direct personnel (needed for complex intervention work).

Industry	Maintenance workforce / (percentage) total workforce
Food	18
Textiles	12
Skins and leather	10
Chemical industries	30
Building materials	15
Steel	22
Metallurgy and electromechanical construction	18
Cork and wood	10
Paper	12
Other	12
Electricity and gas	60
Average weighted figure	22

Source : DGS INTERNATIONAL

The distribution between engineers (cadres), supervisors and workers in the maintenance department can also vary depending on each company.

Nevertheless, the distribution below has produced good results in developing countries :

Group	Distribution
1. Indirect personnel	
Engineers (cadres)	1.1 to 5
Supervisors + technicians	7.9 to 18
2. Direct personnel	
Qualified workers	55 to 59.1
Unskilled workers	28 to 31.9

Source : DGS INTERNATIONAL

In general, indirect personnel will represent 12 to 25 percent of the total maintenance workforce, depending on the size and nature of the work.

Referring to the organization charts, discussed in section 3.2 above in four steps, imaginary manning tables for some of the charts are given below as an example.

The charts discussed under stage 1 concern small factories of which the total workforce is as follows :

(a)   Plants with workforce of 10;
(b)   Plants with workforce of 20 to 30;
(c)   Plants with workforce of 50 to 100;
(d)   Plants with workforce of 80 to 130.

Examples of manning tables for some of the cases discussed are presented below.

1.   First stage

TOTAL WORKFORCE	10		20 TO 30					50 TO 100									
SERVICE/ SECTION	FM	TOTAL	FM	QW2 MEC	QW2 ELEC	SW	Total	T	FM	QW3 MEC	QW1 MEC	SW MEC	QW2 ELEC	SW ELEC	SW	W	Total
MM	1	1	1				1	1									1
PL	X	X	X				X	X									X
INT	X	X		1	1		2		1	1		1	1	1			5
ST	X	X	X			1	1	X							2		2
WS	X	X		X			X				1					1	2
Total	1	1	1	1	1	1	4	1	1	1	1	1	1	1	2	1	10

Table 1a. Three examples for the first chart of the first stage

T   :   Technician
FM :   Foreman
QW :   Qualified worker (level 1, 2 and 3)
SW :   Specialized worker
W   :   Welder
X   :   Function executed by the same person

MM :   Maintenance management
PL :   Planning
INT :   Interventions
ST :   Stores
WS :   Workshop

SERVICE/ SECTION	ENG	SECR	T	FM	QW3 MEC	QW2 MEC	SW MEC	QW3 ELEC	SW ELEC	LO	W	AW	Total
MM	1												1
SECR		1											1
OPL			1										1
INT				1									1
MEC					1								1
PREV					X	2							2
CORR					X	2	1						3
ELECT./INSTR.								2	1				3
SPMS			X			2	1		1				4
WS					1								1
TST					X								X
MT										1			1
MW											1	1	2
REP						2	1						3
Total	1	1	1	1	2	8	3	2	2	1	1	1	24

Table 1b. Example for the second chart of the first stage

ENG	:	Engineer
SECR	:	Secretary
T	:	Technician
FM	:	Foreman
QW	:	Qualified worker (level 1, 2 and 3)
SW	:	Specialized worker
LO	:	Lathe operator
W	:	Welder
AW	:	Aid-welder (helper)
MM	:	Maintenance management
PL	:	Planning
INT	:	Interventions
MEC	:	Mechanics
PREV	:	Preventive maintenance
CORR	:	Corrective maintenance
ELECT./INSTR.	:	Electricians / instrumentists
SPMS	:	Spare parts management and stores
WS	:	Workshop
TST	:	Toolstore
MT	:	Machine-tools
MW	:	Metalworking
REP	:	Repair

2.   Second stage

The charts discussed under stage 2 concern larger factories of which the workforce approaches 200. The following manning table relates to the first chart presented under this heading :

Table 2a

SERVICE / SECTION	ENG	SECR	T	FM	QW3 MEC	QW2 MEC	QW1 MEC	SW MEC	AID MEC	QW3 ELEC	QW2 ELEC	QW1 ELEC	SW ELEC	AID ELEC	QW2 INSTR	AID INSTR	LO QW3	LO QW1	MO QW3	QW2 SMW	AID SMW	QW2 W	AID W	FITTER QW3	AID FITTER	ELECTRO MEC QW2	AID ELECTRO MEC	MAS	TOTAL
MM	1																												1
SECR		3																											3
PL			2																										2
MEC			1																										1
INT																													1
PREV							1	2	2																				6
CORREC				1			1		1																				3
MWS				1																									1
MT			1		1	1																							3
MW				1		1		1	1																				4
REP									1																				2
ELEC/INSTR										1																			1
INT																													1
PREV										1		1		1															3
CORR								1			1	1	1		1	1													4
EWS																													2
SPMS			2														1	1	1	1	1	1	1	1	1				4
GM																													1
UTIL									1															1	1				2
GAR																										1	1		3
CIV																										1	1	2	2
Total	1	3	6	3	1	2	2	3	5	1	1	2	2	1	1	1	1	1	1	1	1	1	1	1	1	2	2	2	**50**

Legend

ENG	:	Engineer
SECR	:	Secretary
T	:	Technician
FM	:	Foreman
QW	:	Qualified worker (level 1, 2 and 3)
SW	:	Specialized worker
AID MEC	:	Aid mechanics (helper)
LO	:	Lathe operator
MO	:	Milling machine operator
SMW	:	Sheet metalworking
W	:	Welder
MAS	:	Mason

MM	:	Maintenance management
PL	:	Planning
MEC	:	Mechanics
INT	:	Interventions
PREV	:	Preventive maintenance
CORR	:	Corrective maintenance
MWS	:	Mechanical workshop
MT	:	Machine tools
MW	:	Metalworking
REP	:	Repair
ELECT/INSTR	:	Electricians/instrumentists
INT	:	Interventions
EWS	:	Electrical workshop

SPMS	:	Spare parts management and stores
GM	:	General maintenance
UTIL	:	Utilities
GAR	:	Garage
CIV	:	Civil works

(Example for the first chart of the second stage)

3.   Third and fourth stage

As the standard chart presented under stage 3 relates to all types and sizes of plants, supplying manning tables would not make sense. Instead, a manning table for the plant presented under stage 4 is given (see appendix 10).

3.3.2. Subcontracting

In industrialized countries, subcontracting of maintenance activities is often recommended for the following reasons :

(a)   To decrease the company workforce, while focusing for on upgrading qualifications;

(b)   To deal with the increasing complexity of production systems with a high variety of technologies.

Western companies are often inclined to call in subcontracting based on strategical, social, economic or other reasons, such as :

(a)   The fact that firing personnel is expensive;
(b)   Restricted time-lines for work execution;
(c)   Lower productivity when the personnel is underoccupied;
(d)   Higher motivation of personnel when there is higher demand for technological knowledge;
(e)   Better mastering of variable costs;
(f)   The anufacturers' guarantee on the equipment;
(g)   Regular inspection controls by accredited organizations.

In developing countries, the problem of subcontracting is more complex.

First it depends on the local infrastructure around the plant. Are there workshops at a reasonable distance which can overhaul diesel engines, grind crankshafts, cut gears, execute surface treatment etc.? This will define whether an important investment is to be made in the workshop or if all machine-tooling or specialized work can be subcontracted.

Secondly, subcontracting of maintenance work with a high standard of complexity will be done currently instead of investing in expensive training of highly qualified personnel.

Often companies in developing countries take into account a socio-economic efficiency rather than a financial efficiency by creating jobs, even though their personnel is not fully occupied.

In most cases subcontracting of specialized maintenance work to local companies is not possible because of poor standards of quality. Companies in developing countries are quicker to call for specialized services on the equipment manufacturer or on specialized technical assistance.

The fields in which subcontracting is justified in most developing countries are :

(a)   Maintenance of specific machines (either through after-sales service or through technical assistance) : turbines, laboratory equipment, computers, photocopiers etc.;

(b)   Intervention with a high complexity : computer numerical control machines, complex automatization etc.;

(c)   Spare parts manufacturing and reclaiming;

(d)   When specialized and very expensive equipment is needed;

(e)   Major work : overhauls, repairs, modernization or small extensions (when a substantial workforce is involved in a limited period);

(f)   Regular (official) inspections.

3.4.   Data collection and information flow (maintenance management information system - MMIS)

3.4.1. Maintenance data

The data which the maintenance department will require in order to carry out its job efficiently are of various types :

(a)   Basic data regarding written procedures on the internal relations and organization of the maintenance department;

(b)   Detailed inventory of machines, apparatus, installations, including technical characteristics;

(c)   Technical data contained in the technical documentation;

(d)   Instructions and information regarding job execution;

(e)   Historical data on machines;

(f)   Information regarding spare parts;

(g)   Necessary data for cost control and maintenance management.

In order to avoid incoherence and discontinuity of work due to turnover of personnel, it is necessary to record all instructions regarding the organization, work methods, information systems, etc. By keeping *written records*, poor application of verbal instructions can be avoided. These concern mainly :

    (a)   The organization chart of the maintenance department;

    (b)   The description of functions and related job descriptions;

    (c)   The interdependencies between the various sections of the maintenance department and internal procedures;

    (d)   The interdependencies between the maintenance department and the other departments of the plant, including related procedures;

    (e)   External relations with the subcontractors;

    (f)   The internal and external information systems of the maintenance department;

    (g)   Maintenance methods, in particular preventive maintenance, lubrication, set-up of machine files and maintenance planning;

    (h)   Coding, storage and management of spare parts;

    (i)   Training of maintenance personnel;

    (j)   Plant safety and hygiene.

A complete inventory of all items to be maintained, with an indication of their location and main characteristics, is the starting point for maintenance strategy and planning.

The *technical documentation* contains all the drawings and documents which are or have been necessary for the design and construction of the plant, as well as for the sound operation of the equipment. It contains all the information regarding operation, maintenance or possible future extension of the plant.

The information regarding *maintenance job execution* concerns :

    (a)   The job request;

    (b)   Gathering all the supports for job preparation, including work specifications (work study);

    (c)   The job-order;

    (d)   The work planning (maintenance programming and scheduling);

    (e)   The feedback of information to the various sections (methods, stock management, accountancy, machine files).

The data regarding the history of machines are collected on a history record card after each maintenance intervention on the machine, and also during the operation of the machine. These data form the basis for the cost and productivity analyses of the machine, on the one hand, and for the preventive maintenance programmes as well as the preparation of capital overhauls, on the other hand. The history data concern essentially the following information :

(a)   The reason for the intervention (type and cause of failure or other reasons);
(b)   The type of intervention;
(c)   The frequency of intervention;
(d)   The parts replaced;
(e)   The time to repair (shut down time);
(f)   The operating hours of the machine.

The documents regarding spare parts constitute, together with the technical documentation, the main information support between the purchasing department, the spare-parts store and the user. These documents concern the codification of the parts, the spare parts management, procurement/reordering and stock movement.

The data which are required for cost control and maintenance management, should permit the calculation of the cost for each maintenance job. This cost should include the following components : labour, materials, subcontracting services (internal and external) and overheads.

The labour cost covers the actual wages paid to the personnel, as well as incentives and social advantages.

The material cost contains all charges for spare parts, raw materials and other maintenance materials.

The external subcontracting services may concern the carrying-out of an actual maintenance job, or the payment of technical assistance or part-time personnel. Internal subcontracting occurs when the maintenance department receives services from other departments of the plant.

The maintenance overheads concern in the first place the charges for rent (i.e. occupied surface, energy), as well as the depreciation of the machines used by the maintenance department, insurance and other constituents of the operating costs of the department.

3.4.2. Data collecting forms

Forms are used to collect the necessary data for maintenance. They form the basis for further processing. Examples of basic forms are outlined below. If a computerized maintenance management system is introduced, several of those forms can be disregarded as data can be entered immediately into the computer. Nevertheless it should be emphasized that the introduction of a computerized system can only be efficient if a manual system is functioning correctly.

(a)   Technical data concerning the equipment

The <u>machine record card</u> (appendix 11) is completed for a machine or a device and contains general information such as type of machine, manufacturer, supplier, inventory number, year of manufacturing and technical characteristics.

The <u>motor card</u> (appendix 12) for electric motors contains general information (type, make, drawing number etc.), physical and electrical characteristics and a list of main spare parts.

(b)   Instructions and information concerning job execution

The <u>job request</u> (JR) (appendix 13) is used to express a request for maintenance work.

The degree of urgency indicated on the JR should be considered as follows :

A   =   very urgent : risk of standstill of a whole section or safety risks for personnel. The JR should be signed by a department head.

B   =   urgent : risk of a breakdown of a machine or small risk for safety of personnel. The signature of a section head is requested on the JR.

C   =   to be programmed : the execution of the work can be integrated into the work programme. Signature of the applicant responsible is sufficient.

The <u>programming register</u> (appendix 14) is intended to register all JR and to follow up their status.

The <u>work-file</u> (appendix 15) contains the JR, drawings, technical notes, schemes and any other support or safety rules.

The <u>job order</u> (JO) (appendix 16) (also called work order (WO)) contains a summary of the work procedures and on the back the hours clocked in by each craftsman. For complicated work a job preparation will be made on a work specification sheet.

The <u>work specification sheet</u> (appendix 17) is intended for job preparation and is completed in case of a complicated job on the basis of a work study. For repetitive work, a standard work specification sheet is made by the methods unit and is added to the job order.

The <u>maintenance card</u> contains the instructions for preventive maintenance (appendix 18). It describes what has to be done to which part of the machines. Furthermore it indicates the frequency and refers, if necessary, to more detailed instructions about how to do the job (Work specification sheet). On the back of the card a drawing or scheme indicates the subassemblies which are the subject of the intervention. Separate maintenance cards are made for mechanical, electrical and instrumentation equipment.

A <u>lubrication card</u> (appendix 19) contains all instructions for oiling and greasing.

The <u>job report</u> provides brief information about the work done during each shift or day by the intervention crews (appendix 20).

(c)   Machine history data

The <u>history record card</u> (appendix 21) provides all information necessary for a summary of the "life" of the machine. The main data contained in this card are :
      (a)   Description of the work done and the parts replaced;
      (b)   Shut-down time of the machine for maintenance interventions;
      (c)   Running hours on a monthly basis.

(d)   Forms used for data collection concerning spare parts

The <u>spare parts list</u> (appendix 22) contains the following main information concerning spare parts to be stored :
      (a)   Designation of parts;
      (b)   Drawing number of manufacturer of machine or subassembly, including item number of spare part;
      (c)   Manufacturer of the part, including reference for ordering;

(d)   Unit price, weight, country of origin, custom code;

(e)   Delivery delay, estimated monthly consumption;

(f)   Initial provisioning.

The issuing sheet (IS) (appendix 23) is used to request a spare part.

The entering sheet (ES) (appendix 24) is completed when entering or returning parts in the store.

A purchase request (PR) (appendix 25) is used for purchase or reordering and for external manufacturing or repair.

A designation card (DCD) (appendix 26) contains the list of parts belonging to a corresponding subgroup in the coding system. It is used to allocate a code number for new parts.

A stock control card (SCC) centralizes all information concerning the "life" of a store item. A form which is based on the Kalamazo system can be found in appendix 27.

The bin card (BC) (appendix 28) contains information concerning movement of parts and gives a constant indication of the state of the inventory. It is stored in the bins of the spare parts.

The inventory check card (ICC) (appendix 29) is used to control the inventory and to update all data.

The store catalogue (SC) (appendix 30) gives a listing of all parts stored in the company. It is distributed to the job preparation sections and to the production department.

3.4.3. Information flow

The information flow should be designed so that job instructions are forwarded and all necessary data gathered. Furthermore the information circuit should allow for the evaluation of data intended both for the maintenance management and reordering of spare parts as well as for the follow-up of machine history, the updating of maintenance methods, the updating of maintenance programmes, the preparation of yearly overhauls and the renewal of equipment.

(a)   Information flow of a job execution

Following is the explanation of the information flow for work execution. The circuit is shown in appendix 31. A job request (JR - appendix 13) is issued for every job except for the work foreseen in the preventive maintenance and lubrication programme or emergency work. The JR is sent to the programming unit of the section concerned which then registers the request (appendix 14). The programming unit opens a work file (appendix 15) which contains the JR, drawings, schemes and all other support and any existing information on job instructions. The work file is transmitted to the preparation unit.

The preparation unit studies the need for a preparation or work specification sheet (appendix 17) and always issues a job order (JO - appendix 16). A work specification sheet is completed if necessary and is attached with the JO to the work file. The latter is returned to the programming unit for integration into the long-term planning (work programme - appendix 32). On the basis of this long-term programme, the programming unit transmits the work file in due time to the work scheduling unit which sets up a workload programme for each crew (appendix 33). In the case of a preventive maintenance or lubrication job, the methods unit opens directly a work file on the basis of the preventive programme and planning, including JO and all necessary support. The unit transmits the work file to the work scheduling section which in turn integrates it in its workload planning. This planning is transmitted to the foreman in charge of execution who distributes the work to his crews. Emergencies are communicated by phone to the foreman who will issue a JO after job execution.

In case of a job to be done by different sections (for instance mechanical, electrical and workshop) the job report is sent to the programming unit of the mechanical section which will coordinate and distribute secondary JRs to the various programming units of the sections concerned.

After job execution, the job order, completed with clocked hours per person, and the work file return to the programming unit. A copy of the job order is forwarded to the methods unit for evaluation. Another copy is sent to the accounting department. The evaluation of the JOs in the methods unit will result in an updating of the history sheet and possibly in an improvement of work methods, an updating of the preventive maintenance programme etc. The data are evaluated further by the maintenance management unit.

In appendix 31 a simplified data processing circuit for job execution is shown. In order to guarantee a good information flow up to the maintenance manager, the foreman or crew leader completes a job report at the end of each shift (appendix 20). This report is sent each day to the preparation unit which, after evaluation, transmits it to the maintenance manager.

(b)   Information flow for spare parts

The information system of spare parts consumption control and file updating can best be explained by the study of data-processing circuits for spare parts.

These circuits are : the circuit of purchase request and the circuit of movement sheets.

The need to stock a part is noted by the user on a purchase request (PR) for initial supply (appendix 25). After checking by the head of the requesting section or department the PR is sent to the spare parts management and stores service (SPMS) for checking and codification (registration on the designation card DCD - appendix 26). From now on these items have entered the spare parts management system. The completed PR is sent to the purchasing department and the ordering procedure is set in motion.

Before being stored the delivered parts are checked both by the purchasing department and SPMS and if necessary by the requesting department. These checks are essential to ascertain quality and correctness of the order. After checking, an entering sheet (appendix 24) is issued by the storekeeper on which any discrepancy between the ordered quantity, received quantity and entered quantity is noted.

Stored items are entered in a store catalogue (appendix 30) together with designation, code number and storage position. This catalogue is frequently updated by the SPMS and distributed to the various departments. Items required from the store are noted on an issuing sheet (IS - appendix 23).

If a user orders too many parts for the actual needs of a certain job, they can be returned to the store by means of an entering sheet on which "Return" is marked.

Each item stored has a bin card (BC - appendix 28) placed in its bin, on which each movement (entry, issue, return) is mentioned by the storekeeper. This allows a continuous inventory of stock, which can be checked by the stock management section by means of an inventory check card (ICC - appendix 29).

A copy of the movement sheets is sent to the stock management section of SPMS where the data of these sheets is entered on a stock control card (SCC - appendix 27). The stock situation (normal, reordering level, minimum stock, stock-out, PR in progress, order in progress, delay exceeded) is indicated on the cards by means of coloured clips. These cards are filed so that the coloured clips are viewed horizontally. This permits a rapid survey of the stock situation. In case the stock level moved below the reordering level (which is defined for each store item depending on the monthly consumption, delivery delay, price etc.) a PR is sent to the purchasing department for ordering. In appendix 34 a simplified data processing circuit for spare parts is presented.

The system described above is very simple and can be implemented manually for up to 30,000 stock items. Nevertheless, experience has proven that with modern electronic data processing techniques (especially microcomputers) a computerized system is already efficient for 1,000 stock items.

3.5.   Maintenance planning

3.5.1. Introduction

The planning of maintenance work in general concerns daily maintenance, the repair schedule, preventive and design-out maintenance, periodic overhauls, planned replacements and the activities of the central workshops.

Daily maintenance concerns cleaning of the equipment, routine maintenance (i.e. tuning, adjustment, alignment, greasing etc.) and the various checks to be made (abnormal heating and sounds, vibrations, leaks, normal operation in general). The daily maintenance also concerns breakdown maintenance, i.e. unscheduled interventions which are often urgent. Emergency work should on the average not exceed 5 percent of the total workload of a well-run maintenance department. It should be stressed here that the maintenance department in industrial plants in most developing countries faces about 60 to 70 percent of unscheduled work. A substantial reduction of these unscheduled interventions can be achieved by implementing a sound, planned maintenance system.

The repair schedule consists of :

(a)   Repairs on site : repairs on the machine will take place when the defective sub-assembly cannot be transported into the workshop;

(b)   Repairs in the electromechanical workshop concern the repair of assemblies or subassemblies, such as pumps, compressors, fans, electrical and pneumatical equipment, electromotors.

Workload planning should be fixed by taking into account the priorities put forward by the production department.

The planning of design-out maintenance is in general a long-range planning, due to the fact that modification or extension work to the equipment require detailed preliminary studies. In practice these plans are made on the basis of the data received from the central maintenance planning office.

As to the planning of preventive maintenance and lubrication (periodic and condition-based maintenance), a distinction should be made between activities with a high frequency (daily and weekly), which often interfere with the activities of routine maintenance, and activities with a low frequency. Activities with a high frequency seldom require the shut-down of the machine, whereas interventions with a low frequency (monthly, three-monthly, half-yearly or yearly) involve more important work, so that it is generally necessary to stop the machine for some time (partial overhauls, exchange of parts, changing oil etc.). The planning of preventive maintenance and lubrication is found in the following sections.

Periodic overhauls are planned on the basis of the manufacturer's instructions and on the analysis of the history of the machine; they generally take a long time. It may be interesting to plan these periodic machine overhauls at a period of the year of general plant shut-down. During this annual overhaul, any problems with the machines which have not been solved during the current year should be dealt with. The planning of an annual overhaul requires long and detailed preparation. Nevertheless, it should be mentioned that the principle of annual overhaul is not always ideal. Regular shut-down of a part of the installation (for example during week-ends) for overhaul or repair is a new trend in many factories. The planning of overhauls and major repairs is found in section 3.5.4 below.

Planned replacements are necessary due to the wearing of parts or subassemblies after a certain time of operation. For instance, bearings, seals, sleeves, drive chains etc. are replaced systematically after a number of operating hours or according to condition-based parameters. The planning of these replacements is based on the history of the machine, on-site experience or on instructions of the manufacturer. The use of condition-based methods should be stressed. By monitoring the equipment, the intervals between replacements are increased, thus reducing the high cost of systematic replacement. A condition-based philosophy should be part of a maintenance strategy taking into account the risks which can be taken in relation to safety, reliability and quality (see section 3.1 above).

The central workshop is concerned mainly with the repairs as mentioned above plus the manufacturing of spare parts or renovation of subassemblies and equipment. The planning of this work will depend on the priorities of the production department and the availability of skilled personnel as well as appropriate machinery.

In the following sections the planning of preventive maintenance and of lubrication will be discussed in detail. Their importance is vital for the availability and life cycle of the equipment.

3.5.2. Planning of preventive maintenance

The preventive maintenance file contains all the information necessary for the execution of preventive maintenance work. This information concerns the work study (work specifications), the parts of the machine to be inspected, as well as the job planning, inspection schedules and check-lists.

A distinction is made between the following types of information :

(a)   Job instructions : the preventive maintenance card;
(b)   Programming of preventive maintenance : work programming;
(c)   Scheduling of preventive maintenance jobs : workload planning;
(d)   Inspection of the work.

Preventive maintenance job instructions contain the detailed operations to be carried out on the machine and the rules which should be respected during interventions. These instructions are written on the preventive maintenance card which is in fact a maintenance programme (appendix 18). It contains the most important information on preventive maintenance. The card is made by the methods unit (MET). The instructions entered on the card are based on the technical documentation from the manufacturer and on experience. Certain instructions will require more detailed information regarding work specification and procedures. In this case, it will be necessary to refer to the documentation or to prepare the job in detail on a work specification sheet (appendix 17). Check-lists can be used to facilitate the inspections. An inspection report is made after each visit.

The implementation of the preventive maintenance card is done by separating the preventive work into mechanical, electrical and instrumentation work. A card is made for each machine, assembly or subassembly. The instructions are given for each periodicity, starting with the highest one. These instructions should be clear, precise and in simple language.

Based on the preventive maintenance programme per machine, detailed planning will be done for all the machines. This preventive maintenance planning will take into consideration the time which is necessary to carry out all the jobs for each subassembly indicated in the programme. It will also consider the periodicity of the interventions. For coordination and practical purposes, the plan will make a distinction between the preventive mechanical maintenance and the preventive electrical maintenance, and will contain also the planning for lubrication. This lubrication planning should be added to the mechanical planning because in most cases, the lubrication job is done at the same time.

Regarding the scheduling of preventive maintenance, reference is made to section 3.4 above, in which the information flow for the execution of maintenance work is explained. In this case, the information flow is not basically different from any other maintenance job, but a distinction is made between high and low frequency jobs.

For high-frequency work (periodicity less than 2 weeks) the scheduling officer will automatically include the jobs in the workload planning (appendix 33) of the intervention section. The list of jobs and their periodicity is only set up once by the methods unit (central maintenance planning office). Copies of the preventive maintenance cards which contain the work instructions and specifications are lodged with the foreman of the intervention section.

For scheduling the jobs, the scheduling officer sends a JO to the foreman in charge with an indication of all relevant preventive maintenance cards/tasks.

After the job has been done and inspected, the completed JO will be returned to the foreman and will then follow the normal circuit as described in section 3.4 above.

Regarding the low-frequency work (periodicity more than 2 weeks) the maintenance methods unit (MET) will make a JO in conformity with the preventive maintenance planning, will add the corresponding preventive maintenance cards, and will send the whole file to the programming section. The programming officer opens a work file (appendix 15) and includes all relevant information. The work file is forwarded to the scheduling officer who transmits it to the foreman of the respective intervention section, according to the workload planning. Execution and further processing of data is done according to the normal circuit.

After preventive maintenance work has been carried out, the craftsman will make a job report (appendix 20).

Inspections are included in the foreman's workload planning or are done by inspectors from the CMPO or PL section. An inspection report is made after each inspection. This report is a form which should already contain all the predetermined checkpoints (type of check-list where the items have to be ticked).

3.5.3. Planning of lubrication

The lubrication file contains all the information necessary for carrying out lubrication. This information concerns work specifications and lubricating points, as well as planning and inspection of the work.

A distinction should be made between the following elements :

(a)   Work instructions : the lubrication card;
(b)   Lubrication planning : work programming;
(c)   The lubrication workload schedule : workload planning.

The lubrication card (appendix 19) contains the following information :

(a)   The designation of the machine;
(b)   the designation of the subassembly;
(c)   The lubrication points;
(d)   The method of intervention;
(e)   The periodicity;
(f)   The lubricant which should be used.

Lubrication planning is done for lubrication which exceeds two weeks. It is based on the lubrication programme and is in line with the preventive maintenance planning, because most lubrication activities which exceed two weeks coincide with those of periodic maintenance.

As to the information flow in relation to lubrication work, reference is also made to section 3.4 above, in which the information flow concerning the maintenance work execution is explained.

For lubrication activities with high frequency (periodicity less than two weeks), the scheduling officer will include them automatically in the workload planning of the greasers (mechanical crew). This planning is only made once in cooperation with the methods unit of the CMPO. A copy of the lubrication card is lodged with the foreman of the mechanical intervention crew concerned. The greasers themselves receive the work instructions from the foreman who makes a combined job order for the jobs to be carried out during the day. This JO follows the normal routing as explained in section 3.4.

For lubrication activities with low frequency, the maintenance methods unit (MET) makes a JO, according to the lubrication planning. The appropriate lubrication cards are added and the whole file is sent consecutively to the programming officer and the scheduling officer who includes the work in the workload planning according to the classic scheme as explained in section 3.4 above.

3.5.4. Planning of overhauls and major repairs

(a)   Introduction

The various operations which are necessary for the implementation of maintenance work can consist of a number of complex tasks. This is especially the case for overhauls and major repairs.

These tasks must be carried out respecting a certain sequence and interdependence. This means that certain tasks are consecutive, others can be done at the same time.

Several methods exist for the planning of overhauls and repairs. One of them is the programme evaluation and review technique (PERT) which is explained in more detail below. The method is based on the calculation of the critical path of all tasks to be executed. The method can be implemented very easily today by using existing microcomputer programmes.

(b)   Implementation of the PERT method

To set up PERT planning, the following steps should be taken :

(a)   Identification and breakdown of the various tasks : listing of all the tasks to be accomplished between the shut-down of the machine/installation and the restarting. This step is an important one, and for major overhauls several work sessions are needed;

(b)   Estimating the time needed to execute the various tasks and estimating costs : this is carried out on the basis of the above list of tasks. Manpower can also be estimated, resulting in a workload and cost forecast for each task;

(c)   Definition of the sequence for execution : the order of execution must be defined in a logical way, taking into account that some tasks must be done consecutively and others simultaneously;

(d)   Definition of the interdependence of certain tasks : this means that the tasks which cannot be started before others are finished must be indicated;

(e)   Set-up of the graph : in order to visualize the execution sequence and interdependence of certain tasks, a graph should be drawn up. Each task on the graph is represented by a number. Consecutive tasks are linked by a continuous line. Interdependence is shown by an interrupted line between two tasks. The time needed to execute a task is written on the line connecting the two consecutive tasks. Interrupted lines have a zero duration;

(f)   Calculation of the earliest and latest start, of the earliest and latest finish, and of the resulting margin of each task : the earliest start corresponds to the follow-up of successive tasks; the latest start corresponds to a follow-up of simultaneous and/or successive tasks taking into account that the next task should not be delayed; the resulting margins are obtained by making the difference between the latest start and the earliest start;

(g)   Definition of the critical path : the tasks for which the total margin is zero are on the critical path. This means that each delay for these tasks will result in a delay for the whole work. Consequently these tasks should be supervised very thoroughly to avoid any delay in the execution.

3.5.5. Work programming and scheduling

(a)   Programming

The programming function as mentioned in chapter II is responsible for making available the human and material resources needed to carry out a work programme : drawings and technical documentation; spare parts and supplies; tools; measuring instruments; machines, machine-tools, accessories and miscellaneous devices; transport and lifting equipment and manpower.

The programming function is thus responsible for the definition and editing of the work programme. Consequently it has a mid- and long-term planning mission.

This function is carried out by the programming officer in the planning section. This function concerns the management of the job orders and plays an important role in the work execution process.

An example of a work programme is shown in appendix 32. This planning can be presented on a larger scale if necessary, or can be introduced in a computerized system.

In order to follow up the various work orders more easily and to have a survey of the job request situation, a programming register (appendix 14) is kept in which is noted each JR and its follow-up. This register shows, at any moment, the exact status of the JR and its execution progress.

(b)   Work scheduling

The job scheduling function has a short-term planning function as explained in chapter II. It is in fact the planning function which is the closest to execution : it is responsible for the work distribution according to a plan (workload planning), which is established taking into consideration the workload of the teams and machines. It shows the necessity for the efficient utilization of manpower and equipment.

The job scheduling should take into account a buffer for unforeseen work, emergencies or delayed jobs. The job scheduling is done by a scheduling officer of the planning section who is also in charge of the follow-up of work in progress. Therefore ad hoc controls will be done during execution. If necessary, appropriate measures will be taken to update the planning or to re-schedule works.

In order to fulfil this task, workload planning (appendix 33) is done. Such planning is represented in this Manual on an A4 format, but can be made on a bigger form if necessary or introduced into the computer for easier access. The JOs in progress are represented by thick lines, the length of which represents the duration of the different work phases (for workshop) or of the job (for interventions).

If necessary, this monthly planning can be split into weekly plannings.

3.6.   Computer-aided maintenance *

3.6.1. Introduction

Efficient and effective maintenance above all requires a structured organization, as already discussed in this Manual. Once this is in place, further improvement can be obtained by computerization.

---

* Contribution by Dirk Deceuninck.

Efficiency will be improved by the computer in reducing administration, replacing manual data processing, and better communication. Quick and easy access to operational and technical data will make maintenance interventions more efficient, but also more effective because the information, if found quickly, will help in analysing and deciding upon the most suitable intervention. Finally, at management level, where strategies and targets are set, the availability of the right management information to monitor performance and the possibility of analysing in further detail the underlying reasons for good or bad performance will improve the overall effectiveness of the maintenance operation.

In section 3.6.2, the different functions which can be computerized in maintenance are explained. It will quickly become clear that nearly all functions of a maintenance department can be computerized, and that every organization will have to choose selectively those which show the most room for improvement. In this section, for better understanding, some topics which have already been discussed will be repeated in a summarized form.

In section 3.6.3 the different phases in implementing a computerized maintenance system are discussed.

In section 3.6.4, condition monitoring with real-time data collection and analysis is dealt with.

Finally, section 3.6.5 deals with the cost-benefit aspects sof a computerized maintenance system.

3.6.2. What can be/should be computerized in a maintenance department

3.6.2.1. Main aspects of computerization

Before discussing the main aspects of computerization, an overview is given below of the different fields which are part of the maintenance operation and which are subject to computerization.

Job execution cycle

Registration of breakdowns of equipment/requests for interventions
Long-term planning (work programming)
Planned corrective interventions
Preventive interventions
Major repairs and overhauls

Job preparation

Reservation of parts, tools

Allocation of trades/staff to jobs

Requests for availability of equipment

Short-term planning (scheduling) with analysis of availability of manpower, parts, tools, equipment

PERT planning for major repairs

Printing of job cards

Issue of parts, tools

Monitoring of works in progress

Reporting back

> Work executed
>
> Tme spent
>
> Machine down-time

Signing off jobs as complete

Spare parts cycle

Reservation of parts

Reordering of parts

Reception of parts ordered/entering

Issue of parts

Stocktaking

These fields deal with a large amount of data which are registered, communicated, consulted and treated in many different ways. In this data processing the computer can play an important role.

Four aspects of computerization are discussed below.

(a)   Database

First of all there is the database, which stores an enormous amount of data in a structured way in one central place. Data are entered only once at one place, and are available to anybody who wishes to consult the database.

The data in the database will be basic, operational and historical.

(i)   Equipment database

This is the structured description of all equipment maintained by the maintenance department. This database will hold :

Basis data : identification, codification; basic details; technical details; bill of material; and structure, relations, classifications.

Operational data : which interventions are outstanding for the equipment

Historical data : all data recorded on past interventions on equipment

(ii)   Parts database

This is the description of all parts used by the maintenance department for maintenance intervention :

Basic data : identification, codification, designation; basic details; technical details; where used (in which equipment); and stock information.

Operational data : which parts are reserved, on order etc.

Historical data : parts consumption.

(iii)   Personnel database

Basic data : maintenance departments; trades; personnel.

Operational data : outstanding work per department, trade, person.

Historical data : history of work per department, trade, person.

(iv)   Maintenance database

Basic data : preventive maintenance schedules; standard maintenance instructions; picking lists of parts; drawings.

(b)   Transactions

Secondly there are the transactions functions. These functions feed into the database the maintenance actions carried out (refer to the overview of actions given earlier, from registration of breakdowns to signing off jobs as complete).

Each of these transactions adds data to or updates data of the maintenance intervention.

Part of the data can be used operationally : date and intervention are scheduled; parts reserved for the job.

Part of the data will be used later as historical data : which interventions and when; cause/action taken; down time; and hours worked, parts used and costs.

(c)   Computer tools

Thirdly, the computer can carry out a number of time-consuming data processing functions :

(a)   Automatic planning of preventive maintenance schedules;

(b)   Analysis of manpower, spare parts, tools and equipment availability for scheduling;

(c)   Reservation and automatic reordering of parts ;

(d)   PERT planning for major overhauls.

(d)   Query facilities

Finally, there is the facility to select, retrieve and treat data from the database to obtain information :

(a)   Basic data : equipment or parts with specific technical characteristics; equipment where a specific part is used.

(b)   Operational data :   (i)   Outstanding work
                                    By type of work, by priority
                                    By equipment, group of equipment, location
                                    By department, by trade etc.

		(ii)	Parts
			Reserved not yet issued
			On order not yet received
(c)	Historical datal :	(i)	Analytical
			Previous interventions on specific equipment
			Similar problems on comparable machines
		(ii)	Management information. Summary information

(c)   Historical datal :   (i)   Analytical
                                             Previous interventions on specific equipment
                                             Similar problems on comparable machines
                                      (ii)   Management information. Summary information
                                             which is based on the detailed data in the
                                             database is discussed here :
                                             Cost by equipment, groups of equipment,
                                             locations, cost centres.
                                             Performance indicators - objectives and actual
                                             results :
                                                   Percentage of downtime
                                                   Mean time between failure (MTBF)

The performance indicators may be calculated and presented on management information screens (or print-outs) under the form of steering charts. These will include targets, ranges and actual results.

For each indicator it must be possible to go into further detail to analyse the underlying data in a systematic way, for instance :

(a)   MTBF below target;
(b)   Evolution of MTBF over time;
(c)   Overview of maintenance intervention within time window;
(d)   Selection of specific interventions (recurring problem).

Based on such an analysis, corrective action can be taken.

It is in this area of retrieving data in a flexible way to obtain valuable information that recent software developments (relational databases) have opened up new horizons.

3.6.2.2. Improvement in efficiency and effectiveness

(a)   Efficiency

The database where basic and operational data are stored, and are available to anybody who wishes to consult the database, will reduce administration significantly.

This central database eliminates the need for multiple individual file systems for different people in the organization, and for multiple files with the same information ordered and grouped in different ways. Retrieval of operational and technical data will be quicker and easier, as a computer system will allow many different ways of selecting the right data, which is often cumbersome or nearly impossible with a manual system.

The computer tools can save a lot of time and administration. Also the fact that these functions can be carried out quickly and more frequently with up-to-date data will improve the efficiency of these operations.

Finally the work involved in creating summarized management information will be greatly reduced.

(b)   Effectiveness

The fact that data can be consulted easily and quickly will improve the availability of the right information needed to analyse and decide upon the most adequate action.

It is in this area that computerization can have an enormous impact. When a break-down occurs, it may be extremely valuable to be able to quickly retrieve information about previous interventions or similar breakdowns on equipment of the same or comparable class. Deciding the right intervention will have an effect not only on the cost, but also on the result of the intervention (down time of the machine, subsequent availability and reliability of the machine).

The same holds true for ex-post analysis. As targets are set for machines, it must be feasible to monitor results against targets, and go into details at the level of the individual interventions to analyse the underlying reasons for good or bad performance. Based on this information one should be able to take corrective action.

(c)   Conclusion

From this explanation it should be clear that improvement in efficiency and effectiveness will have an impact both on direct costs as well as on indirect costs (the "breakdown" cost).

Reference is made again to this in section 3.6.5 below, where the cost-benefit aspect is discussed.

3.6.2.3. Summary

Nearly all functions of a maintenance department can be computerized. Every organization will have to make a selective choice of those functions to see where there is the most room for improvement.

As a general rule it can be said that the bigger the maintenance organization, the bigger the impact of a computer system. However, smaller organizations can also benefit from a computer system, but they will have to be more selective.

It will often pay to work slowly, gradually adding new transactions, with more data, more tools and query facilities. Improving efficiency and effectiveness involves a lot of management time, and can only happen step by step. Computerization should support these steps.

An example of this step-by-step approach is given below :

(a)   Once a coding structure for equipment and parts has been set up, a computer database will soon be interesting to consult the information and keep it up-to-date;

(b)   Registration of work carried out and parts used per item of equipment will give a more detailed picture of the total maintenance cost. This cost can now be charged to each item of equipment;

(c)   selective registration of technical aspects (cause of failure, action taken, down time) for critical equipment will help in analysing this part of the maintenance operation;

(d)   Registration of the requests for interventions, together with preventive maintenance schemes will give overviews of outstanding work and initial support for work programming and job scheduling;

(e)   A further step may be computer analysis of manpower, parts, tools and equipment availability;

(f)   Finally, a management information system (MIS) with performance indicators may be added.

3.6.3. The different steps in implementing a computerized maintenance management system

3.6.3.1. Phased approach

As with every computer project, different phases have to be followed in order to arrive at a successful implementation of a computerized maintenance management system. It is worth stressing again that maintenance must first of all be adequately structured and organized before it is computerized. The different phases of a computerization project are the following :

(a)   Scope of the project :

(i)   Objectives;
(ii)   Identification of what can and should be computerized;
(iii)   Feasibility, cost-benefit analysis, justification;

(b)   Functional specifications. First a general description should be given followed by a more detailed one of the functions to be computerized;

(c)   Technical specifications. A technical description of the functions with the corresponding data model should be given;

(d)   Programming;

(e)   Training;

(f)   Implementation.

Two other phases determine the environment used to develop the system : the choice of software and the choice of hardware.

Each of these phases starts with an objective, and ends with a report. These serve as an input and a time and effort estimate for the following phases.

Management can then monitor the progress of the project, and intervene after each phase (if necessary), when new agreements have to be made. Management thus avoids being dragged into a project where costs and implementation time far exceed the initial idea, or which has grown away from the initial objective.

(a)   Scope of the project

The most important phase is the first one, because it is then that what will be computerized is determined. It has been pointed out that being selective in what should be computerized, by carefully weighing up the cost and benefits, is essential. It has also been indicated that progressive computerization in different steps along with improvements in the organization is strongly advisable, especially for small- and medium-scale enterprises.

(b)   Functional specification/technical specification/programming

The way these phases are carried out will depend on whether it is decided to develop the system internally or to use or adapt an existing software package.

1. Internal development

A great deal of attention should be given to the detailed functional specification. It is in this phase that what the computer should do is determined in detail. Close cooperation and communication with the different people in the organization who know how they have to operate or would like to operate is essential in this phase.

Once the functions are defined and described in detail, they have to be translated into a technical specification, which involves the description and the structure of the data used (data model), the function itself (input, treatment, output), and the user interface (in other words, the screens and the screen handling). In this last part, the user should be involved very closely.

The next phase is the programming. This will take up the major part of the project time. As the user is involved in the very first stages of the project, it is important not to create illusions, and to inform him in a realistic way about expected delivery dates. A progressive step-by-step computerization is therefore advisable, but it is essential that the analysis is done at the global level to ensure future integration of the different steps.

The choice of hardware and software is in principle independent of the functional and technical specification, and can be determined in function of the hardware and software strategy of the company.

2. Package

A great number of software packages for computerized maintenance management are available on the market. They range from small personal computer (PC) packages to big complex packages, are developed in different software languages, run on different hardware platforms, and cover certain ranges of the complete spectrum of maintenance functions that can be computerized. Moreover, the market of software packages is still increasing.

Based on the general functional specification and other criteria (hardware, software language etc.), one (or more) software package(s) can be selected. The package can be used as a basis to compare the functions in it with what is needed. By so doing, the package is used as a "vital" functional and technical description of the maintenance functions to be computerized, and will concentrate on the differences as compared with the needs or on shortcomings of the package.

The report of the detailed specification will be a "correspondence - non-correspondence" report. The technical specification report will be a description of changes to be made to the package.

The choice of hardware and software will be determined by the package, and will therefore be an important factor regarding decision-making.

As programming is now limited to modifications in the package, this phase will be significantly reduced in time. In many cases, this phase will be planned in parallel with the next phases, as these mostly can be carried out for a great part with the standard package.

(c)   Training / implementation

Training is a very important phase of the project. Every user should know exactly what the functions do, how to use them, how information can be retrieved. Training should go on after the system is live, as many questions only come up after the user has worked with the system for some period of time.

The best results are obtained when one or two people in the organization are responsible for the application, and know it inside out. They can train people in charge of the different aspects of the application, who can in turn train users of their unit. They will deal with all questions from the various users, and evaluate possible further enhancements to the applications.

It is also advisable that management be trained, although they may not be working with the system operationally. It is important that they fully support the introduction of the system, that they understand the time needed to start up the system, and that they know what can and cannot be expected from it.

A great deal of data input is needed before the system can become operational. Again, a selection of what is absolutely needed for start-up and what can be entered later is necessary. Also, a good coding structure and classification of equipment and parts is essential.

Once the system is programmed, data are entered and the users are trained, the system can operate correctly.

The manual system may be abandoned right away, or after a short period in which both systems have run in parallel.

3.6.3.2. Package versus internal development

The choice between these two approaches will very much depend on the scope of the project, the computer resources within the company and the market.

The following observations can be made : although every maintenance department is different, many operations will, functionally speaking, be similar. Software companies are therefore able to develop packages which can fulfil 70 percent, 80 percent or possibly 90 percent of the functions to be computerized.

If this is the case, then there is an important economic advantage in using a package and adapting it so that it can incorporate the remaining functions.

An internal development for all functions of a maintenance department can be estimated at least at five man-years of work over a period of two years. Adapting a package will be a matter of months. Market prices of packages augmented by the "adaptation cost" will in many cases be significantly lower than the "internal development" cost.

Beside the savings on implementation time and development cost, there is a number of qualitative aspects which are important. Chances of a successful project are higher with a package which has been implemented in a large number of companies.

Based on this experience, a package will have evolved and operates in a way that is difficult to achieve initially by an internal development.

Software companies committed to their package will continue to develop it, and this will lead to new releases, new modules with extra functions. This will allow a maintenance department to follow new developments in the software market.

Also, user groups in maintenance departments using the same package can exchange experience and discuss or propose new developments.

The advantages are dependent on the quality of the packages available on the market, the degree of matching the required functions (70 to 90 percent) and the possibility of easily adapting the package, either internally or by the software company.

In many cases, local support by the software company in training users and computer people or in programming is absolutely essential.

An internal development may be preferred, when the advantages of a package are less attractive, such as : small application; insufficient local support for the package; difficulty in adapting the package; big or very specific application, where a package does not cover sufficient functions.

3.6.3.3. Choice of software and hardware

The choice of software and hardware is dependent on the overall strategy of the company. In terms of hardware, there is an evolution from one big central computer towards a number of low-cost departmental systems with dedicated applications. These departmental systems may be PCs, PC networks or minicomputers.

The reason for this is the extremely fast development of ever-higher-performance and lower-cost computer processors and memory. This allows small low-cost computers to handle specific applications, which is more economical than one big system handling all applications.

The disadvantage of this development is a more complex data and communication structure, as data are treated and stored on different systems and there must be communication between them.

In terms of software, the most important development is the introduction of relational databases with their own languages and tools. Compared to traditional file or database systems, the relational database offers the advantage of very flexible ways of retrieving data, in any combinations determined at the moment of the consultation.

This is particularly important for database applications where large amounts of data are stored, and have to be consulted as operational and management information, which is certainly the case for a maintenance system.

Secondly, relational databases allow programmes to be used more or less independently from the database, which allows easier modifications to both programmes and database. This is an important advantage where packages must be adapted.

This added flexibility requires a hardware of higher performance, with extra internal and external memory. However, as indicated above, the cost of "performance" and "memory" continues to decline, which explains the fast growth of relational database in the market in recent years.

3.6.4. Condition-based maintenance (condition monitoring)

Condition-based maintenance is becoming an important factor in improving the effectiveness of a maintenance operation.

By analysing the exact state of the equipment, a breakdown might be prevented or an intervention planned for the most suitable time, which may be more economical than corrective maintenance after a breakdown or systematic preventive maintenance based on fixed intervals.

In recent years there have been significant developments both in the technology and the application of this technology in the maintenance operation.

The areas of use, the subject of computerized condition monitoring and the computerization aspects of the implementation of condition-based maintenance systems will be briefly discussed.

3.6.4.1. Areas

Condition monitoring is mainly used in the following areas in developing countries: vibration monitoring; wear debris monitoring; equipment performance monitoring.

Vibration monitoring. This is widely used for rotating machines. The measurement ranges from the simple level measurement to measurement at specific frequencies (discreet frequency monitoring) and more sensitive techniques such as spectral analysis.

Level vibration analysis is commonly used for routine measurements, with simple portable measurement equipment. The measurements can be recorded manually, or entered into a portable data collection device.

The more sensitive but complex spectral analysis has to be carried out by experienced engineers. Recent developments have led to programmable measurement devices, which can be programmed by these engineers, for each specific machine or component. The data collected can be downloaded in a computer for detailed analysis. This allows the "expert analysis" to be integrated into the preventive maintenance operation.

Wear debris monitoring. Wear debris monitoring can be carried out through analysis of the wear debris in oil, using magnetic plugs, ferrography or spectrographic oil analysis (SOAP).

Typical of these methods are the regular manual interventions. Recent developments have led to systems which monitor a machine continuously and retain a sample as soon as the measurements become critical.

Equipment performance monitoring. A great variety of performance monitoring methods are used. Some examples are :
  (a)   Temperature measurement for bearings (thermography or thermoscopy), infra-red thermography for insulation for electronic cards etc.;
  (b)   Output-input analysis : flow-pressure for pumps, electricity/fuel consumption for diesel generator etc.

All these methods are machine specific, and in general only few standard monitoring systems are available.

Typical of these methods is the large amount of data which can be collected. They are mostly recorded in graphical form, for visual analysis.

As with new measurement devices data are available in electronic form; the data can be communicated to a "cell-computer" which stores, treats, and produces data output from different measurement devices.

Important here is the standardization of the measurement devices and the standards of data communication.

3.6.4.2. Computerization aspects

The first objective is to acquire the necessary know-how to translate condition monitoring results into adequate maintenance intervention. This indicates the choice of the right method and measurement device, and a significant learning period to interpret the measurements.

Once a certain know-how is acquired, the attention can shift toward improving the efficiency of collecting, recording and analysing data. As indicated, new computerized measurement devices and electronic data communication will help in turning these condition monitoring activities into preventive maintenance operations.

The computerization will again help in providing the right data at the right moment, in the right format for analysis and interpretation.

3.6.5. Costs and benefits of a computerized maintenance system

3.6.5.1. Cost of a system

The cost of a computerized maintenance system can be expressed as the man-years needed to carry out the different phases of the project, the cost of hardware and the yearly maintenance cost.

The figures given below are examples for an average project, where the man-years indicated refer to the total time spent by the project team and all people involved at various stages (management, users etc.). Figures are given for both an internal development and a package-based project.

Software	Internal development (man - years)	Package based development (man - years)
Scope of the project and functional specifications	1 (a)	0.5
Technical specifications and programming	4	1
Training and implementation	0.5	0.5
TOTAL	5.5	2

(a) This is for small applications. Software for complete integrated packages need 5 to 20 man-years to be written.

(a)   Package price (1991 prices)

Market prices of packages vary depending on the required functions and local situations. Packages are often priced as a function of the number of users.

Package and users	Price range (United States dollars)
PC package	7,500 - 25,000
Multi-user	
10 users	25,000 - 50,000
10 users	50,000 - 125,000

(b)   Hardware (1991 prices)

PC prices range from $ 2,500 to $ 12,000, depending on the make of the processor and memory.

Departmental systems range from $ 20,000 to $ 50,000.

(c)   Yearly maintenance

Here reference is made to market prices for maintenance contracts for hardware and software. These typically range in the order of 10 to 15 percent of the hardware and package price.

3.6.5.2. Benefits of the system

Improvement in efficiency can be measured in terms of the direct cost. Studies have shown differences of 20 percent in maintenance expenses between well and badly organized maintenance departments. A large part of this difference is due to restructuring and improved organization. The savings due to computerization can be estimated at 3 to 5 percent of the maintenance budget.

Improvement in effectiveness is more difficult to measure, and has to do with the availability, reliability and life cycle of the equipment. Some order of savings are found, and again part of these are due to computerization through the availability of the right information.

In conclusion, the total yearly savings due to computerization of maintenance can be estimated at 5 to 10 percent of the maintenance budget.

3.7.   Management tools for maintenance

3.7.1. Maintenance management methods *

The importance of the economic stakes of maintenance are such that a manager will ask the following question : which actions must be undertaken to ensure that maintenance of the equipment is carried out in the most efficient way ?

As mentioned in chapter I, section 1.2, the answer to this question can be analysed more easily by considering two types of management. One is short term, e.g. from year to year, and is defined as maintenance policy; the other is long term, sufficiently long to cover the period of exploitation foreseen, and is defined as "post-investment strategy". Both management types are part of the Maintenance Management Master Plan.

Maintenance policy.

A maintenance policy governs, above all, the technical aspects (knowledge of equipment, foreseeing and prevention of break-downs, carrying out of work, selection of types of maintenance, etc.) aspects of organization (definition of organization chart, administration of operations, planning of studies and work, sub-contracting etc.), accountancy procedures and financial evaluation.

A maintenance policy is a system of organization and management which allows for the coordination of operations in such a way that, year after year, the efficiency of the exploitation of the equipment is optimized. This can be expressed through the following ratio (on a yearly basis) :

$$\frac{\text{Total cost of maintenance}}{\text{Profit withdrawn from equipment}}$$

Post-investment strategy

Once the management methods are defined, their development must be in line with the level of obsolescence of the equipment. This often results in a modification of the maintenance policy, for instance by selecting different types of interventions or deciding

---

* Contribution Robert Leenaerts (Université catholique de Louvain, Belgium)

upon partial or total rehabilitation or technological updating. It is obvious that these preoccupations are done in the framework of optimalizing the life cycle of the equipment, as has been discussed before.

Under these conditions, the final objective during the whole life cycle is to optimalize the ratio :

$$\frac{\text{Total post - investment cost}}{\text{Profit withdrawn from equipment}}$$

This procedure is part of a real strategy which turns post investment -thus maintenance- into an actual profit centre for the manager.

3.7.2. What are management tools and how can they be used ?

For the efficient management of a maintenance service, it is advisable to have condensed, easy and quickly accessible information on hand. Maintenance managers have long known of the necessity to have benchmarks which give an idea of performance of their departments. Therefore indicators must be found that can,on the one hand, situate maintenance in relation to the other services in the factory, and on the other, compare it with active maintenance services in other similar and equally important sectors.

These performance indicators, and related information are generally presented in the form of coefficients or of a relation of two absolute values and are called "Ratios". These ratios become, in fact, real maintenance management tools for monitoring an existent maintenance system. As to the decision upon maintenance priorities and levels, section 3.1, "About maintenance strategies", should be reviewed. In that section is explained how to define the equipment to which maintenance efforts should be directed if resources are limited. These methods are also management tools which are linked to strategic decisions about the maintenance concept.

Comparing the maintenance performance ratios of one plant to those of another even in the same industrial field can be dangerous, particularly for plants in varied situations: different countries, or a different industrial environment.

The deviations in relation to these "foreign" averages do not necessarily imply good or bad maintenance. The results are based on particular situations in the plants concerned and on their own system of data gathering. This can seriously influence the results.

During the definition of ratios, experience has shown that the following principles must be respected :

(a)   Each user must choose their own ratios: the maintenance manager of a factory is not necessarily interested in the same ratios as a manager of another factory or production sector would be;

(b)   The number of ratios on the monitoring chart (steering chart) must be limited. A dozen is considered as sufficient;

(c)   The ratios must be based on data easily available in the factory. A reliable system of data gathering is thus indispensable;

(d)   Updating of the values which make up the ratios must be carried out on a continuous basis;

(e)   The results must be carefully interpreted, so that they can be compared to the previous results. For example, the variations in the exchange currencies will have a marked influence on the value of spare parts used or on the production cost of a product. Differences in production equipment or maintenance resources will also have an influence.

3.7.3. Performance indicators

There are two categories of ratios under which the performance indicators can be presented :

(a)   Economic ratios which allow the follow up of the evolution of internal results and certain comparisons between maintenance services of similar plants;

(b)   Technical ratios which give the maintenance manager the means of following the technical performance of the installations.

3.7.3.1. Economic ratios

(a)   Ratios linked to maintenance costs

Amongst the economic ratios that exist, those which seemed to be the most representative have been chosen. Understandably this list must be completed by "customizing" for each company.

$$\frac{\text{Direct cost of maintenance}}{\text{Added value of products}}$$

The direct cost of maintenance comprises : cost of manpower; cost of materials (spares, parts subject to wear, miscellaneous); cost of subcontracting work; and overheads.

The added value of the product constitutes the total cost of production less the cost of raw materials. This ratio situates the importance of maintenance in a plant. The fact of using the added value and not the total cost of production eliminates the important fluctuations in the plant itself as well as between enterprises due to the fluctuation in the price of raw materials.

$$\frac{\text{Direct cost of maintenance + failure costs}}{\text{Added value of products}}$$

Even though it is theoretically possible to calculate this ratio by type of product , it is easier and just as efficient to calculate it for the whole plant or production unit. Particular attention must be paid when calculating the failure costs.

As already mentioned in chapter I, this takes into account ad hoc circumstances such as profit loss through use of a substitution product, the intermediate stock of a product in the process of manufacturing, the possibility of overcoming the loss in production by overtime, loss of company image, indirect overload of the equipment etc. It is an actual cost because it can be calculated immediately after failure has occurred.

This ratio is important for the maintenance manager because he tends to think that the failure costs are low and do not influence total costs of maintenance. As the direct and indirect costs vary inversely to each other - care must be taken to keep this ratio as small as possible.

$$\frac{\text{Cumulative costs of maintenance of a unit since start-up}}{\text{Number of running hours since start-up}}$$

This ratio links the total direct costs of maintenance to a time unit (apparatus, equipment etc.).

Two precautions are necessary :

(a)   The costs must be calculated in constant monitary values;

(b)   The interest on money spent must not be added to the costs of previous years.

If the entity shows a low rate of utilization, the penalization produced by the valorization of interest will be serious, and will give an erroneous idea of the cost of the entity.

This ratio allows an efficient comparison of similar entities.

Another ratio is :

$$\frac{\text{Total maintenance manpower cost}}{\text{Total direct maintenance cost}}$$

(b) Ratios in relation to spare parts

$$\frac{\text{Average stock value}}{\text{Replacement value of production equipment}}$$

This ratio takes into account the components of maintenance costs in relation to exterior ones. This ratio is significant for indicating the degree of ageing of the equipment.

Likewise it has a comparative value for similar plants or for a developing enterprise.

$$\frac{\text{Cumulated value of issued spares over 12 months}}{\text{Average stock value over 12 months}}$$

This ratio measures the stock level of spares or stock rotation. This means the number of times the value of the stock is issued per year.

The value of the yearly issues is clearly defined. The average stock value is the average value during the period of issues. This eliminates any ad hoc variations in the stock value. This precaution is necessary because if the stock value was taken at the end of the exercise by a company which amortizes regularly at the end of every exercise a considerable stock of spares, non-representative stock rotations would be obtained.

$$\frac{\text{Cumulated value of issues over 12 months - cumulated value of issues of safety parts over 12 months}}{\text{Average stock value without safety parts}}$$

This ratio eliminates the safety-parts issues on the ratio of stock rotation. These parts are generally supplied together with the production equipment. From the accountancy point of view, they are considered together with the fixed assets.

A substantial reduction in the stock value then arises without decreasing the value of the issues. Here too the stock rotation would not reflect the real situation.

Even if it is sometimes difficult to define and classify with precision the safety parts, the last ratio will be more precise than the previous one. When considering 2 types of classifications, it can be seen that the last ratio is hardly influenced by variations, whereas the previous ratio is very sensitive. In other words any error in classification of safety parts will have a limited impact on the last ratio and a strong impact on the previous one.

Two other ratios in relation to spare parts are interesting :

Consumables and spare parts

$$= \frac{\text{Total store issues and purchase}}{\text{Total direct maintenance cost}}$$

Utilization of stock

$$= \frac{\text{Total yearly store issues}}{\text{Average stock value}}$$

(c)   Ratios in relation to manpower

$$\frac{\text{Cost of subcontracting}}{\text{Direct cost of maintenance}}$$

This ratio follows the evolution of the policy adopted for subcontracting.

Subcontracting is defined as the total amount of maintenance operations which are given to outside companies.

$$\frac{\text{Cost of maintenance personnel}}{\text{Direct cost of maintenance}}$$

This ratio gives an idea of the impact of fixed or temporary personnel.

The temporary workforce is described as follows : ad hoc personnel supervised by the company personnel and placed under the orders of the company foreman. The work carried out by the temporary manpower is added to that of the maintenance department.

(d)   Ratios in relation to post-investment

Performance of post-investment will be estimated as part of the whole production activity through the comparison of appropriate ratios; post-investment can then be identified among other financial topics which will result in a more global appreciation. More especially, the following indicators will be mentioned:

Maintenance

$$= \frac{\text{Total direct and indirect costs}}{\text{Total investments}}$$

Post-investment

$$= \frac{\text{Total maintenance, renewing and rehabilitation costs}}{\text{Replacement value of the equipment}}$$

Weighing indicator

$$= \frac{\text{Post-investment cost per production unit}}{\text{Added value per produced unit}}$$

Other ratios exist, based on the same principle and aimed at detailing one or another topic. All must be calculated on a periodic basis, for instance monthly, and are then presented in a time-base graph. This gives a very representative visualization of the maintenance activity and its economic impact.

In these graphs, each variation is an indication of regression or progress which is necessary for sound decision-making.

On the basis of these economic figures, the evaluation of the efficiency of post-investment becomes possible through comparison of the obtained profit and the expenses necessary for ensuring correct functioning.

3.7.3.2. Technical ratios

The technical ratios, far more numerous than the economic ratios, are also much more varied. This is why only those considered to be fundamental and applicable to all companies are described on the condition that the principles of preventive and organized maintenance can be applied.

Contrary to the economic ratios which are often in relation to the whole plant maintenance, the technical ratios concern mainly apparatus, measures or installations. They can be placed under two categories :

(a)   Those which interest the users of the equipment and are a measure of the efficiency of maintenance;

(b)   Those which interest more directly the maintenance manager in measuring the efficiency of maintenance policy.

$$\frac{\text{Hours theoretically available - Hours of maintenance}}{\text{Hours theoretically available}}$$

By hours theoretically available in a period is meant the hours during which, if the machine is technically in working condition, it can really be used. For a 30-day month in a factory running at full capacity,this corresponds to 720 hours.

The hours of maintenance are considered as hours of breakdown, of preventive maintenance, of repairs, inspection, lead time awaiting spares and waiting around for maintenance personnel during micro-stops. In certain companies the hours of down time for accidents are considered as hours of breakdown or repairs. This depends on the agreement between maintenance departments and production. In any case, the details of causes of down time will highlight certain stoppages that necessitate particular analysis.

This ratio indicates the time during which the equipment would have been in production. It is one of the principal performance ratios of maintenance. It also allows calculation of the degree of utilization of equipment.

$$\frac{\text{Number of running hours}}{\text{Number of running hours + down time for maintenance}}$$

It is the ratio of operational availability.

The number of running hours is clearly defined.

Down time for maintenance includes : repairs, preventive and corrective maintenance, overhauls and microfailures.

$$\frac{\text{Number of hours of down time for unscheduled maintenance}}{\text{Number of running hours}}$$

The numerator is calculated based on total down time for maintenance reasons, less the hours for scheduled inspection and maintenance.

This ratio represents the lost production hours due to breakdown for maintenance reasons, during which the production manager could not use the personnel for other jobs.

$$\frac{\text{Number of stoppages}}{\text{Number of running or usage hours}}$$

This ratio characterizes the number of failures in the system per unit of time and is a measure of the failure or breakdown rate. It is generally preferred to the previous one wherever production of wastes at the time of shut-down or start-up is important and expensive. This is the case for paper-mills, spinning units, rolling mills and also when restart takes a long time.

The unit of use chosen should be large enough so that it is representative, for example 1,000 hours, 10,000 kilometres, 10,000 cubic metres etc.

The ratio makes it possible to judge the development of the reliability of the equipment, during its life cycle. Under normal conditions of operation and maintenance, this ratio evolves following the so-called "bath tub curve". For new machines, during the initial working hours, breakdowns which are called "teething troubles" will give a higher ratio. Later this will decrease and stabilize to a lower value. If operation is "normal" and the maintenance well done, this ratio will stay low during a good part of the life of the equipment.

A sudden variation of this ratio, calculated periodically, indicates that something abnormal is taking place during either maintenance or operation of the equipment. If the ratio increases progressively even though conditions are normal, it is time to think about reconditioning or scrapping of the material (see also chapter I, section 1.2).

This ratio also represents the opposite of MTBF when the units of time are used in the denominator.

$$\frac{\text{Number of maintenance hours}}{\text{Number of running hours}}$$

This ratio measures the evolution of the state of material. It can provide a forecast, by material group, of the maintenance workload for the personnel.

This ratio is applied to heavy rolling stock (bulls, cranes, graders) as well as to industrial production machines.

$$\frac{\text{Number of man-hours for troubleshooting}}{\text{Number of man-hours for scheduled maintenance}}$$

This ratio measures the efficiency of the applied maintenance policy.

By troubleshooting is meant the urgent interventions carried out because of the danger of serious accident or stoppage of production as well as those necessary to restart an apparatus under satisfactory conditions. Troubleshooting always causes an immediate disruption in the production programme and maintenance personnel.

Scheduled maintenance includes all maintenance work except that which involves major overhauling work which can immobilize the material during a long time.

$$\frac{\text{Man-hours spent on prepared work}}{\text{Total man-hours spent by maintenance personnel}}$$

This ratio measures the level of work preparation. It is a sign of an efficient maintenance organization.

$$\frac{\text{Sum total of time allocated}}{\text{Sum total of time actually worked for these jobs}}$$

This ratio gives an indication concerning the performance of interventions.

From the foregoing discussion two aspects are apparent and must be considered:

(a)   One is the interdependence of the ratios in general. A ratio on its own rarely signifies anything specific. It must always be backed up or confirmed by examining others in relation to the same topic;

(b)   Another is the need for a precise terminology which is part of the numerators and denominators.

Great care must obviously be taken when examining published ratios in international literature without further explanation. Care should also be taken when comparing ratios of maintenance departments from different enterprises.

To illustrate the foregoing, reference is made to a study for the Arab Industrial Development Organization (September 1987). In this study an analysis was made of 10 ratios in three European industries and has been completed with international literature; the industries were mechanical construction, cement and petrochemicals. The results are given in appendix 41. The same study aimed at giving benchmarks for these ratios in order to orient managers of the same industrial sectors in Algeria. The results are also found in appendix 41.

Other figures are given in chapter I, section 1.2, but as mentioned above, they should all be interpreted with care and cannot be used as points of reference.

3.7.4. Management monitoring chart (steering chart)

(a)   Setting up the monitoring chart

It has been shown above that the ratios, both economic and technical, permit the maintenance manager to follow the evolution of maintenance performance. The results allow the manager to knowingly make any decision necessary for improved management. All the ratios are gathered on a "monitoring chart", also called "steering chart".

The principal objectives of this monitoring chart are :

(a)   To serve as an alarm bell or flashing light if something goes wrong in maintenance practice;

(b)   To allow systematic comparisons with preceding results and so establish the evolution of parameters and deduce the trends;

(c)   To judge the performance of different maintenance services, as far as it is possible within the limits of the ratios.

The frequency of data outputs that influences the calculation of these ratios must correspond to the fixed objectives. It serves no purpose to produce them too often, but they must be sufficiently close together so that action can be taken in time.

The data allow :

(a)   The taking of any immediate necessary action to face emergencies;

(b)   The request for analysis reports and detailed studies on certain topics;

(c)   The correction of deviations, by specific actions, or verifying the effects of any previous corrections;

(d)   The preparation, in detail and with justification, of budgets for operation and investment;

(e)   The informing of management and other services of the technical and economic progress of maintenance in the plant;

(f)   The justification of reorganization or reconstructing and follow-up of the
        results of these modifications by using existing ratios or by new ratios created
        for this purpose.

An efficient and well-designed monitoring chart with satisfactory follow-up not only
gives a precise idea of the performance of maintenance, but also allows for the making of
strategic decisions which directly influence profitability.

(b)   Users of the monitoring chart

In general there are two types of users :

(a)   The staff in charge in the production areas (operators and maintenance
        people);

(b)   The maintenance manager.

Both will compile monitoring charts but the degree of detail will be different. In the
production areas, the following points will be of most interest :

(a)   Number of breakdowns per installation, machine or apparatus;
(b)   Analysis of breakdowns (origin, repetitivity, corrective measures,
        bottlenecks);
(c)   Manning tables by qualification and sector;
(d)   Analysis of work (time spent per machine or per kind of work, parts used);
(e)   Maintenance costs per installation or machine.

For the collection of data, job order, daily job reports from the shifts, the analysis of
work carried out, production reports etc. will be available. If necessary, specific reports will
be made, either to analyse in detail certain situations or to establish budgets for the sector,
in order to make forecasts for material or personnel.

Of most interest to the maintenance manager will be the overall view supplied by
the data collected from the various sectors. The ratios that interest the manager concern
the whole of his or her service. They could be those presented in the previous sections.

A centralized system for data collection allowing rapid access must be installed. A
manual processing of these data is possible for small enterprises, but for large ones
computerization is necessary. In any case, with the progress of micro-computerization, it

would be advisable that a computerized system be introduced either partially or gradually for certain databases, even for small enterprises.

(c)   The monitoring chart as a tool for maintenance management

This monitoring chart will allow the maintenance manager to establish company standards for each ratio after a certain time of implementation. Moreover, he will be able to set objectives for each ratio. By following up the evolution, on a weekly basis for instance, per manager will be able to take the necessary measures. These objectives can then be split up for each production sector or even installation. Each section head or maintenance master will have specific objectives, and the obtained results can then easily be controlled and the measures discussed. A principal topic in this management system is the reporting procedures between the different sections and the maintenance management. Experience proves that a good maintenance management is only possible if the maintenance manager is correctly informed. A reporting system should consequently be installed to assure the transmission of the necessary information based on an efficient distribution for each level of responsibility.

Selected literature

AUTHOR	PUBLISHER	TITLE
ANDERSON R.T. and L. NERI	ELSEVIER APPLIED SCIENCE, 1990	RELIABILITY - CENTERED MAINTENANCE : MANAGEMENT AND ENGINEERING METHODS
BULLOCK J.H.	NATIONAL ASSOCIATION OF ACCOUNTANTS, NEW YORK, 1979	MAINTENANCE PLANNING AND CONTROL
CARA	SINTEF - Safety and Reliability - NORWAY, 1989	COMPUTER -AIDED RELIABILITY ANALYSIS
CONFERENCE COMMUNICATION	CONFERENCE COMMUNICATION 1990	MANAGING MAINTENANCE IN THE 1990S CONFERENCE PAPERS
DGS	DGS INTERNATIONAL - SGS/LAGOS, 1991	SEMINAR ON MAINTENANCE MANAGEMENT

AUTHOR	PUBLISHER	TITLE
GREEN, Dr. Malcolm F.	8th EUROPEAN MAINTENANCE CONGRESS EFNMS - BARCELONA, 1986	USING COMPUTERS IN MAINTENANCE - THE UK SCENE
KELLY A.	CONFERENCE COMMUNICATION, 1989	MAINTENANCE AND ITS MANAGEMENT
Mc. CORMICK N.J.	ACADEMIC PRESS, 1981	RELIABILITY AND RISK ANALYSIS
MILLS P.	CONFERENCE COMMUNICATION - 13TH NATIONAL MAINTENANCE MANAGEMENT SHOW - LONDON ,1990	THE STRATEGIC LINK - MAINTENANCE COSTS VS RISKS
NAKAJIMA S.	SALON INT. DE LA MAINT. IND. - PARIS, 1989	TPM UPDATE AND ITS DEVELOPMENT PROGRAM
NAKAJIMA S.	PRODUCTIVITY PRESS - CAMBRIDGE	INTRODUCTION TO TPM : TOTAL PRODUCTIVE MAINTENANCE
NEWBROUGH E.T.	Mc GRAW HILL - NEW YORK, 1967	EFFECTIVE MAINTENANCE MANAGEMENT
NIEBEL B.	MARCEL DEKKER - NEW YORK, 1985	ENGINEERING MAINTENANCE MANAGEMENT
ROCOF	SINTEF - Safety and Reliability - NORWAY, 1990	COMPUTER PROGRAM TO ANALYSE REPAIR PROCESSES MODELLED BY A NON-HOMOGENEOUS POSSON PROCESS, FOR IBM AT AND PS/2
SAKAKIBARA S.	UNIDO, 1973	APPLICATION OF MODERN PRODUCTION MANAGEMENT TECHNIQUE TO MAINTENANCE FROM THE DEVELOPING COUNTRIES' POINT OF VIEW

```
┌─────────────────────────────────────────────────────────┐
│                                                           │
│                      CHAPTER IV                           │
│               IMPLEMENTING THE PLAN                       │
│                                                           │
└─────────────────────────────────────────────────────────┘
```

4.1.   Introduction

The implementation of a planned maintenance system is only possible if certain preconditions are fulfilled. Amongst these in particular the following should be emphasized:

(a)   An awareness and commitment of the decision-making centres in the company;

(b)   Results of a thorough maintenance audit (diagnosis);

(c)   Availability of a complete technical documentation;

(d)   Availability of spare parts.

The order in which the steps must be taken to introduce a planned maintenance system either from scratch or in the framework of a restructuring project is explained below in section 4.2.

The first step is to obtain the full commitment of the general management and to raise the awareness of the company personnel with regard to the necessity of a good maintenance system. This is explained below in section 4.3 where ideas are also given for a permanent maintenance promotion campaign.

How to execute a maintenance audit is explained in section 4.4.

In sections 4.5 and 4.6, two basic supporting topics of a planned maintenance system, that is technical documentation and spare parts, are dealt with.

The present chapter is the completion of the three previous chapters, in which was explained : what maintenance is; why maintenance must be done; where maintenance is situated in a company organizational structure; how maintenance strategies and organization are designed; who is doing maintenance; and how maintenance is managed.

4.2. How to introduce a planned maintenance system

How to introduce a planned maintenance system is described below using the following two cases as examples :

(a) The introduction of the system starting from scratch in a new plant;

(b) The restructuring of a maintenance department in an existing plant.

4.2.1. In the case of a new plant

Since the maintenance department is generally overloaded with work from the start-up period onward, it is advisable to prepare and introduce the maintenance organization system during the construction phase of the plant. Once the plant has started up, the focus should be on the correct application of the proposed system, on its improvement and its development with regard to the needs of plant operation.

The principles put forward in the preceding chapters cannot be implemented all at once. A start should be made with the most elementary structures in order to have a hold over maintenance and lay down the basis for an efficient organization in the future.

It is of the greatest importance that the future maintenance personnel should be present during the erection of the plant. They should be assigned to the site starting from top level. Here is what they are expected to do at this stage :

(a) The engineers of the maintenance department have to concentrate on the proposed organization chart and prepare procedures so that it becomes operational in the shortest time possible, and in particular :

    (i) To make maintenance personnel aware of the discipline of carrying out the instructions correctly and train them to fill the proposed forms in properly;

    (ii) To prepare the different stages of the implementation of the organizational structures as described in chapter III and appendices ;

    (iii) To coordinate preparatory activities of maintenance personnel;

(b) Mechanical and electrical maintenance intervention teams can benefit from an excellent training if they are involved in the erection of the plant. The periods of installation, tuning, commissioning and starting up are very instructive to those who have to carry out troubleshooting, dismantling and repair of machines later;

(c)   The central workshop should be operational very early (before installing the machines) in order to meet the needs of the construction site and those of the difficult period after start-up;

(d)   The maintenance methods office must be set up gradually so that it is in operation upon arrival of the equipment. Method officers should start :

      (i)   Establishing the lubrication file;

      (ii)   Establishing the preventive maintenance file;

      (iii)   Controlling, centralizing and updating the technical documentation;

      (iv)   Controlling/completing the spare parts forecasts;

(e)   The rest of the central maintenance planning office (CMPO) should be gradually put in place, at least one year before start-up in order to :

      (i)   Design and introduce data collection forms starting with the job request and the job order. The personnel should be shown how to fill in this paperwork carefully, and the information circuits should be explained;

      (ii)   Control the maintenance activities, especially the lubrication work, which should be carried out from the start;

      (iii)   Introduce preventive maintenance which should be implemented step by step from the beginning, and particularly from the moment the intervention teams have more time (i.e. after burn-in period);

(f)   The spare parts management and stores (SPMS) section can already be doing a lot of work during erection. The following can be put in place gradually once the equipment starts arriving :

      (i)   Creation of codification grids;

      (ii)   Codification of all parts being delivered;

      (iii)   Unpacking, control and storage of all the supplied spare parts;

      (iv)   Introduction of all forms, necessary for an appropriate information flow;

(g)   The mechanical and electrical services should concentrate their efforts in the first stage after start-up on ensuring the availability of the machines. All the attention will go towards quick and efficient troubleshooting and repairs, but as soon as possible, priority should be given to preventive maintenance including the introduction of condition monitoring systems.

Once the burn-in period is over, the organization should be improved by putting into practice the measures described in the preceding chapters.

The following priorities should be respected :

(a)   Evaluation of machine data : updating of history cards, preventive programmes, etc.;

(b)   Maintenance management performance indicators;

(c)   Stock management;

(d)   Improvement of work methods and planning;

(e)   Updating of drawings, technical notices and other documents;

(f)   Gradual introduction of a maintenance management information system (MMIS).

4.2.2. Restructuring of the maintenance department in an existing plant

The restructuring of a maintenance department in a plant not only requires a sound knowledge of the internal procedures, but, even more, one must be fully acquaintanced with the attitudes and competence of the personnel. It is therefore impossible to propose a standard scheme.

On the other hand, most plants - burdened with the technical problems which automatically arise when making or keeping their equipment running - do not find the time to consider seriously the setting-up of an organization and an efficient information system. In addition, experience has shown that some systems are more efficient than others and are more suited for application by the personnel. There is no doubt that uniform organizational systems and coherent MMIS in various industrial plants of one group or company will ease the management and the control tasks. In a case such as this, the restructuring of the maintenance department should begin in a pilot section or pilot plant.

Restructuring should be decided on the basis of an in-depth audit either by an internal task force or by an external consultant. This audit should result in conclusions and recommendations along with a plan of action for implementation, together with a cost-benefit analysis.

This audit should help to obtain full commitment of the general management for a plan of action. This should result in the definition of the hierarchical position of maintenance, in the acceptance of the maintenance manager as part of the Board of Directors, and in the setting-up of a maintenance committee at factory level, as explained below in section 4.3.

The order of priority of the restructuring activities once the general management has given the green light will be as follows :

(a)   Definition of the framework of a corporate maintenance management master plan including the principles of the maintenance concept and a plan for human resources development (HRD) for maintenance ;

(b)   Informing the staff : proposing the objectives, asking for cooperation, explaining the evaluation system ;

(c)   Centralization of maintenance activities;

(d)   Introduction of an organization chart for the maintenance department;

(e)   Introduction of some major forms (job request, job order) allowing for an efficient collection of data and follow-up of work;

(f)   Organization of the intervention teams;

(g)   Completion in more detail of the maintenance concept, especially concerning dosage between preventive and corrective maintenance;

(h)   Upgrading of the technical documentation;

(i)   Upgrading of spare parts availability;

(j)   Setting-up of an independent training and upgrading programme, for maintenance staff ;

(k)   Organization of job preparation, work scheduling and programming;

(l)   Upgrading of the central maintenance workshop;

(m)   Launching of preventive maintenance programme;

(n)   Definition of a subcontracting policy for maintenance work;

(o)   Organization of the preparation for the yearly overhaul;

(p)   Introduction of a computerized maintenance management system (CMMS);

(q)   Introduction of a fully fledged maintenance management information system (MMIS);

(r)   Launching of a permanent promotion campaign on maintenance;

(s)   Introduction of a periodic evaluation system.

In order to have an idea about the relations between the above actions, an example of PERT planning is given in appendix 47. This planning is only of an illustrative value and cannot be considered as a standard procedure.

4.3.   Maintenance awareness-raising and promotion

It is becoming increasingly obvious that the implementation of a sound maintenance system depends on the awareness of its importance. This importance is not understood sufficiently by many of the people concerned. This is why a permanent effort must be made to promote maintenance and make them aware of how vital maintenance is to operational performance, productivity, safety and quality.

The aim is to create a real maintenance culture on company level. In order to attain this, the following levels should be involved : general management; various departmental heads; machine operators or production agents; and the maintenance staff.

It is necessary that everyone realizes that maintenance concerns them all. Maintenance, production or operational performance, quality, productivity, safety etc. are all part of the total maintenance concept, and it cannot be obtained without cooperation.

In this way, as an analogy to quality circles, maintenance circles can be imagined, with the objective that maintenance will be improved by a positive contribution by the whole of the company staff. For bigger companies with different maintenance activity centres (e.g. railway companies), the award of quality labels for good maintenance results and the title of "centre of excellence" for maintenance both contribute towards the same objectives.

On a management and departmental level, awareness-raising will mainly concern the micro-economic aspects of maintenance. Thus a comprehensible language at the level of target persons must be insisted upon. It is too often the case that a maintenance manager will use a technical language far too difficult for the understanding of the executives. The terms "bearings", "thyristors" or "PLCs" are common place for technical people. At the executive level, this terminology should focus more on economical topics such as "profit loss as a percentage of turnover", "increase of production cost due to bad maintenance" or "life-cycle costing".

One convincing method is to use figures from one's own company and compare them with the available statistics from other companies in the same sector.

As a consequence, the maintenance manager must be well documented and become used to thinking more like an economist rather than a technician when he or she speaks to the Board of Directors.

Where the machine operators and production staff are concerned, a training in the correct operation of the equipment is important. Statistics show that more than 50 percent of breakdowns or microfailures originate from a poor operation of the equipment. Failures in the operation result, in most cases, in short or medium-term breakdowns. Moreover, people must be taught to immediately signal anything unusual (noises, smells, vibrations, leaks, abnormal function etc.). Then there is a good chance that failure can be avoided before breakdown occurs.

On the level of maintenance personnel, the importance of each job must be ingrained (e.g. greasers), also the necessity of prevention. A continual awareness, even when going to and from one's workplace can help to avoid the worst. On this level, it is also a question of insisting on a high quality level of maintenance work.

The methods used to implement an awareness campaign and promotion of maintenance depend on the different levels concerned.

On the level of the general management, it is, above all, during management meetings that those messages must be communicated. Newspaper articles and selected articles from appropriate magazines can also be circulated. Moreover individual discussions between the maintenance manager and his or her colleagues from other departments are often fruitful. But the most convincing are the results of production, production cost, quality or others following restructuring or improvement of the maintenance system. The availability of quantifiable elements is obviously necessary.

For operating and production personnel as well as the maintenance people awareness-raising actions can be concentrated upon :

(a)   Films, videos or slides;

(b)   Exhibition of photos;

(c)   Distribution of "speaking balloon" posters;

(d)   Organization of maintenance circles;

(e)   Organization of competitions and awarding of quality labels related to attractive prizes : e.g. best worker of the month, the cleanest shop floor, sector with the lowest rate of failures, the department which has made the biggest effort to conserve energy, best design of posters on maintenance or best article in the works magazine or newsletter;

(f)   The introduction of the principle of centres of excellence for maintenance.

The selection of subjects can be done through the maintenance circles or else through a "suggestion box". This suggestion box is well-known in United States and European industry as being the source of clever ideas for improvements in organization, production and even the design of products and machines.

All actions must be coordinated and guided by a task force. The setting up of a maintenance committee composed of representatives from various departments and the social partners is considered a good idea. The committee can act as an intermediary between maintenance and the other departments in the factory. Apart from the technical and organizational aspects, it will be particularly designed to take in hand a continued campaign of promotion and awareness of maintenance. It can also establish contact with other companies. This can result in an exchange of experience and information which can only be positive for the company.

Finally, the maintenance committee (task force) must be in charge of a continual evaluation of the impact created by the campaign and consequently must adapt the implemented methods.

4.4.   How to make a maintenance audit

4.4.1. Introduction

The aim of a maintenance audit is to assess the existing problems in maintenance, both from the organizational and the strategic point of view so as to be able to : suggest measures of improvement; determine the priorities for the recommended measures; and set up a plan of action.

The audit must be prepared and carried out with great care and attention.

The report must set out, objectively and clearly, the actual problems and their causes, as well as the proposals for action to be taken with a view to remedying the situation.

4.4.2. The survey

(a)   Methodology

During an audit survey, it is necessary to form an idea of the prevailing situation as objectively as possible. To this effect, inquiries should be made at the production level as well as maintenance. Questions are asked not only to the service heads but also to the foremen and workers on the shop floor.

In order to carry out the audit, the steps to be followed are listed below.

General information is obtained through meetings with management, during which a programme for the audit is established.

The audit is then started up in the production departments, together with production staff. The visit should be done on the lines described below in section (b).

After gaining an idea about the condition and running of the production equipment, only then should the various maintenance services be visited.

Though not imperative it is better to always proceed in the same order, for example:

(a)   Maintenance organization chart;
(b)   Central maintenance planning office;
(c)   Mechanical workshop and mechanical interventions;
(d)   Electrical workshop and electrical interventions;
(e)   Instrumentation service;
(f)   Management of spare parts and stores;
(g)   General maintenance;
(h)   Maintenance personnel;
(i)   Expenses and maintenance budgets.

It is important to obtain an overall view over and above the specific questions which are listed in the tables later in this chapter.

The interdependencies that exist in a factory can often influence considerably the various topics that are the subjects of the audit. It is only by having an overall view, as complete as possible, that certain questions can be clarified. To obtain this, the best approach is to question all the actors concerned.

Once the visits are over, a list of conclusions can be drawn up on the basis of the answers received and one's individual impressions.

(b)   *Questions and ways to answer*

(i)   General data concerning the plant

General information is obtained regarding the location of the plant, the manufactured products, the process profile, the age of the equipment, the ownership and construction contract, the management, the labour force and the general and industrial infrastructure of the region.

(ii)   Production equipment

The data regarding the production equipment will give an approximate idea of the maintenance problems and workload and about other technical problems which may exist. Some questions which make it possible to evaluate the degree of maintenance are included.

The information concerning the complexity of the equipment, the degree of standardization, accessibility for maintenance work and the variety of suppliers, is set out so that an indication of the qualification and number of maintenance personnel required and the volume of required spare parts can be given.

The evaluation of the data obtained is based on the following conventions :

(a) Variety of manufacturers and suppliers :
     Large : a wide variety of machine manufacturers originating from several countries;
     Average : a wide variety of manufacturers originating from a small number of countries;
     Small : small number of manufacturers originating from a small number of countries.

(b) Complexity of equipment :
     Big : equipment requiring special tools, devices and highly skilled personnel;
     Average : equipment with a technology which requires skilled agents but without specialized training;
     Weak : equipment based on ordinary technology.

(c) In-plant standardization :
     Good : the installed equipment meets the company standards and/or the plant has at its disposal in-plant standards which make reordering of standardized equipment possible;
     Weak : little effort has been made by the machine manufacturer to standardize parts and components;
     Non-existent : no effort has been made to use standard material.

(d) Maintainability :
     Good : excellent conditions for removal of parts and sub assemblies; easy access to several components, even with special tools; easy access for machine-handling equipment (lifting devices, etc.); accessories to ease maintenance are provided;

Average : fair conditions for removal and access; poor access for handling equipment;

Bad : very bad conditions for removal and access. transport of sub-assemblies next to impossible without removal of other machines, removal of walls, etc.

(e) State of equipment :

Good : operation secured, no abnormal wear-out

Average : operation secured but apparent wear-out and ageing

Bad : frequent breakdowns and failures; equipment too old to secure an operation under acceptable conditions.

(iii)   <u>Organization and sections of maintenance</u>

The data with regard to the organization chart of the plant are set out to show the hierarchical level of the maintenance department. For this purpose, questions concerning the centralization of maintenance, its place in the organization chart, and the existence and interdependence of its different services are raised.

The data obtained make it possible to check whether the organization system enables maintenance to fulfil its task or whether maintenance is regarded as an inevitable evil.

The maintenance department can be said to be centralized when all the sections with a maintenance activity come under the authority of one department with one person in charge.

The questions concerning the central maintenance planning office are related to its organization, and its role and efficiency in the plant. If the central maintenance planning office does not exist as such, data have to be collected in order to check whether this function is being executed by other sections.

In addition, questions will be raised regarding the existence and efficiency of : preventive maintenance and lubrication; technical documentation; job preparation; information systems; and computerized maintenance management systems (CMMS).

The results of these enquiries will reflect to which degree maintenance is scheduled or improvised.

It will be checked whether technical documentation is complete. The efficiency is also reviewed and is judged by checking the uniformity of the codification,the access to documentation and its updating :

(a) Good : the parameters mentioned above are adequate for normal maintenance;

(b) Average : the parameters are only partly satisfied but show improvement;

(c) Bad and very bad : the technical documentation is incomplete and no attempt at improvement has been undertaken.

The efficiency of the job preparation can be evaluated as follows :

(a) Good : maintenance work is prepared in such a way that improvisations are reduced to a minimum. The qualifications of the personnel are excellent, and they have at their disposal the material resources they require;

(b) Average : the job preparation only partly carries out the work it is expected to do; a tendency towards improvement exists;

(c) Bad or very bad : the job preparation does not carry out its job and nothing is undertaken to remedy this situation.

Information regarding the situation of the mechanical, electrical and instrumentation services is collected relating to :

(a) The existence of a central workshop and/or decentralized workshops and their locations;

(b) Planning section;

(c) Capacity of the workshop (mechanical and electrical division) or of the laboratory (instrumentation division);

(d) Intervention teams and special teams (hydraulic, pneumatic, electronic etc.);

(e) Tools and equipment;

(f) Quality of work.

The evaluation which relates to the location of workshops can be as follows :

(a) Good : workshops with a central location;

(b) Average : workshops not so central;

(c)   Bad and very bad : badly located workshops with long distances between working-places or decentralized shops all over the plant.

The technical equipment and tools of these divisions are evaluated as follows :

(a)   Good : complete set of tools, special tools included - same for measuring devices;

(b)   Average : sufficient tools available for normal maintenance, some special tools are missing;

(c)   Bad and very bad : the execution of maintenance work is hampered by insufficient or bad tools and measuring instruments.

The review of the quality of work is based on the analysis of the state of equipment, on the one hand, and on the investigation of work in the maintenance workshops, on the other :

(a)   Good : the quality and the precision of locally manufactured spare parts are in conformity with those indicated on the drawings; repairs on site are done in the approved way; sound state of production equipment,

(b)   Average : the quality and the precision of the locally manufactured spare-parts are only partly in conformity with the drawings, nevertheless these parts can be used. The state of equipment indicates improvisations but does not cause breakdowns;

(c)   Bad and very bad : the quality and the precision of the locally manufactured spare parts on site are mediocre. The state of installations is very poor, due to repairs and interventions being carried out badly.

Within the field of spare parts management and stores the following issues are analysed : existence, nature and codification of spare parts; organization and efficiency of stock management; choice of spare parts and their required quantity; forms and information systems; problems of reordering; and storage facilities.

The following criteria are used as far as the data forms and the information flow are concerned :

(a) Good : data-collecting (forms, codification grid, various cards, etc.) is clear and correct. The information systems operate in an excellent way;

(b) Average : although data collecting is not done in the most favourable way it can be used. The information system is acceptable;

(c) Bad or very bad : data collection and the information system do not fulfil the requirements.

The efficiency is evaluated as follows :

(a) Good : work in the various sections is correctly carried out and meets the requirements;

(b) Average : the work in the various sections is not always correctly carried out but attempts at improvement are undertaken;

(c) Bad or very bad : the various sections exist but are not capable of carrying out their tasks properly, which hampers or makes maintenance impossible.

The evaluation of the stores is as follows :

(a) Good : the storage facilities meet the requirements. The parts are properly stored;

(b) Average : the storage facilities do not always meet the requirements and the actual storage of parts is poor;

(c) Bad or very bad : the storage facilities do not meet the requirements at all and actual storage is very poor.

In the field of utilities, the enquiry covers the maintenance of rolling-stock, buildings, tracks, roads, sewerage and equipment for production and distribution of energy and fluids. Both the quality of the work and the means to carry it out (equipment, spare parts) are examined.

An estimation of the degree of complexity of maintenance work makes it possible to have an idea of the required personnel and their necessary qualifications.

The following categories exist :

(a) Routine : maintenance of machines based on simple technology

(b)   Special work : maintenance of machines and equipment with an average rate of automation

(c)   Very special work : maintenance of very complicated and automatic machines with a high precision rate.

(iv)   <u>Personnel</u>

The maintenance workforce is the complete personnel belonging to sections which have a maintenance task and which are included in the maintenance organization chart as it exists in the plant.

Questions regarding *vocational training* of maintenance personnel will essentially relate to the actions which have been undertaken in this field.

Attention will also be given to the discipline of the personnel (follow up of orders, filling in of paperwork, present for work etc.) and to the safety of work (respect of safety orders, fire-prevention measures and devices etc.).

(v)   <u>Maintenance cost and budget</u>

The existence and the application of accounting in the field of maintenance is reviewed by analysing the cost accounting systems in the company. Special attention will be given to the degree of analytic accounting and whether maintenance costs are treated independently.

With regard to investments, the survey will examine whether investments in maintenance are treated independently from other investments. In addition, questions dealing with the value of stocks and the amount of subcontracted maintenance work are raised.

It will be determined whether breakdown costs are known and evaluated and whether detailed maintenance budgets exist.

(vi)   <u>Maintenance management</u>

Does a corporate maintenance management master plan exist ? If so, what are the headlines in relation to : human resources development; acquisition and renewal of equipment; computer-aided maintenance; subcontracting policy of maintenance work; maintenance concept;

relations with other departments (production, quality control); safety; and protection of the environment.

With regard to reliability-centered maintenance, following questions arise :

(a)   Are FMECA, FTA, PARETO (ABC), MTBF, MTTR or other availability, reliability or maintainability analyses done ?

(b)   Which are the condition-monitoring systems used by the maintenance department ? Are they computer-assisted ?

(c)   As to implementation, does a separate section dealing with these topics exist ? If so, where is it located ?

As a complement to the maintenance cost and budget chapter and to the questions under the CMPO and personnel chapters, are there other management ratios (both technical and economic) which are followed up ? How is the maintenance monitoring (steering) chart used for strategic decisions ? What is the relation to the CMMS ?

A tabular summary of results is given in appendix 43.

4.4.3. Analysis of the survey

The analysis of the collected data aims at assessing the existing maintenance problems in a company in order to recommend improvements.

In the case of an audit in different companies or production units, the results of the enquiries should be split up according to the age of the equipment, e.g. : older than 1965; manufactured between 1965 and 1980; manufactured after 1980.

Based on the tabular summary of the results of the survey (see appendix 43), the following topics will then be subject to an in-depth analysis and a description of their impact on production, quality, safety and the environment. When possible, figures or quantifiable outputs should be given :

Average distance from the plant to the industrial centre of the region. Analysis of the possibilities for subcontracting;
Type of construction contract (in case of a plant) ;
Process profile;
Delays in construction as compared with initial scheduling;
Complexity of machinery and equipment;

Variety of manufacturers and suppliers;

Standardization of mechanical and electrical equipment;

Accessibility to the equipment for maintenance work;

State of machinery and equipment (figures should be given concerning availability and reliability);

Corporate maintenance management master plan ;

Position of maintenance within the plant's organization chart;

Existence and efficiency of maintenance divisions or sections mentioned in the previous chapters;

Amount and quality of technical documentation and the access to it;

Maintenance concept ;

Forms and data processing;

The efficiency of data collection;

Workshop : organization and equipment ;

The study of spare-parts needs;

The uniform codification of parts;

Efficiency of spare parts management and reordering;

Level of stocks of spare parts;

Efficiency of storage facilities;

Degree of satisfaction of requests for parts;

The qualifications of the maintenance labour force;

The training carried out;

Collection of data on maintenance costs;

Data-processing of maintenance costs;

Maintenance management systems;

Figures concerning performance ratios (technical and economical).

4.4.4. Conclusions and recommendations - plan of action

Based on the above survey and analysis the following conclusions and recommendations can be drawn.

They should be subdivided into the following chapters :

(a)   Equipment including actions to be taken when acquiring new equipment ;

(b)   Human resources ;

(c)   Material resources (spare parts, technical documentation, tools, measuring and monitoring instruments, equipments etc.);

(d)   Organization and management including computerization ;

(e)   Social, infrastructural and cultural environment.

Recommendations should be subject to pre-set priorities. This will result in a plan of action in the short, medium and long term. In order to highlight the interdependence of the various actions proposed, these can be presented in PERT planning together with a related bar chart. The plan of action should address both corporate as well as maintenance management.

A cost-benefit analysis should also be included, which will facilitate decision-making.

In appendix 46 a framework is given explaining how to use a maintenance audit in structuring the priorities for further actions.

4.5.   Equipment documentation

4.5.1. Introduction

The lack of equipment documentation is a major problem faced by maintenance services in developing-country factories today. Maintenance without a comprehensive documentation is nearly impossible. Equipment documentation is necessary to ensure maintenance management, repair work, manufacturing of spare parts, rapid troubleshooting, work safety, a correct choice and management of spare parts and an efficient training of personnel.

In the process of technology transfer, technical documentation is a priority link without which efficient transfer would be impossible.

During hundreds of surveys carried out in industries in developing countries by the author, it was noted that only about 5 percent of the factories have   complete documentation; 15 percent possess sufficient documentation which permits correct maintenance; 55 percent have incomplete documentation often in a language other than their own; and 25 percent of the plants have no documentation at all.

When purchasing production equipment, technical documentation is generally neglected both by the supplier and by the customer.

The supplier aiming at the export market often lacks experience in running plants in a non-industrial environment. The gullible client accepts everything; he has no time during construction to check if the supplier has fulfilled his obligation and notices, too late, that his documentation is incomplete.

Complete documentation is expensive. For a new factory it can cost between 8 and 22 percent of the value of the equipment. For existing plants, full documentation should only be prepared for priority equipment, as this can lighten expenses. In any case, the investment for setting up or improving technical documentation will only become profitable if the documentation is used efficiently. For this, the documents must be up-dated regularly and dispatched judiciously.

4.5.2. The objectives of equipment documentation

The principal objectives of technical documentation which interest in particular the purchaser concerning plant construction, testing and start-up are :

(a)   Follow-up and control of civil works;
(b)   Control of conformity of the machines, at the time of reception from the constructors, the subcontractors or upon arrival on site;
(c)   Follow-up and control of erection;
(d)   Follow-up and control of tests and start-up of installations;
(e)   Transfer of technology;
(f)   Training of personnel.

In the exploitation of the plant a comprehensive technical documentation permits :

(a)   Maintenance and correct operation of production equipment;
(b)   Mastering of the production process (quality and efficiency);
(c)   Set-up of a preventive maintenance file;
(d)   Set-up of a lubrication file;
(e)   An efficient preparation of intervention works;
(f)   Decrease in time of research into breakdowns and troubleshooting;
(g)   Decrease in disassembling and reassembling errors;
(h)   Increased safety during maintenance work;
(i)   Efficient training of maintenance personnel.

An adequate documentation is equally necessary for efficient management of spare parts. It permits :

(a)   A sensible choice and correct designation of spare parts and consumables to be kept in stock;

(b)   Adequate coding of parts;

(c)   A correct choice of parts and assemblies to be manufactured locally or subject to reconditioning;

(d)   A rapid and correct manufacturing of spare parts.

4.5.3. Content of equipment documentation

Technical documentation can be split up into three parts : study and engineering; construction and start-up; and exploitation.

Above all, it is the third part which is vital for the efficient running of the factory, because most of the documents concerning engineering, construction and start-up are not often used once the factory is in production.

So, in this Manual, it is to this part of the documentation that most attention has been paid. The equipment documentation necessary for exploitation deals in particular with :

(a)   Mechanical drawings and general documents;

(b)   Drawings, diagrams and documents concerning electrical installations, and control and regulation;

(c)   Drawings and documents concerning circuits of fluids;

(d)   Information about spare parts;

(e)   Service instructions for various machines and apparatus;

(f)   Exploitation instructions.

The whole of the documentation must be classified carefully and be easily accessible. For this, a simple system of codification should be adopted. Particular attention must be paid to the presentation.

4.5.4. Codification of documentation

The coding structure of equipment documentation is based upon the factory being divided into different sections so that a code can be given to each machine, assembly, subassembly and apparatus. It also allows the allotment of the maintenance expenditure of each machine and the follow-up of interventions which have been carried out. It is an invaluable tool in maintenance management. This coding is, moreover the basis for filing and administration of the technical documentation.

In this division, a distinction should be made between the utilities found all over the factory and the production machines located in specific areas. This coding according to location is called itemization.

It is on the basis of these principles that itemization and documentation classification can be included in the terms of reference during the purchasing of new equipment.

It is therefore preferable to do the itemization at the beginning of the project. The industrial architect should submit the layout drawings of the installations, together with the list of machines, to the supplier. From these it is then possible to draw up a proposal for itemization.

Codification can be done in different ways. A coding system based on a code number which comprises three groups is proposed here. The first group (2 or 3 figures according to the importance of the factory) determines a zone. It can be a single production function or a complete production unit (see appendix 35). This group is also used to indicate the cost centre of the machine. The second group of two figures determines the machine (see appendix 36). The third group of two figures determines the subassembly of the machine. These three groups form also the basis for the coding of the drawings (see appendix 37).

4.5.5. Presentation and structure of the documentation

All the documents should be presented in hard cover DIN A4 binders. The type and colours can be decided in advance. The different headings will be separated by numbered insertions so that each heading is easily accessible.

Equipment documentation is classified in four different types of files, established by zone, department or production line : general file, machine files, utility files and standard files.

(a)   General file

This file consists of :

    (a)   Technical specifications of the installation;

    (b)   Flow-sheets showing the machines and apparatus and the information concerning the raw materials, consumption of fluids, etc., the plant layout and section drawings of installations showing clearly the interconnections of the different machines;

(c)   The operation and service instructions.

In order to obtain an overall view of the equipment belonging to the installation, an "inventory of machines" will be set up including the machines, apparatus and important accessories. The list shows the machine-file numbers as well as the principal characteristics of the components (see example in appendix 38).

(b)   Machine files

In the machine files a distinction is made between the important/complex machines and the simple ones.

The file of an important or complex machine is composed of eight headings under which the equipment documentation is classified.

For the simpler machines and equipment, the same sort of classification is used, but the content will be reduced.

The different headings comprise the following documents, separated by numbered insertions.

1.   Technical information

      Machine record card
      Layout drawings
      Description of functioning

2.   Installation and start-up

      Foundations and installation
      Transport and handling
      Instructions for assembling
      Commissioning

3.   Instructions for operation

      Safety instructions
      Operation
      Instructions for tuning
      Troubleshooting

4.   Service instructions

Maintenance
Lubrication

5.   Drawings and nomenclature

Mechanical
Electrical and automation
Instrumentation
Hydraulic
Pneumatic
Other fluids

6.   Recommended spare parts

7.   Prospectus and catalogues

8.   Control certificates and commissioning reports

Details concerning the content of each heading above are given in appendix 42.

(c)   Utilities file

The utilities file deals with the distribution network of energy and fluids, such as electricity, compressed air, water, steam, gas, combustibles etc.

The drawings and documents dealing with the machines for the production of energy and fluids can be found in the appropriate machine files.

The utilities file also contains eight analogous headings as above comprising the following :

1.   Technical characteristics

2.   Description of the installation

3.   Exploitation manual of the installation

4.   Maintenance

5. Prospectus and service manuals of apparatus and devices

6. List of recommended spare parts

7. Drawings and diagrams

8. Control certificates and commissioning reports

(d)   Standard files

The documentation for the standard apparatus and accessories (valves, motors, pumps, measuring devices etc.) which are found on various machines or in different installations is classified in the standard files.

There are three types of standard file : mechanica; electric/automation; and instrumentation.

These files also contain the same eight headings as above, but will be simplified as to the content.

4.5.6. Management of equipment documentation

(a)   Filing : when and how

The room in which technical documentation is stored should be dust-free and with no daylight so that the documents do not deteriorate.

Drawings should be stored in drawers, according to codification number and size (DIN A0 to DIN A4). The machine files, standard files and utilities files should be stored in metal cabinets, according to the file number.

The catalogues of standard and commercial parts and products such as manufacturers catalogues will also be stored in metal cabinets. Filing will be carried out alphabetically.

(b)   Dispatching

Proper administration of documents requires a central documents room which contains all originals, catalogues of suppliers and technical magazines.

The administration of documentation does not require much personnel : one file-keeper and one or two helpers can handle the technical documentation of a large factory. In small plants, this job can even be carried out by the technicians in charge of job preparation.

In larger factories, it is advisable to have on hand copies of the documentation, or part of it, close to the equipment. Each section concerned should therefore have facilities for adequate storage of documents, for being permanently available in case of break-down, even at night.

The person in charge of documentation should also dispatch updated documents to the different sections.

(c)   Updating

Each modification, however small, must be immediately recorded on the original documents and made known to the users.

Updating is important because it concerns mainly the drawings (electrical, mechanical etc.). It must be carried out by the methods section together with the drawing section of the CMPO. Everybody must realize that any modification to the equipment must be signalled immediately to the methods section. Each modified drawing will carry a new index. The updates are also noted on a sheet in each machine file. In this way it is possible to see at any time if the plan or document in one's possession is the latest and most up-to-date version.

(d)   Reviews and technical books

In order to enable maintenance staff to be kept informed about new techniques in the field, it is recommended to encourage them to read professional magazines. A dispatching system should be set up so that magazines may be distributed regularly to the staff. Once circulated, the magazines will be stored at the central documentation room.

All factories should have at their disposal a technical library with books regarding general mechanics, surface treatment, electricity, maintenance, spare parts management etc.

4.5.7. Basics for terms of reference for equipment documentation

It is recommended to make sure that separated terms of reference which deal with documentation to be supplied by the manufacturer are available. These terms of reference are added to the specific terms of reference that deal with general and detailed conditions of purchase.

The objectives of these terms of reference are :

(a)   To determine exactly which documents, drawings and diagrams are to be delivered by the supplier;

(b)   To define precisely the standards, formats and other particular demands which the above documents should satisfy;

(c)   To define precisely the form of presentation in order to obtain a uniform documentation easy to classify and consult;

(d)   To define precisely the delivery conditions of the documentation (where, when, how, number of examples, originals etc.);

(e)   To determine the responsibilities of the supplier and to fix penalties in order to have leverage against him if the contract is not fulfilled.

Proposals to improve the situation of equipment documentation concern various levels or stages :

(a)   During the pre-investment studies, sufficient financial resources should be provided for technical documentation. A complete technical documentation, including engineering work and drawings can cost between 8 and 22 percent of the value of the equipment, depending on the type of plant. Expecting such an investment from a supplier without payment is impossible;

(b)   The plant constructors, the manufacturers of equipment and their subcontractors, must make a considerable effort to prepare a technical documentation which meets the local operational needs of their clients :

        (i)   Technical documentation should be comprehensive. Concerning maintenance, the items listed in section 4.5.5 must be included by the main suppliers and their subcontractors;

(ii)   The technical documentation must be in the language of the customer;

(iii)   The documentation must be delivered on time (first draft before arrival of machines), permitting the customer to carry out the necessary checks and to prepare the maintenance service and training of the personnel; .

(iv)   The technical documentation must be "as built" at the final acceptance;

(v)   The technical documentation must be clear and understandable for a workforce which does not always have the technical knowledge of that found in industrialized countries. Abundant use of photographs, exploded views and explanatory sketches are essential;

(c)   The purchaser of equipment or the plant operator must clearly specify in separate terms of reference what he expects from the supplier in the field of technical documentation. He must define the content, the form, the delivery conditions and the penalties in case of failure. Moreover, he must create a correct administration system for his documentation which should be centralized in the plant (coding, classification, updating, system for consultation and distribution etc.). In case of non-supply of machine files by the manufacturer, he has to make them up himself at least in the first stage for the priority production machines. For this reason he should send trainees to companies specialized in the making-up of machine files and technical documentation. It should be emphasized that since a sound documentation is expensive, sufficient budgets should be provided.

4.5.8. Improvement actions in the plant

At plant level, the following improvement actions are recommended :

(a)   *In the short term, steps should be taken :*

(i)   To centralize all technical documentation in one area of the plant;

(ii)   To codify and classify the documentation and create a system for updating and dispatching;

(iii)   To specify priority machines with a high risk of production bottlenecks and make up detailed machine files for them;

(iv)   To establish standard terms of reference for technical documentation which must be imposed on the suppliers of equipment.

(b)   *In the medium and long term, steps should be taken :*

(i)   To train personnel both in the preparation of machine files and in the administration of technical documentation;

(ii)   To complete gradually the technical documentation for machines other than priority ones, according to their importance in relation to safety, reliability, production etc.;

(iii) To assemble workshop drawings for the manufacturing of spare parts, in particular, from those manufacturers who have disappeared from the market.

4.6.   Spare parts

4.6.1. Introduction

The shortage of spare parts is one of the major causes of headaches for plant owners in developing countries. It has been stated for example that at least 50 percent of the unavailability of machines in developing countries is due to a lack of spare parts.

The following common problems have been noted :

(a)   A wide variety of equipment manufacturers and little effort made to standardize machinery and components, resulting in a large investment in spare parts stock;

(b)   A poor selection of spares to be stored. This is due to two reasons : a lack of information in technical documentation supplied by the manufacturer, and a lack of experience in operation of production equipment in a developing country environment of those who must make the selection;

(c)   An incorrect designation of spare parts. The designations are given, based on the information supplied by the manufacturer. In most cases, the designation which is given is the one of the machine manufacturer and not of the part manufacturer. The use of designations, conforming with international standards, is not always done because some manufacturers think that by neglecting this important fact they can protect the spare parts market. The problem is even greater for the spare parts of subassemblies or individual components (the manufacturers of which are sub-contractors of the machine manufacturer, often to the third degree);

(d)   A non-existent uniform in-plant codification of parts. The reasons being:

(i)   A non-existent internal coding system;
(ii)   Incorrectly identified spare parts;
(iii) Poor application of codification systems (where they exist);

(e)   An insufficient or non-existent stock management, due to a lack of stock management systems or to a lack of information concerning the management parameters (average monthly consumption, price, delay, minimum and maximum stock levels, reordering point). Poor data collection (issuing or entering quantities, repairability etc.) or belated treatment (manual or by computer) jeopardizes reliable data. Moreover, unreliable information about frequency of part replacement or priorities for planned overhaul does not allow for the establishing of consumption parameters;

(f)   Lengthy reordering delays, due to protracted internal delays in the company, delivery delays by the supplier, delays in payment or in the setting-up of financing (mainly for imported parts in countries with non-convertible currency), customs delays (heavy administration, work overload of customs services etc.) and finally due to transport delays between place of arrival and destination;

(g)   A lack of hard currency for imported spare parts which obliges plant management to reduce its stock. This reduction is done indiscriminately, which leads to stock-outs of vital parts;

(h)   A random allocation of import quotas in certain countries;

(i)   A poor storage due to insufficient storage and handling facilities or to a lack of part conservation arrangements (cleaning, antishock or anticorrosion protection and coating). It has been found that approximately 15 percent in terms of value of the stored parts is useless when needed, due to poor storage conditions;

(j)   A poor knowledge of stock. There is an important percentage of oddments (often between 15 and 20 percent of the items). Stock analysis (i.e. method of Pareto) is not carried out and therefore spare parts for machines that have been scrapped continue to be stored.

Apart from the above problems, it must be stressed that detailed contractual clauses concerning spare parts are missing or are unclear when purchasing equipment. Specific tender documents for spare parts rarely exist in this case.

Added to these problems there is a lack of facilities and capabilities for local manufacturing of spare parts. The industrial network surrounding the factories in developing countries is very limited. This often forces the factories to become self-sufficient in this field. But it is still not enough to encourage adequate investment to meet these needs.

Techniques for reconditioning of spare parts (protective coating through welding techniques, metallization, application of antifriction metal, adhesives, Metalloc system etc.) are little known, and almost no effort has been made to develop them. Nevertheless they represent a cheap way to make up for the lack of spare parts in many cases.

Finally, very little action has been taken in the field of human resources development for :

(i)   The choice, codification and designation of parts;
(ii)   Stock management.

4.6.2. Selection of spare parts to be kept in stock

(a) Types of articles

The stock in a maintenance store can be divided into three types of articles :

(a)   Specific parts of an installation, machine or device. These parts are especially manufactured for the above equipment and are not interchangeable with parts of another make (for instance, machine frames, valve levers, spiral gears, switch contacts, piston rings, connecting-rods, etc.);

(b)   Standard parts which have characteristics corresponding to international standards and/or which are interchangeable with parts of another make. The manufacturer of the parts is not necessarily the manufacturer of the equipment on which they are installed. Examples of standard parts are bearings, O-rings, lip-seals, fuses, cocks and fittings, roller-chains and V-belts;

(c)   Maintenance consumables and current store items which are generally found on the market include sheet metal, profile iron, castings, bolts and nuts, pipes, building materials, sealing compounds, cleaning products, rags, glues, lubricants, grinding paste etc.

The selection of parts to be stored is based on the study of the components of the equipment. This study should deal particularly with the following factors :

(a)   Parts subject to wear;
(b)   Parts which rarely wear out, but their good condition is a prerequisite for the correct functioning of the machine;

(c)   The stress on the equipment and its components in relation to the degree of utilization of the machine;

(d)   The age of the equipment;

(e)   The technical level of operators and maintenance personnel;

(f)   The motivation of personnel;

(g)   The management and care of the production equipment;

(h)   The general organization of the company and of maintenance in particular.

(b) Estimation of stock level

The stock levels in a company, apart from the factors already mentioned above, depend on :

(a)   The number of identical parts installed;

(b)   The reordering delays;

(c)   Commercial and administration aspects of the purchasing and reordering of spare parts;

(d)   The degree of in-house standardization of equipment;

(e)   The possibilities of local manufacturing.

During the various surveys carried out by the author in developing countries, it was observed that the selection and quantity of materials and parts kept in stock are not in accordance with the needs of local operating conditions. The quantity of specific parts was insufficient, and standard parts and consumables were generally not provided at all.

To estimate a correct stock level, the following procedure should be applied:

(a)   The study of components of the equipment as explained above;

(b)   The determination of the spare parts to be kept in stock;

(c)   The analysis of the quantities proposed by the manufacturer of each machine; this study should be completed by preparing estimates or by available experience in relation to prevailing field conditions;

(d)   The setting-up of recapitulative tables, which would gather data for identical parts;

(e)   A forecast of monthly consumption;

(f)   The study of delivery delays and unit prices;

(g)   The study of possibilities for local manufacturing or repair;

(h)   Preparing estimates of quantity for an initial stock.

Attention should be paid to the fact that the stock level depends on the availability of a rational stock management system, thus allowing a strict follow-up of consumption of parts. If this system does not exist from the very beginning, levels of initial supply should be increased. Consequently the introduction of a sound stock management system is essential.

4.6.3. Parts designation and codification

(a) Introduction

Without a uniform and common language, it is impossible to centralize spare-parts management and stores for different production areas. It is therefore vital to set up one single codification and designation system for spare parts and current store items.

The way in which codification is carried out will determine :

(a)   The quality of stock management;
(b)   The quality of storage and consequently efficiency of serving the users;
(c)   The accuracy in which the user can express his needs;
(d)   Correct reordering by the purchasing department;
(e)   Proper delivery by the supplier.

Correct codification is even more important when stock administration and purchasing are handled by electronic data processing.

A coding system has to meet the following requirements :

(a)   A code number must correspond with one item only;
(b)   An item must correspond with one code number only;
(c)   A code number must be definite. A change of code number which is already known to the users, applied in the stores and registered in the stock management section and purchasing, is a constant source of confusion and should be avoided;
(d)   The code number must be logical, i.e. it is given according to a codification grid which takes into account the main characteristics of the item which has to be coded.

(b) Parts designation

The designation must be studied very carefully :

(a)   It has to be complete and should exclude ambiguity;
(b)   It has to be clear and comprehensible to each user;
(c)   It has to be known all over the company;
(d)   It should be adapted to the restrictions imposed by electronic data processing and purchase procedures (i.e. the designation must be clear to an "outsider");
(e)   It should be the only one existing in the company.

Correct designation is indispensable in order to :

(a)   Avoid stocking identical parts under a different name in different places in the store, and consequently avoid "false" stock-outs (where one stock item is out of stock while the same part with another designation is available in sufficient quantity);
(b)   Ease filing in the purchasing department and the stock management section;
(c)   Speak the same language among users, purchasers and suppliers;
(d)   Allow the supply of standard parts from the world market and not only from one supplier.

Correct designation means a designation :

(a)   According to a standard (international, national, company or in-house) for standard parts;
(b)   According to the references of the manufacturer of the part or of the machine for specific parts;
(c)   According to references commonly used on the market for maintenance consumables and current store items.

A systematic designation of standard parts according to the references of the machine manufacturer should be prohibited.

When acquiring new equipment, the manufacturer or supplier should be informed in detail of how the parts must be designated. Immediately after delivery of the equipment a team in charge of the study of spare parts should check whether this request has been fulfilled. This check should be done in different steps, as follows :

(a)   Identification of the parts;
(b)   Gathering of standard and specific parts on separate lists;

(c)   Checking of the correct designation of the parts with the help of standards or manufacturers' catalogues;

(d)   Checking of the designation of specific parts based on detailed drawings supplied by the manufacturers.

(c) The codification system

The codification system which generally provides good results in developing countries is based on a codification according to the nature of the spare parts. It is a morphological codification. First there is a broad classification of products which is in fact a sorting process, divided into 10 classes (from 0 to 9). The classes are then each subdivided into families, subfamilies, groups and subgroups. A code number composed of eight figures for instance is enough even for very large stores.

By means of an example, the principle of an eight-figure coding system is explained in appendix 39 for a hexagon socket head cap screw M20 x 100 DIN 912-8.8.

In order to proceed with codification, first a codification grid should be designed, adapted to the equipment in the company. This must be done by the spare parts management and stores service, assisted by a methods section and/or technicians in charge of the job preparation.

The following steps should then be followed :

(a)   Check whether parts designation is complete with the help of :
  (i)   Technical documentation of the manufacturer;
  (ii)   International standards;
  (iii) Identification of the part in the store or on the equipment ;
(b)   Define the family and the subfamily in the corresponding class of codification system;
(c)   Define the group and subgroup;
(d)   Attribute the last three figures of the code number;
(e)   In case of an existing subgroup, check whether the part has not already been codified.

After designation and codification of the part the store catalogue (appendix 30) should be completed in which all stored items are listed with an indication of their storage position. The store catalogue must be regularly updated and distributed to all users in the company.

4.6.4. Spare parts management

(a) Stock management parameters

The function of stock management (or stock administration) is to ensure the availability of spare parts according to the demands of the users. It must keep stock levels optimal so that the production equipment operates correctly with the minimum risk of stock-outs and under the best economic conditions.

The solution of the problem of availability of parts passes inevitably through the acceptance that future consumption will be based on past consumption. If data concerning past consumption is not available, it can be obtained by comparing present cases with previous analogous ones. Obviously past results can be adapted according to technical, economic or financial considerations. The main historical data used is the average monthly consumption.

To obtain its objectives, the stock management section must :

(a) Calculate a reordering level and a reordering quantity for each article;
(b) Make a forecast of future consumption, based on past consumption, obviously after thorough analysis;
(c) Issue purchase requests at the right moment;
(d) Define dead stocks (oddments);
(e) Correctly define minimum and maximum stocks.

The basic parameters which are commonly used in stock management are : monthly consumption; unit price; delivery delay; reordering level; minimum stock level; and maximum stock level.

(b) Stock management and re-ordering systems

1. Introduction

A rational stock management system does not mean that there should be a minimum of stored items. On the other hand, overstocking must also be avoided. The best solution can only be found by a systematic approach.

Rational stock management must lead to the following condition when considering the reordering quantity and frequency :

Purchase price + acquisition cost + owner costs = minimum

where

Acquisition cost   =   all administration costs in connection with purchasing

Owner costs   =   all costs resulting from stock composition and conservation (interest loss on invested capital, storage costs, personnel costs, distribution and conservation costs etc.)

The type of stock-management system chosen will depend on the nature of the item, and its average consumption is the first element of decision. In general, two main categories can be established :

(a) Consumables and non-durable items, current store-items, standard parts, certain specific parts. These are items which are often used, their lifetime is limited, and they are subject to wear. They are called fast movers;

(b) items which are rarely used, but which must be in stock, in case of unexpected breakdown, incident or wear. A prolonged stoppage of the machine can occur if they are not kept in stock (they are called "safety, security or insurance parts", and are always "slow movers").

It is evident that stock in the first category will have a large turn-over (also called turnaround), whereas stock in the second category will be "sleeping". The criteria for classifying an item into one of these two categories is its monthly consumption. If consumption exceeds 0.25, then an item will be listed as a fast mover, and if less then or equal to 0.25, than it will be listed as slow mover.

In order to avoid stock-outs due to a longer delivery delay then expected or to accelerated consumption, a "protection stock" or "minimum stock" is determined. This stock is expensive because it is permanent, it takes up precious storage space, it uses capital, and it causes owner costs (conservation, personnel etc.).

A graph illustrating various consumption models and a minimum stock level can be presented as in the following figure VIII.

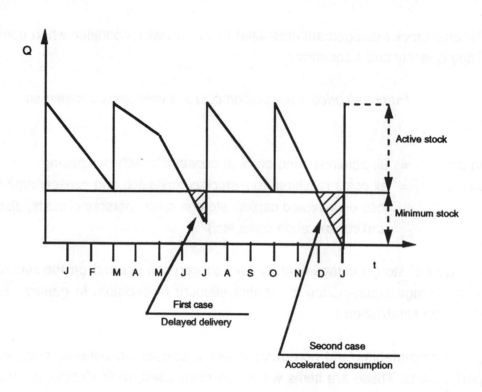

Figure VIII. Consumption models

2. The management of fast movers

When considering management of items of which the monthly consumption exceeds 0.25, the following should be noted :

(a)   Care should be taken to ensure that sufficient parts are in stock. For a minimum stock to be established, possible abnormal consumption or delivery delays should be taken into consideration. There is a mathematical method to calculate minimum stock but because all necessary data for theoretical calculation is rarely found in developing countries, an empirical value of 10 percent of active stock is commonly accepted;

(b)   Reordering must be done in time. Firstly, the reordering level for each item should be determined. This level will depend on the stock level, the quantity already ordered ("expected") and the quantity subject to purchase request. The re-ordering level is determined by the sum of consumption during the internal re-ordering delay plus the consumption during the delivery delay plus minimum stock. The internal reordering delay is the time needed in the plant before ordering. The delivery delay is the time between the date of ordering and the date of delivery. The reordering delay is the internal reordering delay plus delivery delay;

(c)   Care must be taken to avoid accumulating too many parts in stock. A maximum stock will be determined, corresponding to the sum of stock at the reordering level plus the quantity of orders in progress.

These considerations help to determine the economic quantity to be ordered, which takes into account the utilitarian price (Pu) of the item (unit price increased by transport and handling costs etc.), the interest on invested capital (i) and sundry costs (d) (storing, personnel etc. expressed in percentage of average stock).

The economic quantity is calculated according to the formula of Wilson :

$$Q = \sqrt{\frac{24 \times CA}{i+d}} \cdot \sqrt{\frac{Ma}{Pu}}$$

where   Ma = average monthly consumption
         Q = quantity per order
         acquisition cost/item = C_A/item

This quantity should be considered as a tentative quantity to be stored. It is rounded off upwards to the next packing quantity, or should be adjusted in relation to projected maintenance events, such as big repairs or important overhauls.

It must be emphasized that formulae for reordering should only serve as guidelines. They help the decision maker to take into consideration all the parameters, but a considerable number cannot be translated into formulae. This is why permanent follow-up and updating of the files are required.

The use of the formula is not applicable to items with a low monthly consumption. Wilson's formula is further based on the fact that a realistic estimate of the average monthly consumption is available.

The use of abacuses can ease the application of the Wilson formula. Abacuses should be established in order to find Q, starting from Pu and Ma (appendix 48).

3. Management of slow movers

These parts are not supposed to be subject to much wear. Therefore, it is the safety stock which is at stake if unforeseen breakdowns occur.

In order to determine the quantity of these items to be stored, answers must be provided for the following two questions :

(a)   What is the impact of a broken part on production ?

(b)   What are the possibilities of local repair or reconditioning of the part ?

On the basis of this information and taking into account the price of the items, a decision concerning the quantity to be kept in stock is possible according to a re-ordering type such as that explained below in section 5. In some cases a zero stock may be acceptable (e.g. a repaired part can be used provided the frequency of incidents permits it).

4.   Consumption and stock level control

To be able to follow up the evolution of the actual stock and to ensure a rational stock management, correct data are indispensable and should be easily accessible.

In practice for the follow-up of consumption and the stock level of an item (i.e. its history), the following data processing forms are used (see chapter III, section 3.4) :

(a)   Each article has a stock control card (appendix 27) which is updated by the stock management section. The main information on this form is a current overview of stock movements;

(b)   Each article has a bin card (appendix 28) which is kept in its respective bin and updated by a storekeeper. Stock movement and current inventory are the principal topics on this card;

(c)   each movement of an item (issue, entry/return) is recorded on a specific form, i.e. an issuing sheet (appendix 23), or an entering sheet (appendix 24)).

A procedure for data collection and processing should be formulated. A permanent check between what is written on the stock control card and the physical stock is possible through a continuous inventory system. An inventory check card (appendix 29) can be used for this purpose. When the stock level reaches the reordering level (calculated for each item), a purchase request (appendix 25) for reordering is filled in and sent to the purchasing department for further processing.

5.   Reordering

Different types of re-ordering are possible, both for slow movers as well as for fast movers.

(a)   Reordering based on a re-ordering level. Each time the stock reaches the level which equals the sum of the consumption during the internal re-ordering delay plus the consumption during the delivery delay plus the minimum stock, a quantity determined by means of the economic quantity calculated by Wilson's formula is reordered.

(b)   Periodical reordering. A consequence of reordering based on the reordering level is that orders are placed at variable dates. The inconvenience of this is that each item must be considered separately. Grouping would reduce the number of orders. The two main criteria for this grouping relate to the supplier and the geographical location. The stock of items from one supplier would be checked at regular intervals t, t+P, t+2P etc. After grouping one could then switch easily to fixed-date ordering, for which the standard to optimize costs becomes the delay between the intervals of stock checking. The disadvantage of this system is the increase in the stock level.

(c)   Reordering in the case of low consumption. When the consumption becomes very low, i.e.less than one unit per delivery delay, the quantity to be stocked will be calculated in accordance with the consumption during the time between two deliveries (also called "reordering systems by allotment").

(d)   Reordering by contract. This is more a purchasing technique than a method of stock management. It consists of a contract with a supplier which specifies the quantity to be supplied over a certain period of time. The contract details all the purchasing conditions, particularly price and delay.

Regarding the reordering system based on the re-ordering level, the following considerations should be taken into account :

(a)   The use of Wilson's formula is often onerous, especially when no electronic data processing is available to facilitate the calculations. The use of abacuses mentioned before makes the work much easier, but their set-up can be tedious (slide-rules do exist in this field). Also, Wilson's formula is only useful if the monthly consumption is sufficiently high. A continuous stock control for each item is indispensable if this method is used;

(b)   Wilson's formula does not take into account the optimal number of orders per year. This means that the programme of reordering depends on the turnover of consumption. In practice it is necessary to consider an optimal number of orders per year, determined mainly by cost analysis of bulk shipping in relation to detail-transport;

(c)   The economic and political system is in constant evolution, thus creating frequent changes :

        (i)   Parts consumption of production units (expansion, recession, new technologies);

        (ii)   Delivery delays;

        (iii) Transport (ways and means);

(d)   For reasons of close and permanent follow-up of the actual situation of the company, a continuous updating of the reordering level and minimum stock is essential. But in reality, these parameters are usually only updated when :

        (i)   There is a stock-out, with expensive production losses as a result of an urgent reordering under exceptional conditions;

        (ii)   The annual inventory check shows overstocking;

(e)   The only advantage of the method is that the economic reordering and transport quantity can be fixed exactly. This means that many items of low value - which represents a major part of stock - are grouped by family of products, in order to increase the reordering quantity of one supplier;

(f)   A part is only reordered when the reordering level is reached. If consumption decreases suddenly, there is no automatic way in the manual system to discover if this item is not on the way to becoming dead stock (oddment). It can only be seen during an annual inventory check, where movement has been registered. Then it is often too late, especially for products with a limited shelf-life.

The periodical reordering system is a type of stock management based on fixed-date ordering of variable quantities. The quantity to be reordered in this case is :

$$Q = (d+a+P)\ Ma - (S + c)$$

where c = Quantity on orders in progress

        S = Quantity in stock

      Ma = Average monthly consumption

        d = Reordering delay = internal reordering delay + delivery delay (delay between the date of stock revision and entering date in the store)

        a = Risk factor, defining minimum stock in months

        P = Period between two re-orderings

        Q = Reordering quantity

This method can improve a reordering system based on the reordering level and permits the setting-up of a real ordering schedule.

Various methods exist concerning the consumption forecast.

(a)   With the method of mobile average, the forecast is based on data of past consumption (i.e. monthly) for which an average value is taken. It should be noted that it is necessary to analyse the reasons for consumption. Parts, for instance, used during a major overhaul, cannot be considered as normal consumption.

(b)   The method of exponential smoothing provides a new forecast. This is done by adding to the previous forecast a correction which takes into account the difference between the last forecast of consumption (for which historical data was available) and the actual consumption during the period.

In a formula :

New forecast = previous forecast + μ (difference between the actual consumption and the previous forecast for the same period).

Factor μ is called "exponential smoothing constant", and can vary between 0 and 1. Most common values vary between 0.1 and 0.3. Higher values are used in special circumstances.

(c) Stock analysis

Regular stock analysis permits the fine-tuning of an existing system of spare parts management and should be part of a general policy. It determines the parts which need particular attention and for which the decisions taken directly influence the efficiency of spare parts management.

The process of stock analysis consists of putting the items, subject to the study, in a decreasing order of value (unit price). Subsequently a graph is drawn up with the abscissa representing the accumulated items in the same order as mentioned above and the ordinate representing the corresponding cumulative values (this method is called ABC-Analysis or PARETO analysis).

In most cases an analogous graph as shown in figure IX below is obtained :

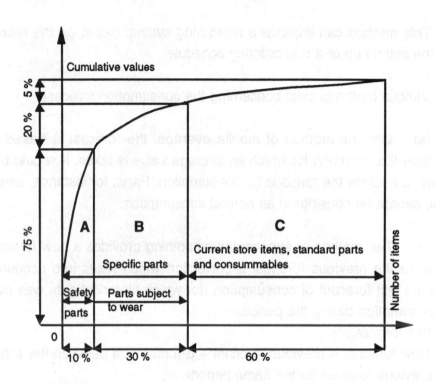

Figure IX : ABC Analysis

This graph consists of three fields :

(a)   Field A corresponds to 10 percent of the items representing 75 percent of the value;

(b)   Field B corresponds to 30 percent of the items representing 20 percent of the value;

(c)   Field C corresponds to 60 percent of the items representing 5 percent of the value.

The spare parts in Field A are of great value, and are in general specific parts of low consumption. The parts in Field B are of medium value and are in general specific parts subject to wear. The parts in Field C are of low value and concern mainly standard parts, current store items and maintenance consumables.

The conclusion reached is that a major part of the invested capital is tied up in a small number of items. Studies aimed at reducing their number will be the most efficient because of the considerable financial impact. This in turn will serve to optimize stock management.

(d) Data processing and file updating

This topic is dealt with in chapter III, section 3.4, where a data processing circuit for spare parts, including the necessary forms, has been explained.

Various good computer programmes are available on the market, and are not too difficult to implement. Preconditions for computerizing are :

(a)   Correct designation and coding;
(b)   Correct fixing of management parameters;
(c)   Informing, preparing and training personnel;
(d)   Well-defined data collection and information flow system;
(e)   Available experience of an efficient manual system is a plus and in most cases indispensable.

4.6.5. Storage systems

The following factors are essential to ensure optimal storage :

(a)   Spacious stores with well-designed storage systems, allowing easy access for handling equipment;
(b)   Suitable handling equipment in sufficient quantity;
(c)   Suitable shelves, bins, racks and other storage facilities;
(d)   Order and cleanliness,
(e)   Methods for conservation of parts (protection against dust, rust and humidity, suitable conditions for the storage of perishable parts etc.).

From the organizational point of view, a centralized spare parts management and stores service produces the best results. Auxiliary (buffer) stores (pick-out stores) in production areas are possible, but the stored items are then considered as being consumed.

The storage capacity is determined by the number of items, the quantity per item, the dimension of parts, their weight and the type of storage. Shelf units should be considered for small-sized parts whereas high racks (maximum height of 8 meters) are more appropriate for medium-sized parts. Heavy parts should be kept in a place easily accessible for the handling equipment or an overhead crane. Small-sized parts can also be stored in special bins and medium-sized parts on pallet boards. Adequate handling equipment should be provided.

Close attention should be paid to the maintenance and preservation of items kept in stock. The following measures should be considered :

(a)   The original packing for vulnerable parts should always be kept (bearings, electronic components);

(b)   Maximum use should be made of plastic bags for storing items which are no longer in their original packing (electronic components, bearings, special springs, seal rings, hydraulic and pneumatic devices);

(c)   Articles with sensitive surfaces such as bearings and certain bulbs should never be touched with bare hands;

(d)   Electrical elements should be protected against dust and humidity (contactors, relays, motors etc.);

(e)   A plastic coating should be applied to surfaces with a low tolerance (gears, tools, bearing-bushes, shafts etc.);

(f)   In areas with a high humidity, the big electric motors and solenoids should be kept charged with a small electric current;

(g)   Modular bins should be used instead of storing parts one above the other;

(h)   The shelves must be cleaned regularly.

Selected literature

AUTHOR	PUBLISHER	TITLE
BANLY P.	CHAPMAN AND HILL, 1969	PURCHASING AND SUPPLY MANAGEMENT
BROWN W.	UNIDO, 1970	HANDLING AND STORING OF SPARE PARTS AND MATERIALS FOR MAINTENANCE PURPOSES ON THE PLANT LEVEL
DGS	DGS INTERNATIONAL-SGS/LAGOS, 1991	SEMINAR ON MAINTENANCE MANAGEMENT
DUNLOP C.L.	BUTTERWORTHS, 1990	A PRACTICAL GUIDE TO MAINTENANCE ENGINEERING
FILE T.W.	BUTTERWORTH HEINEMANN , 1991	COST EFFECTIVE MAINTENANCE - DESIGN AND IMPLEMENTATION
GELDERS L and VAN LOOY P.	JOURNAL OF THE OPERATIONAL RESEARCH SOCIETY, 1978	AN INVENTORY POLICY FOR SLOW AND FAST MOVING ITEMS IN A PETROCHEMICAL PLANT : A CASE STUDY
GOTOH F.	PRODUCTIVITY PRESS - CAMBRIDGE	EQUIPMENT PLANNING FOR TPM : MAINTENANCE PREVENTION DESIGN
HARRIS M.	TEROTECHNICA, 1979	AN INTRODUCTION TO MAINTENANCE STORES ORGANISATION AND SPARES INVENTORY CONTROL
KELLY A. and HARRIS M.	BUTTERWORTHS, 1978	THE MANAGEMENT OF INDUSTRIAL MAINTENANCE
MORROW L.C.	MC GRAW HILL - NEW YORK, 1959	MAINTENANCE ENGINEERING HANDBOOK
TSIKURIN N.	UNIDO, 1973	STANDARDIZATION AND MATERIAL SAVING IN MECHANICAL ENGINEERING
WOLF T.	IN.COM. TEC., 1967	IMPROVING THE EFFICIENCY OF MAINTENANCE STORES

CHAPTER V
HUMAN RESOURCES DEVELOPMENT FOR MAINTENANCE

5.1.   Introduction

The problems which are found in industries in developing countries in the field of human resources development (HRD) for maintenance can be summarized as follows :

(a)   Non-existence of a corporate HRD policy;

(b)   Absence of clearly defined organization charts and related job descriptions;

(c)   Poorly defined needs for maintenance personnel;

(d)   Deficient recruitment policy;

(e)   Poor or non-existent motivation system : career prospects, incentives;

(f)   Poor knowledge of training needs leading to inadequate programmes;

(g)   Poor knowledge of training facilities (centres, schools, institutes etc.) existing at national and international level;

(h)   Incoherence and poor coordination between training programmes of the various training institutes (national and international);

(i)   Absence of a maintenance discipline in high school education in most of the developing countries;

(j)   Inappropriate training methods (too far removed from daily practice);

(k)   Insufficiency or absence of training programmes and facilities for technicians in the following fields : maintenance management (including CMMS); maintenance organization; maintenance methods; work study for machine tooling; spare parts management; condition-based maintenance including use of monitoring instruments; electronics/automation maintenance; hydraulics/ pneumatics maintenance; new technologies : expert systems, artificial intelligence etc.; design-out maintenance : maintainability, reliability, standardization etc.;

(l)   Inadequate training programmes for maintenance engineers;

(m)   Poor supervision and control of results of fellowships, mainly abroad;

(n)   Poor or insufficient qualification and experience of trainers;

(o)   Insufficient budgets for maintenance training.

This chapter deals with several topics related to HRD for maintenance.

In section 5.2 consideration is given to maintenance personnel administration in relation to recruitment and salaries and incentives policies. The reason for selecting these two topics especially is that in maintenance practice, both represent a time-consuming

---

activity for the maintenance manager. Moreover, they are very important and as they are often underestimated and neglected, they are the origin of many practical problems.

Section 5.3 concerns an enterprise policy for HRD for maintenance, and in section 5.4 the focus is on some recommended actions to be undertaken at enterprise level.

5.2.   Considerations on maintenance personnel administration

(a)   Recruitment

The general lack of qualified workers influences the design and the implementation of a recruitment and promotion policy in factories and companies in developing countries. A form of competition springs up amongst them to lure away competent workers. Vague offers of work and poor selection often leads to an inadequate recruitment of personnel. As a result of sketchy or non-existent job descriptions, the profiles of candidates applying for work is not in line with what is actually needed.

To correct this situation it is necessary that the recruitment offer should be accompanied by a job description as detailed as possible. This should be the basis for the selection of candidates. They must then be submitted both to practical as well as to theoretical tests.

For management, cadres (engineers) and supervisors it is only if there is no possibility of internal promotion that recruitment will take place from outside. Poor chances of promotion create uncertainty among the better elements resulting in their premature resignation.

Nevertheless, internal promotion must be done with caution. A worker, for instance, normally possesses 95 percent technical capabilities and 5 percent organizational. If one wants to promote an older worker to foreman, complementary training in organization and shop-floor management will be necessary. Supervisors appointed at a young age and adequately trained present better chances of acquiring qualities of organization, but they will have a problem because of lack of field experience, so that substitutes must be found.

The job preparation desk is composed, in most cases, of an excellent nursery of supervisors already having had intensive training in the organization.

Job preparation (work study) officers deserve particular attention. They are recruited from amongst the best workers between the ages of 25 and 30. This combines maximum knowledge with a malleable character. They must be conscientious, have an open mind, have notions of drawing, technology and elementary mathematics, write well and like office work. Finally they must be willing to deal with practical inspired job preparation.

These workers will follow one or two theoretical training programmes.

The qualified workers will be recruited and the candidates have to undergo :

(a)   A short professional examination (4 to 8 hours) including :

   (i)   A practical part. The exact professional qualification can be judged by the speed, accuracy and accomplishment shown in carrying out tasks and the method followed;

   (ii)   A theoretical part. This will show general technical knowledge, including reading drawings, rules of construction and safety, scientific knowledge which is indispensable but, naturally, adapted to the level of the candidate;

(b)   A trial period of 15 to 30 days to determine before the definitive recruitment, physical capacities, human contact with the rest of the factory, resourcefulness, logical way of thinking, loyalty, eventual slackness.

(b) Salaries and incentives

Salaries and incentives for the maintenance personnel have always been a delicate subject in the salary structure of a factory. They have been the object of many studies which have served to show that the problem is very complex and not easily solved, even in developed countries. This chapter deals with the subject as it relates to the field of maintenance.

The salary structure of the company should be based upon : a classification of jobs; a comparison of tasks inherent to each job; and job evaluation criteria (training, responsibility, effort, work conditions).

Salaries of the maintenance personnel must be equal to those of the production personnel, that is, on an equal footing. Also, the possibilities of obtaining incentives and advantages must be the same, taking into account the global production of the factory.

In the case of output related evaluations, certain precautions must be taken :

(a)   The incentives should not be constant, but should fluctuate in accordance with the actual output by the personnel;

(b)   A simple system easily understood by the workers should be applied;

(c)   The incentives should be paid separately from the main salary.

The setting-up of an output related evaluation system for intervention work (i.e. based on a comparison between allocated time and real time worked on a job) is done by means of the job preparation desk which first will prepare the work including a time study, and then during a minimum of one year will assess the time worked. In this way, a serious and objective data bank with company standard times can be established.

Promotion is a way for the personnel to climb up to a higher grade and wage scale; it is an efficient tool for company directors to manage their personnel. This could also be a useful tool for motivation, as long as it is not abused and is handled with objectivity.

In order to be able to offer everyone the same conditions and guarantee the best objectivity possible, it is necessary that :

(a)   The personnel feel concerned and informed about the activities of the company;

(b)   The personnel is trained in relation to their results and personal merit;

(c)   The allowances take into account the kind of work, the constraints encountered and certain difficult working conditions.

Promotion and career planning should be part of a corporate plan including a system of objective evaluation of the quantity and quality of work and experience gained throughout a career.

This evaluation should be based on a grouping of all job functions into several families : executives, engineer levels 1 and 2, supervisors, foreman, execution and low execution. Each family is subdivided into grades : Director General, department manager, head of service, senior and junior engineer etc.

For each group of functions and grade a basic index is given, which corresponds with the starting-point of a pre-established career curve on a diagram (index/years of experience), related to progress indicators.

The classification of grades must strictly conform with the rules and regulations of the general status of the worker in the country. The index which links the wage scale to the progress indicators must also respect the national regulations.

5.3.   Enterprise policy for HRD for maintenance

(a) Note

An enterprise or corporate policy for HRD for maintenance can only be efficiently carried out if all the actors involved are conscious of the importance of maintenance in the company.

Thus the definition of an enterprise policy for HRD for maintenance must be preceded by awareness-raising actions. See chapter IV, section 4.3 concerning this matter.

(b) Objectives and prerequisites of HRD for maintenance

The principal objectives of HRD in the field of maintenance are as follows :

(a)   Remedying in as short a time as possible the lack of qualified personnel;

(b)   Adapting the men to their work;

(c)   Mastering the imported technology;

(d)   Adapting the men to the technological evolution ;

(e)   Increasing productivity;

(f)   Filling the gap between real needs and the national education system ;

(g)   Following the rapid changes in the industrial society.

Before launching any training programme it is essential that the following problems should be resolved based on an in-depth analysis of the maintenance problems :

(a)   Organization of maintenance in the company (organization chart, job descriptions);

(b)   Assessment of the training needs;

(c)   Training policy (who, how, where , when and with whom);

(d)   Planning of recruitment and training with regard to the needs in terms of personnel and qualifications;

(e)   Designation of a head of training for follow-up, checking and evaluation of results;

(f)   Administrative problems linked with training and recruitment.

(c) Organization of maintenance

The implementation of a maintenance organization in a company not only requires the technical know-how of equipment functioning and that of the internal mechanisms, but also demands an excellent knowledge of attitudes and the intellectual level of the personnel.

A project of maintenance organization must be established :

(a)   In the case of a new factory,with the help of the constructor or the consulting engineer;

(b)   After visits to similar plants in other countries in order to obtain the maximum profit from existing experience and discussion with the users;

(c)   After visits to factories of the same size in the country. This type of visit must be viewed seriously because it can be a valuable source of information and experience.

In the case of new factories, these actions should be carried out by the future maintenance manager together with his or her closest staff and the head of training.

In existing factories, the technical problems are so numerous that generally, the engineers do not have the time for the reflection necessary to cope with the setting-up of an organization and to deal with an efficient information flow. Consequently, a task force composed of dynamic and experienced people, under the leadership of the maintenance manager, should be created. This group will be in charge of picking up the weak points in the factory and setting-up the organization within a given time span.

(d) Assessment of the training needs

Training needs are assessed on the basis of an in-depth analysis of maintenance practice in the company.

The following chart explains the methodology (abbreviations defined below) :

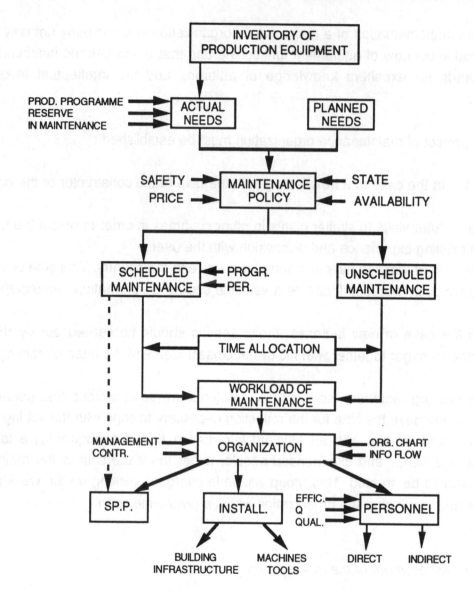

Based on the assessment of the present inventory of the production equipment, the actual and future needs are defined taking into account operational needs such as production programmes (load of the machines), reserve (i.e. margin to cover unexpected breakdown of machines) and shut-downs for maintenance reasons.

The application of a maintenance policy for this production equipment, in relation to the aspects of safety, price, state (i.e. protection of environment, comfort etc.) and availability, will give an estimate of the amount of scheduled and unscheduled work.

Time allocation can be calculated based on maintenance programmes and periodicities (for scheduled work) and on an estimation for unscheduled work. In this way a forecast of the workload of the maintenance department can be formulated.

The organization of the work can then be defined including the organization chart, the information flow, management and quality control aspects.

Finally this will result in the definition of the needs for : direct and indirect personnel (depending on the rate of efficiency, quality and qualification); installations : buildings/infrastructure, machine tools; and spare parts.

For the personnel, detailed manning tables can then be set up (see chapter III, section 3.3 "Staffing").

A comparison between the existing personnel and the needs, which have been defined according to the above methodology, can then be made. This will result in detailed training needs for both workers (direct personnel) as well as for supervisors and engineers (indirect personnel).

Training needs should be expressed on the basis of a detailed job description for which an example is added in appendix 40. The following topics should be indicated when expressing training needs : number of trainees; minimum qualification and experience before training; expected qualification after training; short curriculum of training programme.

In the case of a new factory, the training needs are defined on the basis of an appraisal of the forecast of the supplier and with an indication of the above information.

The qualitative requirements (required profile) can be fulfilled on the basis of the following possibilities : either with personnel already in situ, or by recruitment of trained personnel, or by preliminary training of personnel recruited for this purpose.

An overview of the major necessary maintenance trades in developing countries is given in appendix 44.

Training programmes should be defined on the basis of : the job description; a trade-related training analysis, including retraining and upgrading (an example of a master chart for such analysis is given in appendix 45).

The curriculum of the training programme should include the following components : access level; tasks; content of training programme (theoretical, technical, practical, managerial); duration; and expected qualification after training.

(e) Development of appropriate training methods

1.   Training of cadres

Training of engineers and maintenance managers consists mainly of two types : technical training; and training in the field of maintenance management.

As to the technical training, the best method consists of organizing short studytours to the machine manufacturers or to analogous plants, completed with in-service training during plant construction or with a specialized technical assistance programme.

It is recommended that training in the field of maintenance management should be carried out in the framework of specialized upgrading seminars completed with short-term practical applications in selected plants.

2.   Training of supervisors

The most difficult level in training for maintenance is that of foremen, for which the best recipe is the accumulation of years of professional experience.

The foreman is the keystone of a maintenance department. A management without competent foremen will lose its efficiency. Workers without competent foremen will become uncontrolled.

The few foremen and crew leaders that there are, are always saturated with problems. They are asked to foresee and execute the work, to follow it and to control the workers. They are halted by difficulties that they, young foremen themselves, do not know how to solve in the context where bureaucracy and lack of supplies force them to waste precious time searching for a part or a tool which is missing. The result is that the worker is often left to his own initiative.

To alleviate this, substitutes must be found through a rapid training of foremen, starting, in a first stage, with thoroughly experienced workers. The training of the supervisory level (technicians, foremen and crew leaders) is thus to be considered in another framework than that of the training of the workers. Here the training-within-industry (TWI) approach (training within industry) has produced excellent results in the past.

(i)   Crew leaders

Only part of this training can be carried out in a training centre or institute where a purely theoretical training is given which brings them up to the basic technical level needed. They are often recruited amongst the young qualified workers and are selected for their intelligence and their ability to explain and to control a group. After the appropriate period of industrial activity and after having obtained the level of qualified workers, they will become crew leaders, responsible for four or five men. They are chosen not only for their professional qualities, but for their human qualities as well.

(ii)   <u>Technicians and foremen</u>

The training and practicals must be designed and adapted thoroughly to the needs of each of the levels :

(a)   The maintenance technicians should first be part of an intervention crew before being appointed as method officers in the engineering office or in the spare parts management section;

(b)   The job of foremen is to direct the personnel in the maintenance workshop or during maintenance interventions. Generally they will be in charge of 10 to 15 workers, including the crew leaders. If, amongst the workers, some are old crew leaders with years of practical experience behind them and they can command respect and impose discipline, then it is recommended that they should receive further training using audiovisual and upgrading programmes in order to be promoted to foremen ;

(c)   For future supervisors, after their basic technical training and after having mastered the procedures of the plant (discipline, salaries, information circuits etc.), they are then placed together with an older foreman or a supervisor from the technical assistance. After this practical stage, they have to follow theoretical courses on preparation for command and psychological studies. There they will see, to which practical experience this training is aimed at. Finally they will be placed in effective command as the definite head of a team;

(d)   Job preparation should be selected from experienced workers, crew leaders or foremen. A training in work-study techniques and a guided on-the-job training lasting several months will create the prerequisites for the job preparation function.

3.   Training of qualified workers

Qualified workers in almost all maintenance trades are rare in developing countries (see section (d) above for major necessary trades). The training must, therefore, be designed to stimulate all qualifications. The programmes should further be studied and conceived in such a way that the trainee learns not only a technique but also work habits. To achieve this, one must be demanding, but at the same time teach the trainee and give him or her real responsibilities.

The training-within-industry method is also the most appropriate way of training for the workers' level. Especially the on-the-job training is most appropriate. This training consists of assimilating practical knowledge of the work. A worker proceeds by trial and error and so can get a concrete idea of what the work is all about.

This method can only be effectively applied on the condition that the hierarchy is motivated and accepts to play the role of instructor (thus taking the necessary time for explaining to the worker).

The practical on-the-job training must still be completed by theoretical courses for which the workers can attend training centres.

As mentioned before, on-the-job training for maintenance workers during the construction stage of a plant is indispensable and thus recommended. One efficient solution is to integrate the maintenance workers into the teams of the constructor. They stay under the responsibility of the constructor, but are followed and controlled by their own training head and his staff (future crew leaders for example). Final responsibility will have to be defined in the case where work has been badly carried out or when there is a delay in the planning of the construction.

An assiduous follow-up and control of the trainees is vital in order to guarantee success of the training programme. Weekly controls and regular examinations can help to eliminate or reactivate the weaker elements.The training programme can be adapted more efficiently by use of these intermediary controls. They can spotlight whether the training programmes take into account sufficiently the realities of the environment (qualifications, experience of trainees, intellectual aptitudes).

As to the training of young workers, the apprenticeship programmes should be promoted. Experience has proven that apprenticeship is one of the most efficient methods for training new maintenance workers. As mentioned before, small nuclei composed of a foreman, a qualified worker and an apprentice have produced excellent results.

The question as to multi-skilling is often asked. The experience of the author concerning this topic can be outlined as follows:

(a)   As the need for qualified workers is generally high, a decisive element in the design of training programmes is the time factor. Training a mechanic and an electrician needs less time than training an electromechanic;

(b)   For this reason, multi-skilling covering a wide range of more or less related trades is for the time being not recommended for developing countries although it is the trend in modern industry;

(c)   Nevertheless training of workers must include a certain degree of multi-skilling, especially for organizational reasons, for example :

(i)   A mechanic must be able to disconnect an electric motor;

(ii)   An electrician must be able to align a coupling;

(iii)   A mechanic must have practical notions of welding, of basic hydraulics and of pneumatics;

(d)   Training programmes for workers for various trades should include basic notions of related trades to a certain extent and certainly not at the cost of time-consuming programmes;

(e)   As to the machine operators, training should include some first-level maintenance tasks, limited to visual controls and regular checks (see chapter II, section 2.3);

(f)   The problem is more complex for engineers and higher technicians dealing with automation : there is no other way out but to train in depth the various related trades, so that in this case multi-skilling must be considered. This is especially the case when it concerns new technologies.

4. Training of trainers

The success or failure of a training programme depends largely on the quality of the training given and the motivation of the trainer. Consequently, the selection, training and upgrading of trainers are very important.

Generally, future trainers are recruited amongst the company personnel by rigourous selection. The criteria of selection are principally human qualities (ability to teach), practical professional experience, general and particular technological skills.

The training of trainers for maintenance must be planned early. They must be trained more in a practical or didactic way than by listening and assimilating text books. On top of the pedagogical principles of teaching, the accent must be put on each detail of the course they will have to teach, and most importantly on the spirit of maintenance.

Notions on safety, general organization of the plant, and the environment are equally indispensable. A final examination is required, as well as regular control and upgrading.

5. Fellowships abroad

Fellowships, study tours and seminars are particularly valuable for the supervisory level, technicians and engineers. Their objective should be upgrading or retraining.

Trainees should not be sent abroad for basic training. This must be given, as far as possible, on site, as it does not justify the high related cost.

The only exception to this rule is specialized training for a particular machine at the manufacturers or for a specialized technique.

(f) Structural and administrative arrangements

1. Head of training

It is necessary to appoint a head of training as soon as possible so that the setting-up of the training programme and the coordination of all stages are guaranteed.

The person chosen must be experienced in dealing with human relations and must be accepted by the hierarchy. He should have a thorough practical experience and work closely with the maintenance manager and his staff. The trainees should be able to refer to him throughout the whole training period.

He will take part in : the development of the training policy; the assessment of training needs ; establishing the training programmes; and determining the necessary resources for the implementation of the training.

He will be in control of budgets accorded by the company for training, and will himself instruct in certain programmes, both theoretical and practical.

He will be responsible for follow-up, control and evaluation of the practical and theoretical results.

For larger companies, the training activities can be overseen by a fully fledged section including all necessary administrative and logistic staff.

For smaller companies, the head of the personnel department could be assigned as head of training activities.

2.   Administrative arrangements

The following administrative arrangements should be foreseen :

(a)   The establishing of sound contracts with the trainees, including fidelity clauses, so that they will not leave the company in order to capitalize on their knowledge in another company;

(b)   Development of clear career prospects for the after-training period;

(c)   The inclusion of extensive training for maintenance specifications in the terms of reference when purchasing equipment and involving the supplier in the final results;

(d)   Thinking of a "continued" training, upgrading or recycling activities parallel with the professional life of the maintenance staff;

(e)   Stimulating internal training and upgrading through in-service training activities. In this sense, the training of company trainers can be extremely efficient;

(f)   The definition of detailed evaluation procedures, including a link between results obtained by the trainees and the chances of promotion.

(g)   Budgetary provisions for financing training activities

Figures ranging from 2 to 5 percent of the total maintenance budget for financing training activities in developing countries are not exaggerated.

Based on the assessment of training needs and the selection of training organizations, or methods, detailed budgets should be foreseen.

It is recommended that separate budgets for maintenance training be defined, both when purchasing equipment as well as in the operational budget. This will allow a permanent budget control and an efficient monitoring of training activities.

Including the ratio "total expenses for training/total maintenance cost" in the management steering chart as described in chapter III, section 3.7, is an obvious suggestion.

(h) Environmental problems

Although environmental problems do not only concern maintenance, and are within the framework of this chapter not directly relevant, it is worth giving a passing thought to this important topic.

The problem of the lack of qualified personnel is accentuated by the lack of an appropriate social infrastructure, in particular : insufficient lodgings; limited means of transport; and few local medical centres.

As such the problems of absenteeism and instability of the workers is far more serious than that which is found in industrialized countries.

In order to remedy this situation, it is sometimes essential for the enterprise to deal with topics which are not part of its business, but which are necessary to solve the environmental problems.

(i)   Technical assistance

The real role of technical assistance in the process of technological transfer is not yet universally accepted. Often, technical assistance is treated as a palliative to the lack of qualified personnel. This can be justified in case of short-term specialized technical assistance. Questions arise when one wants to use technical assistance on a long-term basis.

The management of production units and the training of personnel for these units are two inseparable elements.

Technical assistance has a double function : that of contributing to the efficient running of the factory and that of training personnel. But a fundamental point must be insisted upon. It cannot be expected that technical assistance can both run the factory and be the perfect trainer at the same time. The reason is simple : good management demands work methods other than those for giving good training.

It is certain that the exact definition of the role of technical assistance is not easy : type, condition and age of the factory, as well as the demands of the market can all have an influence.

The technical assistant finds himself in a difficult position. On the one hand, if he wants to have a hand in training, he must take the necessary time to explain each break-down, to describe how the intervention will be prepared, to rehearse it etc. During this time the rest of the installation is halted, a fact which is not accepted because the reason for having technical assistance is to avoid just such an eventuality. On the other hand, if he wants to run the factory well, he must have the chance to intervene anywhere, at any time, without wasting time on explanations to trainees. Then he is reproached for not having taken enough time to help with the training programme.

One of the first priorities for the assignment of technical assistance in a factory is to define a coherent policy for it. It is too expensive for it to be used merely as a stopgap.

Too often, technical assistance is called in at the last moment, when the installations are in an advanced state of dilapidation. A "fire brigade" situation risks giving poor satisfaction.

The position of the technical assistant should be made official so that any psychological barriers can be overcome. Thus his efficiency will be improved and he will work to the best of his ability.

Technical assistance must not become the easy way out. It must not be dragged out interminably, but its influence should be gradually reduced, thus enabling nationals to take over while continuing to be provided through advisers during a certain period of time.

It is often very useful to complete technical assistance to the maintenance department with a reduced assistance to production. In this way damage to installations due to poor operation can be avoided.

5.4.   Actions at enterprise level

The problems concerning human resources development for maintenance laid out above concentrate on the following five topics for which actions for improvement are a necessity : information; coherence and coordination/planning; suitability/efficiency; human resources, in terms of capability and motivation; and financial resources.

The following actions should be considered at an enterprise level :

(a)   The setting-up of a corporate policy for HRD for maintenance . This policy should take into account the following topics :

(i)   Programmes to provide specialized awareness-raising for cadres (engineers) and technical supervisors;

(ii)   The role of education and planning concerning HRD for maintenance in particular;

      (iii)   The development of appropriate training methods in the field of maintenance;

      (iv)   Structural and administrative arrangements for the implementation of these methods;

      (v)   The organization of training at the company level through appropriate structures;

      (vi)   Budgeting provisions for financing training activities;

  (b)   Arrangements to improve and correct training for maintenance by :

      (i)   Adapting maintenance training programmes to the specific needs of the users;

      (ii)   Supervising fellowships more thoroughly and checking the results (mainly abroad);

      (iii)   Integrating trainees in the construction teams during plant construction;

  (c)   Provision of the necessary resources for the implementation of the programme: human (trainees, trainers, administration, etc.); material (facilities, equipment didactic aids, etc.); and financial;

  (d)   Development of a corporate career plan for all levels of maintenance personnel, in particular for maintenance engineers.

Selected literature

AUTHOR	PUBLISHER	TITLE
BASKER B. and HUSBAND T.	MAINTENANCE MANAGEMENT INTERNATIONAL, 1992	SIMULATING MULTI-SKILL MAINTENANCE : A CASE STUDY
CORDER G.	UNIDO, 1970	HUMAN RELATIONS IN INDUSTRY WITH SPECIAL REFERENCE TO THE MAINTENANCE/ PRODUCTION RELATIONSHIP
CROSS M.	11TH NAT. CONF. ON MAINTENANCE ENG., 1986	MAINTENANCE MANPOWER, UTILISATION AND TRAINING
DE GROOTE P.	UNIDO, 1989	PLAN OF ACTION FOR TRAINING OF INDUSTRIAL MANPOWER IN MAINTENANCE IN DEVELOPING COUNTRIES
HERZBERG F.	HARVARD BUSINESS REVIEW, 1986	ONE MORE TIME : HOW DO YOU MOTIVATE EMPLOYEES
INTERNATIONAL LABOUR OFFICE	ILO/BIT, 1970	UPGRADING OF MAINTENANCE AND REPAIR PERSONNEL
NACHI-FUJIKOSHI	PRODUCTIVITY PUBLISHING - CAMBRIDGE, 1990	TRAINING FOR TPM A MANUFACTURING SUCCESS STORY
SMITH A.R.	ILO - GENEVEA, 1988	TECHNIQUES FOR MANAGERIAL MANPOWER PLANNING

CHAPTER VI
THE NEXT STEP

6.1. Introduction

In the preceding chapters it was explained how to introduce a planned maintenance system and how to manage maintenance.

The proper implementation of the methods proposed make it possible to obtain a satisfactory - even excellent - level of maintenance.

As there are no standards concerning the degree of satisfaction or excellence in maintenance (as discussed before, figures can vary tremendously), only the study of the evolution of internal indicators can be a means for measuring maintenance performance.

The effort which is made by the company to obtain a satisfactory maintenance performance should only be considered as a first step. In fact, maintenance will frequently face problems in relation to both external and internal influences which need continuous and imaginative action for fine tuning or adaptation.

In this chapter two of these influences are highlighted as a next step once a planned maintenance system has been set up :

(a)   How can maintenance face constant technological evolution in terms of methods, techniques, training, control devices etc ?

(b)   How can a higher degree of attention to maintenance be secured even when satisfactory performance has been reached ?

6.2.   Maintenance and new technologies *

6.2.1. Fields of application

The need to be competitive in order to survive and progress has forced industry to reduce manpower costs and to increase the qualitative and quantitative performance of production equipment. Constant research to enhance performance standards results in continuous technological evolution and in an increased use of new technologies.

New technologies which have been developed especially in the last decade deal with, amongst others : new materials, such as optic fibres or composite materials; and advanced techniques, such as artificial intelligence, expert systems, computerized automation and laser applications.

The equipment using new technologies is mostly found on manufacturing or transformation lines or in the processing industries using programmable logic controllers, automatic or semi-automatic workstations, robots etc.

The principal differences vis-à-vis traditional technology are :

(a)   The increased use of microelectronic components in new technologies, with high reliability rates which differ very much from the traditional hydraulic or electromechanical components;

(b)   The reduction in volume and weight because of miniaturization of components. This presents both advantages and disadvantages as regards repairs and trouble shooting ;

(c)   The use of special materials which need specialized techniques for processing, repair or reconditioning.

6.2.2. The impact of new technologies on maintenance

(a) Consequences of failures

High-level technology might require a very large investment. The profit loss resulting from a breakdown or failure, being a function of the performance of the equipment, will increase with the introduction of new technologies. The smallest production stoppage and, in particular, microfailures will have very serious consequences resulting in

---

* Contribution by Claude Georges and Patrick De Groote.

a reduction of the benefit gained by new technologies in case maintenance cannot keep up.

The reliability and the ratio "loss of production per unit of time" because of unavailability, which are the responsibility of maintenance, thus take on a far more serious aspect.

(b) Maintenance equipment

The necessity to shutdown production at the last minute before breakdown occurs compels maintenance management to set up more efficient maintenance systems directed more and more towards condition-based maintenance. Reliability-centered maintenance and the use of advanced diagnostic or operational research techniques such as failure mode effects and criticality analysis, fault tree analysis and hazard and operability studies become a necessity. This introduces the need for much more sophisticated maintenance instruments, tools and equipment such as: instruments for vibration or shock wave analysis, thermovision, analysis of waste debris and of effluents and analysis by ultrasound, and oil scan equipment.

(c) Personnel requirements

The personnel must be capable of understanding the functioning, the content, the possibilities, and the failure modes and their effects which can occur in new technologies.

The use of increasingly sophisticated instruments for measuring, analysis and control is essential. Personnel must rapidly become familiar with the equipment.

It is obligatory for maintenance management to adapt the strategies and policies of maintenance so that the maximum benefit can be obtained from new technologies. This obligation involves action on three levels :

1.   Before acquisition of new technologies

The maintenance manager must be involved in the search for equipment with a higher level of performance. He must be aware of every latest innovation, know what the research institutes are doing, and attend trade fairs,demonstrations and seminars. Faced with the improvements in performance and the consequential impact, the maintenance manager must change his approach towards failures, particularly microfailures.

As to the design of the equipment to be purchased, internal diagnostic and failure-finding systems such as the early warning system (EWS) or built-in test equipment (BITE), are expert systems which can ease fault analysis and troubleshooting. These techniques should be used as much as possible especially for equipment with a high automation component.

In this way the maintenance manager will be fully prepared to thoroughly advise the management board concerning the purchasing of equipment.

2.   After the decision to acquire new technologies

The maintenance manager must organize training and continuous upgrading sessions for himself and his personnel. He must purchase the specific maintenance equipment (tools, instruments) which is necessary to maintain the new production material. He must also gather all related technical documentation.

He must be involved in the recruitment of suitable personnel.

The aptitude of the maintenance personnel to be able to "catch on" is a very important criteria. Taking into consideration the extremely rapid progress of material (technological obsolescence has changed from 15 years to 2 and sometimes less in very advanced fields), maintenance personnel must follow this evolution.

3.   During and after the starting-up of the equipment

This is the period for organizing the technical documentation, its updating, the preparation of work specifications, and the training of personnel both in-service as well as at the plant of the manufacturer.

This means that a continuous training and retraining policy must be designed for the maintenance of new technologies.

Training programmes should be developed in the fields of : fault detection; component and system reliability; fault prevention; use of specialized equipment; updating of technological knowledge.

A consequence of this is that the required qualifications of maintenance personnel will increase : it will be necessary to recruit more and more technicians of a higher level or engineers in order to face the maintenance problems.

6.3.   Maintaining excellent maintenance *

Imagine an enterprise in a developing country which has, with great effort and perseverance, set up an organization whose efficient procedures have resulted in an acceptable maintenance performance. Considerable time has been spent on the progressive implementation and running-in of this organization as well as the familiarizing and training of the personnel regarding the new procedures.

Undoubtedly the results are convincing. The maintenance interventions, having been well prepared, are carried out efficiently, gaining time and improving quality to the satisfaction of the job requestor as well as the maintenance personnel. The improvement - even though relatively minor for the time being - in the availability of the production equipment proves the success of the implemented reorganization and leads one to expect rapidly growing results. Data-gathering permits an easy follow-up and a quick evaluation of the results obtained.

It is the moment to feel deserved satisfaction. Maintenance is not causing any of the problems previously encountered . They now appear to be a thing of the past.

Nevertheless this satisfaction has hidden risks, namely complacency. The minute that maintenance does not cause any more problems, is the minute that less importance starts to be attached to it.

Management, at every level, must play an important role in the continued application of maintenance procedures.

Without a regular follow-up by the technical people in charge, the personnel will give in slowly, sometimes even unconsciously, to the easy way out. For example, an important form will be ignored because its reordering has been delayed; some history cards will not be kept up to date due to a sudden work overload or illness etc.

More important still is the influence of general management. It is they alone who can guarantee that efficient maintenance continues to be considered a vital factor for the health of the factory, just as vital as reaching the production objectives, the quality of products, sales promotion etc. Even though managers feel its importance, the awareness that most company objectives can only be obtained through successful maintenance, especially in the fields of productivity, quality, continuity of production, safety and environment, has yet to be grasped by many.

---

* Contribution by Maurice Depraetere.

The Japanese "total productive maintenance" (TPM) concept is a success story based on this integrated approach.

The aim of TPM is to optimize the productivity of the equipment. Among the basic principles and ideas the following are worth mentioning :

(a)   Maintenance must always be considered as a productive function, to the same extent as production;

(b)   TPM must be the concern of every department in the plant, not only maintenance, but also production, planning etc;

(c)   Every level must have the will to cooperate with TPM, from the general management to the lowest echelon.

The TPM model attaches an enormous importance to the motivation of personnel, and it is this motivation, found in every department and on every level, which constitutes the principal factor of success.

Even if it is understood that "zero break down" is not a goal - this would entail huge and unjustified expense - the Japanese model is difficult to imitate because of the great difference in mentality. But an important lesson can still be learned. Without the motivation of the workforce the perfect organization which has been established will not produce the optimal result required and will not resist the erosion of time.

The motivation of the Japanese is more spiritual: they take pride in being able to contribute to the expansion of their company and country, the honour of being singled out as an exemplary employee etc.

This is not necessarily the case in developing countries, even if the personnel have a sense of duty, pride and satisfaction in a job well done. A motivation of a different sort is needed, one that is understood by all that of material gain, and as maintenance involves everyone, the results obtained should be felt by the whole workforce. In the same way, good production results will have a direct influence on the wages and bonuses of the maintenance personnel.

Even so, it would be a mistake to think that material incentives are the only things that can stimulate the workforce. On the contrary, it is recommended that a list of honour be placed in the entrance hall, or published in the newsletter of the bigger companies, on which could be noted : the cleanest workshop, the production area with the lowest down time due to breakdowns, the name of the worker who has, through his own vigilance, prevented a breakdown from taking place etc.

But to return to bonuses. These are proportional to the salary level and subject to the individual evaluation of the worker.

The evaluation of each worker must be established according to various criteria of personal appreciation, but also criteria of appreciation of the total result which stimulates the solidarity of a team, a workshop or the whole plant.

The criteria of personal appreciation concern: punctuality, perseverance,discipline, quantity and quality of jobs done, relations with superiors, colleagues or subordinates etc. These are the classic evaluations, already used in a number of companies (see also chapter V).

As to the criteria of appreciation of the total result, several formulas are possible, the simplest being that at the end of the year each member of the workforce benefits from the annual profits of the company. Unfortunately this idea rapidly causes them to lose interest, because they do not realize the impact of their individual effort on the total results. In addition, they forget throughout the 11 months that an end-of-year bonus is awaiting them, and when they get it, they then consider it as their due.

Thus, it is much better to set up monthly appreciation criteria. They will be based, principally, on the direct results of the work carried out by a unit, but will nevertheless be influenced by those of other units and services. Two examples: if a production worker is interested in positive "maintenance" results, this will incite him to be concerned about the state of his equipment, or a worker in the purchasing department will be inclined to treat an urgent order for one or another spare part more favourably. The result is a spirit of partnership and a positive sense of cooperation.

Even if the bonuses are only distributed quarterly, the appreciation should be done monthly and communicated monthly in detail, so that the personnel is reminded regularly of the stimulation the appreciation is supposed to induce.

An easy way to assess the appreciation criteria of the total results is to use ratios.

Certain ratios, those to which an important coefficient is accorded, concern the results of the crew or section itself. Others, with a smaller coefficient, concern the results of the whole service or department. A final group, with the lowest coefficient, covers the results of the entire plant.

This system of appreciation could be implemented through the setting-up of maintenance circles as discussed in chapter IV, section 4.3.

It is important that the workforce can see that general management attaches the utmost importance to the question of maintenance.

Thus, it is equally important that any service or departmental report, brief but thoroughly explicit, must catch the attention of management. They in turn must not hesitate to ask for extra information or explanations on a particular point or decreasing results.

An occasional brief visit to the shopfloor and offices by management can be a considerable encouragement to the foremen as well as to the maintenance personnel. During these visits particular attention should be paid to the cleanliness of the machines and installations, updating and respect for the preventive maintenance schedule, or to important rehabilitation work being carried out at that moment.

This overall interest in the maintenance function and the creation of an attitude "to do better than others" could still be expressed more concretely through the creation of centres of excellence for maintenance as introduced in chapter IV, section 4.3. The sections or departments which had obtained exceptional results in maintenance practice, based on predefined corporate standards, would be awarded a quality label. The challenge will then be to maintain excellent maintenance in order to keep that quality label.

The action "maintaining excellent maintenance" should be sustained and coordinated by the maintenance committee as proposed in chapter IV, section 4.3.

To conclude: maintenance is undergoing an impressive turnaround. Its importance and productive role are being admitted and recognized more and more. Maintenance techniques are the subject of intensive research, and they will continue to be modernized and perfected in the years to come.

Without knowing the evolution of methods nor the interest of implementing some of them in the companies concerned, prior to the setting up of any system it is imperative to have a rational organization with well-thought-out and respected procedures. Computerization and automation are only considered as tools to help and optimize human intervention and decision-making.

Thus it is necessary to be well prepared for this evolution by ensuring the constant dedication of everyone in the implementation of the organization.

Selected literature

AUTHOR	PUBLISHER	TITLE
ASSCHER H & FEINGOLD	MARCEL DEKKER INC. - NEW YORK, 1984	REPAIRABLE SYSTEMS RELIABILITY, MODELING INFERENCE, MISCONCEPTIONS AND THEIR CAUSES
BALDIN A.	TEROTECHNICA, 1979	CONDITION BASED MAINTENANCE : A POWERFUL TOOL FOR MODERN PLANT MANAGEMENT
BENNETT K.	PROCEEDINGS OF 6TH NAT. CONF. ON COMPUTERS FOR MAINTENANCE MANAGERS, 1985	EXPERT SYSTEMS IN MAINTENANCE
BOUCHE-PLANCHU-RETOUR	UNIVERSITE DES SCIENCES SOCIALES DE GRENOBLE, 1988 EUROMAINTENANCE 88, HELSINKI	"INDUSTRIAL MAINTENANCE AND TROUBLE SHOOTING EXPERT SYSTEM : SOME HUMAN, MANAGERIAL AND ORGANISATIONAL CONSIDERATIONS"
CANNON A.G. and BENDELL A.	ELSEVIER APPLIED SCIENCE, 1991	RELIABILITY DATA BANKS
CROSBY P.	McGRAW-HILL, 1984	QUALITY WITHOUT TEARS, THE ART OF HASSLE-FREE MANAGEMENT
GIBSON N. and WITTAKER J.	BIT/ILO - GENEVE , 1989	RESULT-ORIENTED MANAGEMENT DEVELOPMENT : THE CASE OF THE ETHIOPIAN MANAGEMENT INSTITUTE
HIRSCH A.	COMPUTER AND ELECTRONIC, 1984	ARTIFICIAL INTELLIGENCE IN COURSE OF AGES
KELLY A.	FACTORY, 1972	WORK MEASUREMENT FOR MAINTENANCE MANAGER
TAKAHASHI Y.	TEROTECHNICA, 1981	MAINTENANCE-ORIENTED MANAGEMENT VIA TOTAL PARTICIPATION
TAKAHASHI Y.	UNIDO, 1973	PRACTICAL ASPECTS OF APPLICATION OF MODERN PRODUCTION MANAGEMENT TECHNIQUES TO MAINTENANCE
WALZ D.	THE A.I. MAGAZINE, 1983	ARTIFICIAL INTELLIGENCE
WIIG K.	ILO/BIT - GENEVE , 1990	EXPERT SYSTEMS : A MANAGER'S GUIDE

GLOSSARY

As there is no extensive internationally standardized maintenance glossary in existence today, the authors thought it would be of interest to list selected terms which are commonly used in the maintenance profession.

The list and explanation of terms given below are based on the following sources :

W.M.J. Geraerds : Glossary in the MAINTENANCE MANAGEMENT MANUAL, published by SAMSON BEDRIJFSINFORMATIE, THE NETHERLANDS
BS 3811 : BRITISH STANDARD GLOSSARY OF MAINTENANCE MANAGEMENT IN TEROTECHNOLOGY
AFNOR : INDUSTRIAL MAINTENANCE
DIN 31051 : TERMINOLOGY FÜR INSTANDHALTUNG
DGS : COURSE ON INDUSTRIAL MAINTENANCE MANAGEMENT
P. DE GROOTE : personal research and experience

ENGLISH	DEFINITION	FRENCH
ABSOLUTE FAILURE	A failure on an item whose intended function becomes completely unable to be performed	DEFAILLANCE CATALEPTIQUE
ACCELERATED TEST	The item to be tested is submitted to an accelerated testing programme (i.e. submitted to higher speed or load compared with its normal functioning) in order to detect quickly any failure	ESSAI ACCELERE
ACCESSIBILITY	Possibility to have access to a place, a part or an accessory. The accessibility is a qualitative design property ; it will determine the time needed for removal and reassembling of a subassembly or a part	ACCESSIBILITE
ACCIDENT SEQUENCES	Different ways in which accidents might occur	SEQUENCES D'INCIDENTS
ACQUISITION COST	The total costs at the charge of the owner for acquiring an item or a material and for bringing it into the condition where it is capable of performing its intended function	COUT D'ACQUISITION
ACTIVE REDUNDANCY	The redundant item is in operation in parallel to the basic item. If one fails the other takes over	REDONDANCE ACTIVE
ADAPTATIVE MAINTENANCE	See DESIGN-OUT MAINTENANCE	MAINTENANCE ADAPTATIVE

ENGLISH	DEFINITION	FRENCH
ADAPTION	Action to modify an item with the objective to conform or adjust. The design-out maintenance function will deal with adaption in order to make the equipment for example more reliable or accessible	ADAPTION
AFNOR	(Association Française de Normalisation) - French national standards institute	AFNOR
AGE REPLACEMENT	The replacement of a group of identical parts, when one part is subject to failure. Age replacement (or group replacement or bloc replacement) is done for cost saving reasons based on the knowledge that if one part is worn out, the others will follow soon (is justified for instance in case of bad accessibility)	REMPLACEMENT EN BLOC
AGE-SPECIFIC FAILURE RATE	Numbers of failures per time unit during life cycle. See also failure rate, instantaneous failure rate, force of mortality, hazard rate. Also expressed as 1/MTBF. It is in fact the probability of failure	TAUX DE PANNE
ALGOL	Algorithmic language - computer language used for programming algorithmic mathematics	ALGOL
ALGORITHM	Path followed to obtain an expected result through deviding the problem into a number of sequences	ALGORITHME
ALLOTMENT REORDERING BY)	Reordering system in case of low consumption	PAR DOTATION
AMIS	(Asset Management Information Service) Index which allows to measure maintenance management performance	AMIS
ANSI	American National Standardization Institute	ANSI
API	American Petroleum Institute	API
APPRENTICESHIP	Learning a trade by being employed in it for an agreed period at low wages	APPRENTISSAGE
AREA MAINTENANCE	Maintenance teams are assigned to specific production area. Also called assigned maintenance	MAINTENANCE DE ZONE MAINTENANCE ASSIGNEE
ARTIFICIAL INTELLIGENCE	A more developed expert system which can generate subsystems on its own	INTELLIGENCE ARTIFICIELLE
AS BUILT	In conformity with the real situation as it is built	AS BUILT
ASCII	American Standard Code for Information Interchanges - used to interchange computer languages	ASCII
ASSIGNED MAINTENANCE	See AREA MAINTENANCE	MAINTENANCE ASSIGNEE

ENGLISH	DEFINITION	FRENCH
AUDIT	A maintenance audit is composed of following topics : - Survey of production equipment, maintenance strategy, maintenance organisation, material and human resources - Formulation of recommendations for improvement - Formulation of a plan of action - Cost-benefit analysis of the proposed actions	AUDIT/DIAGNOSTIC DE MAINTENANCE
AUSCULTATIVE MAINTENANCE	See CONDITION-BASED MAINTENANCE	MAINTENANCE AUSCULTATIVE
AVAILABILITY	Property of an item to be able to fulfil a function under defined conditions	DISPONIBILITE
AVAILABILITY OF SPARE PARTS	The proportion of stored items in relation to requested items. Also called the degree of satisfaction of requested parts	DISPONIBILITE EN PIECES
AVAILABILITY RATE	Fraction between MTBF and MTBF + MTTR. This rate concerns the comparison of the time during which an item can be used and the total time during which it can be used without stoppage due to failures or maintenance	TAUX DE DISPONIBILITE
AWG	American Wire Gage	AWG
BAR CODE	Code of which the characters are composed of parallel bars from different thickness and distance to each other. They are read by transversal scanning	CODE A BARRES
BATH TUB CURVE	Graphical representation of a phenomena on time basis, the form of which is a bath tub. In maintenance this is the case with the failure rate curve : decreasing in the beginning, the failure rate will increase after a period during which it is, on average, constant	COURBE DE BAIGNOIRE
BENCH TEST	A test of a component or an equipment on a special test bench.	ESSAIS SUR BANC
BETTERMENT MAINTENANCE	Identifies how technical and managerial performance is monitored and how opportunities for improvement are identified within the regular management process. Is a part of DESIGN-OUT MAINTENANCE	MAINTENANCE AMELIORATIVE
BINARY	Fixed-base two-digit coding - in computer techniques the numerical binary system is composed of the figures 0 and 1	BINAIRE
BINARY CODE	Code of which the characters are composed of binary elements	CODE BINAIRE
BIT	Binary digit	BIT
BITE	Built-in Test equipment. Systems foreseen in the design of equipment, to test certain functions	BITE
BLOCK REPLACEMENT	See AGE REPLACEMENT	REMPLACEMENT EN BLOC

ENGLISH	DEFINITION	FRENCH
BLOTTER TEST	Test to estimate the magnitude of metal parts in lubrication oil. By regular testing, one can get an idea about failure expectance	BLOTTER
BOROSCOPY	See ENDOSCOPY	BOROSCOPIE
BREAKDOWN	Unexpected interruption of function due to failure	PANNE
BREAKDOWN COST	See FAILURE COST	COUT DE DEFAILLANCE
BREAKDOWN MAINTENANCE	See FAILURE-BASED MAINTENANCE	MAINTENANCE ACCIDENTELLE
BS	British standards	BS
BSI	British Standards Institute	BSI
BUILT-IN CAPABILITY	See INHERENT RELIABILITY	FIABILITE INHERENTE
BURN IN	Initial period after start-up - also called INFANT or GREEN PERIOD - see also PREMATURE FAILURE	DEVERMINAGE RODAGE
BUROTICA	Techniques and resources aimed at automizing office activities principally related to word processing, communication, writing and publishing	BUREAUTIQUE
CA	Criticality analysis - a method to group failures of a technical system according to the importance of their consequences. Failure criticality - the potential failures in the various parts of the product or service system are examined to determine the severity of each failure effect in terms of lowering of performance, safety hazard, total loss of function etc.	AC
CALIBRATION	All the operations for the purpose of determining the values of the errors of a measuring instrument (and, if necessary, to determine other metrological properties)	CALIBRAGE
CALL RATE	Intensity of job requests for a certain item	DEGRE D'APPEL
CANNIBALIZATION	Removal of a part from a machine in order to use it for repairing or maintaining another machine	CANNIBALISATION
CATASTROPHIC FAILURE	A failure with very heavy consequences	DEFAILLANCE CATASTROPHIQUE
CAUSE - CONSEQUENCE DIAGRAM	Diagram based on a choice of critical events and the most related sequential problems	DIAGRAMME CAUSE ET EFFET
CD-ROM	Compact disk read-only memory	CD-ROM
CENTRAL PROCESSING UNIT	See CPU	PROCESSEUR CENTRAL

ENGLISH	DEFINITION	FRENCH
CENTRALIZED MAINTENANCE STRUCTURE	A maintenance organization according to which all maintenance work in the plant is part of one organizational structure and depends on one head	MAINTENANCE CENTRALISEE
CFR	Constant failure rate	TCD
CHIP	See INTEGRATED CIRCUIT	CHIP
CM	Condition monitoring	CM
CMMS	Computerized maintenance management systems	GMAO
CODING (CODIFICATION)	Action to set up an organized and rational system. Coding a spare part in a machine (i.e. with figures, letters or other signs such as bars) will facilitate its computerized management	CODIFICATION
COMMISSIONING	The advancement of an installation from the stage of static completion to full working order according to specified requirements	MISE EN ROUTE
COMPLETE BREAKDOWN	Result of a total failure	PANNE COMPLETE
COMPLETE FAILURE	See TOTAL FAILURE	DEFAILLANCE COMPLETE
COMPLIANCE	An affirmative indication or judgement that the supplier of a product or service has met the requirements of the relevant specifications, contract or regulation ; also the state of meeting the requirements	RECEPTION
COMPUTER-AIDED (ASSISTED) MAINTENANCE	Some years ago, computerized systems in maintenance dealt with management topics. Due to the evolution of condition-monitoring techniques and the related computer assistance, today a difference is more and more made in the terminology between CMMS (computerized maintenance management systems) and computer-assisted (aided) maintenance, the latter dealing more with the technical aspects such as oil scan, vibration analysis, thermography etc.	MAO MAINTENIQUE
CONDITION-BASED MAINTENANCE	This type of maintenance, also called predictive or auscultative maintenance, is a breakdown prevention technique requiring no dismantling, and based on inspection by auscultation of the equipment involved	MAINTENANCE CONDITIONNELLE
CONDITION MONITORING	Continuous observing of an item in order to detect possible deviation of normal behaviour or to be informed about its condition and related evolution	SUIVI CONDITIONNEL
CONFORMANCE	An affirmative indication or judgement that a product or service has met the requirements of the relevant specifications, contract or regulation; also the state of meeting the requirements	RECEPTION
CONFORMITY	The fulfilment by an item or service of specific requirements	CONFORMITE

ENGLISH	DEFINITION	FRENCH
CONSIGNMENT	See PERMIT TO WORK - an item is subject to consignment when it is not allowed to work on it	CONSIGNATION
CONSUMABLE ITEM	An item with a monthly average consumption exceeding 0.25 - see also FAST MOVERS	CONSOMMABLE
CONSUMPTION ITEM	An item (spare part) which cannot be used anymore after removal	PIECE DE CONSOMMATION PIECE CONSOMPTIBLE
CO-PROCESSOR	Processing unit which extends the capacity of a main processor in a computer through direct access to the memory of the main processor, but which is unable to operate automatically.	CO-PROCESSEUR
CORRECTIVE MAINTENANCE	Also called breakdown maintenance, palliative or curative maintenance. Form of maintenance which consists of : - Troubleshooting on machines whose poor condition results either in a total or partial stoppage of the equipment, or in its operation under intolerable conditions - Machine repairs	MAINTENANCE CORRECTIVE
COST CENTRE	A location, person or item or equipment (or group of these) in respect of which costs may be ascertained and related to cost units, e.g. processes cost centre, production cost centre, service cost centre etc.	CENTRE DE FRAIS (OU DE COUTS)
COSTS IN USE	See RUNNING COSTS	DEPENSES COURANTES
CPU	Central processing unit - a unit of a computer that includes circuits controlling the interpretation and execution of instructions	CPU
CRITICALITY ANALYSIS	See CA	ANALYSE DE LA CRITICITE
CRITICALITY INDEX	The product of the ratings P x S x D with P = probability of each failure mode occurring S = criticality of the failure D = difficulty of detecting the failure before the product or service is used by the consumer	INDICE DE CRITICITE
CURATIVE MAINTENANCE	See CORRECTIVE MAINTENANCE	MAINTENANCE CURATIVE
DAMAGE	Failure resulting in partial or complete material deterioration of a piece of equipment	AVARIE, DEGAT
DATA FLOW	Routings of information which are defined in the company in an organized way	FLUX DES DONNEES
DATA BANK	A group of data related to a certain field of knowledge and organized to be consulted by users	BANQUE DE DONNEES
DAILY MAINTENANCE	See ROUTINE MAINTENANCE	MAINTENANCE JOURNALIERE

ENGLISH	DEFINITION	FRENCH
DEAD STOCK	See ODDMENT and SURPLUS ITEM	STOCK MORT ROSSIGNOL
DECENTRALIZED MAINTENANCE STRUCTURE	A maintenance organization according to which each production area has its own maintenance crew, without any relation between them	MAINTENANCE DECENTRALISEE
DEFECT	A departure of a quality characteristic from its intended level or state that occurs with a severity sufficient to cause an associated product or service not to satisfy intended normal, or reasonably foreseeable, usage requirements	DEFAUT
DEGRADATION FAILURE	A failure (malfunction process) which happens gradually during a certain period of time	DEFAILLANCE PROGRESSIVE
DELIVERY DELAY	Time between issue of order for spare parts and entry in the stores	DELAIS DE LIVRAISON
DESIGN-OUT MAINTENANCE	This is also known as plant improvement maintenance, and its object is to improve the operation, reliability or capacity of the equipment in place. This sort of work usually involves studies, construction, installation, start-up and tuning	MAINTENANCE CONCEPTUELLE
DFR	Decreasing failure rate	TDD
DIAGNOSTIC	Identification of failures based on symptoms. Evaluation of a situation - Identification of the cause of a failure by way of a logical way of thinking based on a compilation of data as a result of inspection, control, tests etc.	DIAGNOSTIC
DIN	Deutsche Industrie Normen - German Standards	DIN
DIRECT MAINTENANCE COST	Costs which are directly linked to the execution of maintenance. They are composed of : - Regular maintenance costs - Labour costs - Equipment costs - Material costs - Training costs - Subcontracting costs - Costs for technological updating	COUT DIRECT DE MAINTENANCE
DISCARD-AT-FAILURE MAINTENANCE	A repair by removal for which the removed part is not reconditioned but scrapped	REMPLACEMENT PAR DESAFFECTATION
DISPOSAL	Discarding or otherwise disposing of material when it has failed or is no longer required for any reason	REFORME, DESAFFECTATION, DECLASSEMENT
DOM	See DESIGN OUT MAINTENANCE	DOM
DORMANT FAILURE	A failure which is not necessarily seen when it occurs, for instance when it concerns a redundancy or a sub-function which is only in operation from time to time	DEFAILLANCE DORMANTE

ENGLISH	DEFINITION	FRENCH
DORMANT STOCK	See SLEEPING ITEM	STOCK DORMANT
DOS	Disk operating system	DOS
DOWN TIME	The total duration during which an item is out of order (i.e. not in condition to perform its intended function)	TEMP D'ARRET
DROP TEST	See BLOTTER TEST	ESSAIS A GOUTE
DURABILITY	Property of an item to fulfil an intended function under defined operational conditions until a limit is reached	DURABILITE
EARLY DIAGNOSTIC	Examination and interpretation of "weak signals"	DIAGNOSTIC PRECOCE
EARLY FAILURE	See PREMATURE FAILURE	DEFAILLANCE PRECOCE
ECHELON	Maintenance echelon is the degree of complexity of a maintenance intervention. Generally five echelons are considered. MAINTENANCE "LEVEL" is also used	NIVEAU DE MAINTENANCE
ECONOMIC QUANTITY	See WILSON FORMULA	QUANTITE ECONOMIQUE D'ACHAT
EEDPM	Electronic and EDP maintenance	MIE
EMC	Electromagnetic Current	EMC
EMERGENCY MAINTENANCE	Urgent maintenance intervention due to unexpected failure	MAINTENANCE D'URGENCE
ENDOSCOPY	Condition-based maintenance technique executed with an endoscope, which is an optical instrument equipped with a lighting device designed to be introduced in cavities	ENDOSCOPIE
EQUALIZED MAINTENANCE	A maintenance form according to which manpower-intensive maintenance activities are split up into approximately equal subpackages. The objective is to limit the call for maintenance	MAINTENANCE EGALISEE
ERA	Elementary risk analysis	AER
EWS	Early warning system	SAP
EXAMINATION	A comprehensive inspection supplemented by measurement and physical testing in order to determine the condition of an item	EXAMEN
EXCHANGE UNIT	The removal and replacement of an item subject to failure through exchange of an identical one (new or reconditioned) by the supplier against payment of a relatively low price, defined by the reconditioning cost	ECHANGE-STANDARD

ENGLISH	DEFINITION	FRENCH
EXPENDABLE ITEM	A non-repairable spare part - see also CONSUMPTION ITEM	ARTICLE CONSOMPTIBLE
EXPERT-SYSTEM	Computer system (software) which has the knowledge and know-how of an expert in a certain field. This system must use, treat and represent knowledge so that it can be used by a non-expert. In maintenance, expert systems are used for instance in failure diagnostics or troubleshooting programmes	SYSTEME-EXPERT
EXPLODED VIEW	Tridimensional representation of all parts of an assembly in such a way that their position one to another after assembling can be seen	VUE ECLATEE
EXPLOITATION	All operations which contribute to the production and circulation of goods and resources	EXPLOITATION
EXPONENTIAL SMOOTHING	A method for forecasting the consumption of spare parts. This is done by adding to the previous forecast a correction which takes into account the difference between the last forecast of consumption (for which historical data was available) and the actual consumption during the same period	LISAGE EXPONENTIEL
FAIL SAFE	A design method, so that in case of failure or human error, catastrophic consequences are excluded	SUR
FAILURE	The inability of an item to meet a desired standard of performance. Failures occur when an item is not longer in the physical condition which is considered as being necessary for its correct functioning	DEFAILLANCE
FAILURE ANALYSIS	Statistical analysis of failures with the objective of defining the appropriate maintenance method	ANALYSE DE DEFAILLANCE
FAILURE BASED MAINTENANCE	A form of corrective maintenance which is done after failure has occurred	MAINTENANCE ACCIDENTELLE
FAILURE COST	A cost which corresponds to production losses due to unavailability of equipment. This cost is composed of the following costs : - Reduction of production or service - Alteration in the quality of production or service - Longer delivery delays - Higher depreciation costs - Increase of work accidents - Alteration in the work place and environment - Demotivation of personnel Also called BREAKDOWN COST or INDIRECT MAINTENANCE COST	COUT DE DEFAILLANCE
FAILURE CRITICALITY	See CA	CRITICITE DE LA DEFAILLANCE
FAILURE MODES AND EFFECTS ANALYSIS	See FMEA	ANALYSE DES MODES DE DEFAILLANCE ET DE LEURS EFFETS
FAILURE EFFECTS	See FMEA	EFFET DE LA DEFAILLANCE

ENGLISH	DEFINITION	FRENCH
FAILURE RATE	See AGE-SPECIFIC FAILURE RATE - also called HAZARD RATE	TAUX DE PANNE
FAST MOVERS	Spare parts with an average monthly consumption exceeding 0.25	CONSOMMABLES
FAULT	A lack in the functioning of an item due to failure or to other reasons including human operation	DEFAUT, ANOMALIE
FAULT TREE ANALYSIS	See FTA	ANALYSE DE L'ARBORESCENCE DE DEFAILLANCE
FERROGRAPHY	Observation of metallic parts in lubrication oil, which are attracted and kept in a magnetic field. Regular microscopy observation of the precipitated parts give an idea about the degree of wear and the related wearing process. See also under SOAP	FERROGRAPHIE
FFT	Fast Fourier Transformation. Serial transformation algorithm of an imput signal into a signal which can be treated by computer	FFT
FIFO	FIRST IN FIRST OUT Method used in stock management on a set of items, aimed at defining their price. It is based on a systematic choice to issue first the oldest set. Stock value is calculated on the basis of the most recent entries. This method is principally used for raw materials in important quantities	FIFO
FIXED TIME MAINTENANCE	See SYSTEMATIC MAINTENANCE	MAINTENANCE A PERIODICITE FIXE
FMEA	Failure mode and effects analysis - A method to analyse reliability of equipment or an item, including a systematic analysis of all possible failures which can occur during well-defined applications. Failure mode = the anticipated conditions of operation, which are used as the background to study the most probable failure mode, location and mechanism of the item or system and its components. Failure effect = the potential failures, which are studied to determine their probable effect on the performance of the whole item and the effects of the various components on each other	AMDE
FMECA	Failure mode effects and criticality analysis - a combination of FMEA and CA	AMDEC
FOM	Force of mortality : number of failures per unit of use	TAUX DE PANNE
FORCE OF MORTALITY	See AGE-SPECIFIC FAILURE RATE	TAUX DE PANNE
FORCED OUTAGE	Outage due to the unscheduled putting-out of service of an item	MISE HORS D'USAGE FORCEE
FREQUENCIAL ANALYSIS	See SPECTRAL ANALYSIS	ANALYSE FREQUENTIELLE

ENGLISH	DEFINITION	FRENCH
FRL	Filter, regulator, lubrication points	FRL
FSI	Functionally by significant items	FSI
FTA	Fault tree analysis - a systematic fault analysis of an item by representing the relation between the main function and the possible faults which can occur both for maintenance as well as for operational reasons. This representation is done in the form of a decision tree. This inductive analysis consists of an investigation of which sub failures can lead to a major failure	ANALYSE DE L'ARBORESCENCE DEFAILLANCE
FUNCTIONAL FAILURE	Inability of an item to meet a desired standard of performance	DEFAILLANCE FONCTIONNELLE
GAN	See GOOD-AS-NEW	RECONDITIONNE
GOOD-AS-NEW	Term used to describe a system after it has been repaired, whether the repair has restored it to its original condition, or whether it still contains some used or worn parts	RECONDITIONNE
GRADUAL FAILURE	See DEGRADATION FAILURE	DEFAILLANCE PROGRESSIVE
GROUP REPLACEMENT	See AGE REPLACEMENT	REMPLACEMENT PAR GROUPE
HARD TIME MAINTENANCE	See SYSTEMATIC MAINTENANCE	
HARDWARE	The physical equipment used in data processing, as opposed to computer programs, procedures, rules and associated documentation	HARD WARE
HAZARD RATE	See AGE-SPECIFIC FAILURE RATE	TAUX DE PANNE
HAZOP	Harzard and operability study - an extended FMEA technique by including operability factors in addition to equipment fault modes. It is a systematic analysis of an installation or system to find the possibilities and effects of deviations in the process which are not directly expected by the designers	HAZOP
HEAT RECLAIM	The principle whereby heat that might otherwise be discharged to waste is passed through a suitable form of heat exchanger and thereby recovered for other uses	RECUPERATION DE CHALEUR
HEAT RECOVERY	A process that enables waste heat to be stored or transferred for the purpose of performing a useful function elsewhere	RECYCLAGE
HELI COIL	A reconditioning technique of worn-out threads. Externally and internally threaded inserts with the original internal diameter are screwed in the worn-out thread after reboring and rethreading on a higher diameter	HELI-COIL

ENGLISH	DEFINITION	FRENCH
HEURISTIC	Failure solution technique using a step-by-step strategy where each step is based on the previous result - mainly implemented in artificial intelligence for its quickness	HEURISTIQUE
HIDDEN FAILURE	See DORMANT FAILURE	DEFAILLANCE CACHEE
IDLE TIME	The period of time during which an item is available to perform its intended function, but is not used due to shortage of work, tooling, material, operators etc.	TEMPS MORT
IFR	Increasing failure rate	TDC
IMPERFECTION	A departure of a quality characteristic from its intended level or state, without any association with or conformance to specification requirements or to the usability of a product or service	IMPERFECTION
INCIDENT	See CATASTROPHIC FAILURE	INCIDENT
INCIDENT FREQUENCE ANALYSIS	See FTA	AFI
INCIDENT FREQUENCE ANALYSIS	See FTA	ANALYSE DE LA FREQUENCE D'INCIDENTS
INDIRECT MAINTENANCE COST	See FAILURE COST	COUT INDIRECT DE MAINTENANCE
INFANT MORTALITY	See PREMATURE FAILURE - See BURN-IN	MALADIE D'ENFANCE DEFAILLANCE PRECOCE PANNE DE JEUNESSE
INHERENT RELIABILITY	Performance standard of an item which indicates what it is capable of achieving (also called BUILT-IN CAPABILITY)	FIABILITE INHERENTE
INITIAL PROVISIONING	A forecast and supply of spare parts for new equipment to cover needs during a first period of use	PREMIERE DOTATION
IN-PLANT TRAINING	Training in the plant without sending trainees outside	FORMATION DANS L'USINE
IN-PLANT STANDARDIZATION	Action which aims at reducing the number of types and makes of items. This action is based on the set-up of rules, descriptions and procedures which allow to acquire items according to pre-established specifications	STANDARDISATION
IN-SERVICE TRAINING	See ON-THE-JOB TRAINING	FORMATION EN SERVICE
IN SITU	Under real operational conditions	IN SITU

ENGLISH	DEFINITION	FRENCH
IN SITU TEST	A test under real operational conditions of an item or component which does not necessitate the removal of the component or the transfer of the item towards a test bench	TEST IN SITU
INSPECTION	Assessment of the value of one or more properties of equipment compared to defined limit values; the process of measuring, examining, testing, gauging or otherwise comparing the unit with the applicable requirements	INSPECTION
INSPECTION ROUNDS	Technical inspections, followed by a report, executed by specialized "inspectors" who are in charge of preparing maintenance programmes and verifying the quality of the work done on the equipment	VISITES
INSPECTIVE MAINTENANCE	See CONDITION-BASED MAINTENANCE	MAINTENANCE AUSCULTATIVE
INSTANTANEOUS FAILURE	A failure in which a malfunction process happens instantaneously. Also called SUDDEN FAILURE	DEFAILLANCE INSTANTANEE
INSTANTANEOUS FAILURE RATE	See AGE-SPECIFIC FAILURE RATE	TAUX DE DEFAILLANCE SOUDAINE
INSTRUMENTIST	Technician specialized in maintenance of control and measuring devices	INSTRUMENTISTE
INSURANCE ITEM	Spare parts which, under normal operational conditions, are not subject to wear, but whenever they brake down, the whole machine is out of order. Therefore they are kept in stock as a kind of "insurance". They are always slow movers. Also called SECURITY or SAFETY ITEM	ARTICLE (OU PIECE) DE SECURITE
INTEGRATED CIRCUIT	Electronic device whose components and connections are manufactured in a semiconductor substrate, allowing to produce a complete function	CIRCUIT INTEGRE
INTERACTING	Allows a dialogue in real time between computer and user	INTERACTIF
INTERFACE	Function between computer and peripherals	INTERFACE
INTERMITTENT FAILURE	Repetitive and momentary malfunction followed by normal operation	PANNE INTERMITTENTE
INTERNAL RE-ORDERING DELAY	Time between issue of a purchase request and issue of an order for spare parts	DELAIS DE REAPPROVISIONNEMENT INTERNE
IRAN	Inspect and repair as necessary - a maintenance method which is used when the process of wear is irregular or not mastered. Maintenance intervention is decided after inspection. This is a kind of condition-based maintenance	IRSB

ENGLISH	DEFINITION	FRENCH
ISO	International Standards Organization	ISO
ITEM	- A part, equipment, subsystem or system that can be individually considered and separately examined or tested - An actual or conventional object on which a set of observations may be made - Defined quantity of material on which a set of observations may be made - An observed value, either qualitative (attributes) or quantitative (measured)	ITEM
JIT	Just in time	JIT
JOB CARD	See JOB ORDER	BON DE TRAVAIL
JOB ORDER	A written instruction detailing work to be carried out - see WORK ORDER	ORDRE DE TRAVAIL
JOB PREPARATION	The job preparation function determines operation procedures, job specifications, material resources, requirements, time allocation and workload. Also called WORK PREPARATION, WORK SPECIFICATION or WORK STUDY	PREPARATION DE TRAVAIL
JOB REPORT	A statement recording the work done and the condition of the item	RAPPORT DE TRAVAIL
JOB REQUEST	A document requesting work to be carried out - see WORK REQUISITION	DEMANDE DE TRAVAIL
LCC	Life cycle cost : the total cost of ownership of an item of material, taking into account all costs of acquisition, personnel training, operation, maintenance, modification and disposal, for the purpose of making decisions on new or changed requirements and as a control mechanism in service, for existing and future items. The term LCP - Life cycle profit - is also commonly used.	COUT DU CYCLE DE VIE
LEVEL	See ECHELON	NIVEAU DE MAINTENANCE
LIFE CYCLE	It has become usual to compare production equipment with living organisms. For each item there is the phase of design followed by the phase of manufacturing or construction. Then comes the period of use which is limited of necessity because of the progressive deterioration, and finally after a certain time, total breakdown and ruin. This total process is called life cycle	CYCLE DE VIE
LIFE CYCLE COST	See LCC	COUT DU CYCLE DE VIE
LIFE CYCLE PROFIT	See LCC / LCP	PROFIT DU CYCLE DE VIE
LIFE SPAN	See LIFE TIME	DUREE DE VIE

ENGLISH	DEFINITION	FRENCH
LIFE TIME	Period during which an item assures a required function under defined operational and maintenance conditions until it reaches its limit condition	DUREE DE VIE
LIFO	Last in first out. Method used in stock management on a set of items, aimed at defining their price. It is based on a systematic issue of the last entered sets. This method is principally used for raw materials in important quantities	LIFO
LOAD RATE	The total time of utilization or production in relation to the total availability	TAUX DE CHARGE
MACHINE FILE	The totality of documents containing technical information concerning a machine	DOSSIER MACHINE
MACHINE HISTORY	Listing of data concerning machine life including, in chronological order, each failure, malfunction and intervention on the machine	HISTORIQUE MACHINE
MAINTAINABILITY	Property of an item which indicates the ease of maintenance under defined operational conditions (i.e. ability of an item to be maintained easily). A good maintainability means a low MTTM or low MTTR	MAINTENABILITE
MAINTENANCE	Maintenance is the function which has as objective to ensure the fullest availability of production equipment, utilities and related facilities at optimal cost and under satisfactory conditions of quality, safety and protection of the environment	MAINTENANCE
MAINTENANCE PLANNING	A time-based plan allocating specific maintenance tasks to specific periods	PLANNING DE MAINTENANCE
MAINTENANCE PROGRAMME	A comprehensive list of items and the maintenance required, including the intervals at which maintenance should be performed	PROGRAMME DE MAINTENANCE
MAJOR MAINTENANCE INTERVENTION	Is an intervention of important magnitude and duration, and which is a necessity to avoid shortening of technical lifetime	INTERVENTION MAJEURE
MAJOR REPAIR	See MAJOR MAINTENANCE INTERVENTION - here the intervention is limited to repair activities	REPARATION MAJEURE
MALFUNCTION	A failure for which the requested operation does not happen when the related function is activated (for instance an electrical switch)	DYSFONCTIONNEMENT
MARGINAL MAINTENANCE	Type of condition-based maintenance along with a systematic effort to find possible improvements aimed at reducing variations in lifetime between simular equipment and at increasing the average lifetime	MAINTENANCE MARGINALE
MAXIMUM STOCK	Sum of spare parts stock at the reordering level + quantity of orders in progress	STOCK MAXIMUM

ENGLISH	DEFINITION	FRENCH
MEAN TIME BETWEEN FAILURES	See MTBF	MOYENNE DES TEMPS DE BON FONCTIONNEMENT ENTRE PANNES
MEAN TIME BETWEEN REMOVALS	See MTBR	MOYENNE DES TEMPS ENTRE REMPLACEMENTS
MEAN TIME BETWEEN UNJUSTIFIED REMOVALS	See MTBUR	MOYENNE DES TEMPS ENTRE REMPLACEMENTS INJUSTIFIES
MEAN TIME TO FAILURE	See MTTF	MOYENNE DES TEMPS TOTAUX DE BON FONCTIONNEMENT
MEAN TIME TO MAINTAIN	See MTTM	MOYENNE DES TEMPS DES TACHES DE MAINTENANCE
MEAN TIME TO REPAIR	See MTTR	MOYENNE DES TEMPS DES TACHES DE REPARATION
MECHANALYSE	A condition-based maintenance technique according to which vibrations from rotating parts are measured. The evolution of the amplitude is in direct relation with the evolution of wear. See also SPM	MECHANALYSIS
MEFO	Most expensive first out. Method used in stock management on a set of items, aimed at defining their price. The most expensive sets are issued first. This method is principally used for raw materials in important quantities	MEFO
METALLOCK SYSTEM	Method to repair split cast-iron parts (for example, engine blocs). It concerns a cramping technique, developed by the Metallock Company of Hamburg, Germany. It consists in driving in cramps transversally to the split	METALLOCK (SYSTEME)
METHODS	The methods function consists of thinking ahead and making the best possible preparation for maintenance department work through the use of suitable techniques and appropriate means	METHODES
MINIMUM STOCK	Care should be taken to ensure that sufficient parts are in stock. A minimum stock should be established to take into consideration possible abnormal consumption or delivery delays.	STOCK MINIMUM
MIS	Management information system	SIG
MISUSE	This represents the application or stresses which are outside the usual capability of the product or service system	MAUVAIS EMPLOI
MIXED MAINTENANCE STRUCTURE	A maintenance organizational structure according to which a part of maintenance activity is centralized (planning office, workshop, stores, general maintenance) and another part is assigned to the production areas without any relation between them	MAINTENANCE MIXTE

ENGLISH	DEFINITION	FRENCH
MOBILE AVERAGE	A method for forecasting the consumption of spare parts based on data of past consumption (i.e. monthly) for which an average value is taken. It should be noted that it is necessary to analyse the reasons for consumption. Parts used, for instance, during a major overhaul cannot be considered as normal consumption	MOYENNE MOBILE
MODIFICATION	A change of the construction/design of equipment in order to improve quality, performance or safety of production. See also DESIGN-OUT MAINTENANCE	MODIFICATION
MP	Maintenance prevention	PM
MPI	Management performance indices	MPI
MSI	Maintenance significant items	MSI
MTBF	Mean time between failure - the average of intervals between failures, during a certain period of time, in case the failure can be solved through maintenance intervention	MTBF
MTBR	Mean time between removals - average interval between the moment that the removals took place	MTBR
MTBUR	Mean time between unjustified removals - average interval between the moment that unjustified removals took place	MTBUR
MTTF	Mean time to failure - the same as MTBF, but involving non-repairable items (i.e. light bulbs)	MTTF
MTTM	Mean time to maintain - the average duration of all preventive and corrective maintenance activities during a certain period of time	MTTM
MTTR	Mean time to repair - the average duration of all repair activities during a certain period of time	MTTR
MULTI-SKILL	Having knowledge, capabilities and expertise in various fields related to a basic field. A multi-skilled mechanic has competence in mechanics, hydraulics, pneumatics, and basic electricity	POLYVALENCE
NON-CONFORMITY	A departure of a quality characteristic from its intended level or state that occurs with a severity sufficient to cause an associated product or service not to meet a specification requirement	PAS CONFORME
NON-EFFICIENCY COST	See FAILURE COST	COUT DE NON-EFFICACITE
NORMAL WORKLOAD	Relation between the activity and the capacity on the basis of practical feasibility	CHARGE NORMALE DE TRAVAIL
NORMATIVE FAILURE	A failure which occurs when a normative limit value of a failure-related condition is reached	DEFAILLANCE NORMATIVE

ENGLISH	DEFINITION	FRENCH
NUGATORY TIME	That portion of time for which payment is made but for which no service is rendered	TEMPS IMPRODUCTIF
OBSOLESCENCE	Going out of use due to technological evolution and not due to wear	OBSOLESCENCE
OBSOLETE	Disused, discarded	OBSOLETE
ODDMENT	See DEAD STOCK	STOCK MORT ROSSIGNOL
OEM	Original equipment manufacturer	FOE
OFF-LINE MAINTENANCE	See SHUT-DOWN MAINTENANCE	MAINTENANCE A L'ARRET
OIL SCAN	See SOAP	ANALYSE D'HUILE
ON-CONDITION MAINTENANCE	See CONDITION-BASED MAINTENANCE	MAINTENANCE CONDITIONNELLE
ON-LINE MAINTENANCE	Maintenance activities while the equipment is in operation	MAINTENANCE EN CONTINU
ON-THE-JOB TRAINING	Training during execution of the job, outside of classrooms	FORMATION SUR LE TAS
OPERATING SYSTEM	Software for controlling the execution of computer programs, and which may provide scheduling, debugging, input/output control, accounting, compilation, storage allocation, data management and related services	SERVEUR
OPERATING TIME	The period of time during which an item performs its intended function	TEMPS OPERATOIRE
OPERATION INTENSITY	The average use of the equipment per unit of time	INTENSITE D'OPERATION
OPERATION ITEM	An item (spare part) which can be used again after removal. Also called NON-EXPENDABLE ITEM	PIECE DURABLE
OPERATION PROCEDURE	Procedure to execute various operations based on a preliminary study or experience ; operation procedures are for example : used in job preparation for maintenance work (work study)	MODE D'OPERATION
OPERATION PROFILE	The repetitive pattern of periods of time during which production tools are put into operation	PROFIL OPERATOIRE
OPPORTUNISTIC MAINTENANCE	Maintenance intervention when the occasion occurs, for instance when equipment is shut down for other maintenance activities	MAINTENANCE OPPORTUNISTE
OUTAGE	The state of an item being unable to perform its required function	HORS D'USAGE, ARRET DE FONCTIONNEMENT

ENGLISH	DEFINITION	FRENCH
OUTAGE DURATION	Within a specified period of time, the period of time during which an item is not available to perform its function because it is withdrawn from service	PERIODE D'ARRET
OUTAGE RATE	For a particular class of outage and a specified period of time, the quotient of the number of outages to the up-time for an item, e.g. scheduled outage rate, forced outage rate	DEGRE D'ARRET
OUTDATED	See OBSOLETE	DEPASSE
OVERHAUL	Total reconditioning of an item, subject to gradual wear	REVISION
OVERSTOCKING	When the stock level is higher than the maximum stock (see MAXIMUM STOCK)	SURSTOCKAGE
OWNER COSTS	All costs resulting from stock composition and conservation (interest loss on invested capital, storage costs, personnel costs, distribution and conservation costs etc.)	COUTS DE POSSESSION
PALLIATIVE MAINTENANCE	See CORRECTIVE MAINTENANCE	MAINTENANCE PALLIATIVE
PARETO LAW	Law of economic optimum by VILFREDO PARETO (1848-1923). Also known as 20/80 rule - analysis based on a classification of a magnitude according to its decreasing importance in relation to another magnitude	LOI DE PARETO
PARTIAL FAILURE	The item does not work or the service is not provided as well as expected, but it has not completely failed	DEFAILLANCE PARTIELLE
PARTS LIST	A definitive list of all items which form the material	LISTE DE COMPOSANTS
PASSIVE REDUNDANCY	The redundant item must be put into operation if the basic item fails	REDONDANCE PASSIVE
PERIODIC MAINTENANCE	See SYSTEMATIC MAINTENANCE	MAINTENANCE PERIODIQUE
PERIODICAL REORDERING	A consequence of reordering based on the reordering level is that orders are placed at variable dates. The inconvenience of this is that each item must be considered separately. Grouping would reduce the number of orders. The two main criteria for this grouping are the supplier and the geographical location. The stock of items from one supplier would be checked at regular intervals t, t+P, t+2P etc. After grouping one could then switch easily to fixed-dates (periodical) reordening for which the standard to optimize costs becomes the delay between the intervals of stock checking. The disadvantage of this system is the increase in the stock level	REAPPROVISIONNEMENT PERIODIQUE
PERMIT TO WORK	A signed document, authorizing access to an item, which defines conditions, including safety precautions, under which work may be carried out. This may include a document, signed on completion of maintenance, stating that an item is safe and ready for use	PERMISSION DE TRAVAIL DECONSIGNATION

ENGLISH	DEFINITION	FRENCH
PHA	Primary hazards analysis - preliminary identification of the system elements or events that lead to hazards	ARP
PHASED INSPECTION	See PROGRESSIVE MAINTENANCE	INSPECTION ECHELONNEE
PHYSICAL ASSET REGISTER	A list of items, including information such as constructional and technical details about each. This may be combined with an inventory	INVENTAIRE DES IMMOBILISATIONS
PHYSICAL STOCK	The real stock level of stored parts expressed in terms of quantity or money	STOCK PHYSIQUE
PICK-OUT STOCK	A buffer stock in the workshop or production areas which can immediately be issued by the workers without time-consuming procedures. It concerns especially consumable standard parts of a low value (fasteners, screws, bolts, fuses, O-rings etc.).	STOCK TAMPON
PLANNED MAINTENANCE	Maintenance for which the necessity for execution is known sufficiently in advance so that the normal planning and job preparation procedure can be followed	MAINTENANCE PLANIFIEE
PM	Preventive maintenance	MP
POST-INVESTMENT	The total of actions aimed at valuating the existing capital for optimal use in terms of efficiency and longevity during the whole lifetime of the equipment. Other aspects are the pre-investment studies, technology transfer, cost control, training, the correct utilization of the equipment, the quality of production etc.	POST INVESTISSEMENT
POSTPONABLE MAINTENANCE	When the execution of maintenance intervention can be postponed until an opportune moment	MAINTENANCE DELAYEE MAINTENANCE DIFFEREE
PRA	Primary risk analysis. Analysis of primary failures	APR
PREDICTIVE MAINTENANCE	See CONDITION-BASED MAINTENANCE	MAINTENANCE PREDICTIVE
PREMATURE FAILURE	Failure which occurs too soon compared to the expectations concerning the behaviour of the item concerned. This type of failure occurs for instance during the initial period after start-up (childhood disease)	DEFAILLANCE PRECOCE (PANNE DE JEUNESSE)
PREVENTIVE MAINTENANCE	The principle of preventive maintenance is always based on thinking ahead. It is put into practice in two forms : systematic (periodic) maintenance and condition-based (predictive) maintenance	MAINTENANCE PREVENTIVE
PRIMARY FAILURE	The failure on an item which is not the consequence of another failure up-stream	DEFAILLANCE PRIMAIRE
PRINTED CIRCUIT	Card with electronic components related to each other through printed connections on the card	CIRCUIT IMPRIME

ENGLISH	DEFINITION	FRENCH
PRODUCTION PROFILE	See OPERATION PROFILE	PROFILE DE PRODUCTION
PRODUCTIVE MAINTENANCE	See TPM	MAINTENANCE PRODUCTIVE
PROGRAMMING	See WORK PROGRAMMING	ORDONNANCEMENT
PROGRESSIVE MAINTENANCE	See EQUALIZED MAINTENANCE	MAINTENANCE PROGRESSIVE
QA	Quality assurance	QA
QUALITY CIRCLE	Method of exchanging ideas or joining efforts aimed at improving the quality of a product, a process or a service	CERCLE DE QUALITE
RAM	Random access memory (computer)	
RATIO	Coefficient or relation between two absolute values. It is a criteria for comparison.	RATIO
RCM	Reliability-centred maintenance : a process used to determine the maintenance requirements of any physical asset in its operating context	RCM
REAL TIME	Data processing by computer related to an exterior process under respect of the time constraints imposed by the exterior process	TEMPS REEL
REBUILD	See OVERHAUL	RECONSTRUCTION
RECLAIMING	See RECONDITIONING	RECONDITIONNEMENT
RECLAIMING BY WELDING	A repair technique which is based on a deposit of a skin of material on an item through welding. This deposit can be obtained through welding with welding rods, spray-welding or powder metalization	RECHARGEMENT PAR SOUDAGE
RECONDITIONING	Said of an item which can be put into its original condition through appropriate techniques such as spray-welding. See also REPAIRABLE ITEM	RECONDITIONNEMENT
RECOVERABLE ITEM	A repairable spare part. See REPAIRABLE ITEM	PIECE REPARABLE
REDUNDANCY	Provision of more than one component in equipment or an item in an installation aimed at increasing reliability or, in case of failure, to ensure that the redundant component takes over the function	REDONDANCE
REHABILITATION	Operation which is done on an item having lost a part of its ability and which aims at obtaining the original or, through modernization, a higher capacity	REHABILITATION

ENGLISH	DEFINITION	FRENCH
RELIABILITY	The probability that an item performs a required function under well-defined conditions during a certain interval	FIABILITE
RELIABILITY-CENTRED MAINTENANCE (RCM)	Maintenance based on the inherent reliability of each item of manufacturing equipment in its operating context. RCM provides a method of identifying, for each piece of equipment, the cost-effective measures necessary to maintain its reliable performance	MAINTENANCE CENTREE SUR LA FIABILITE (FIABILISATION)
RENEWAL	Exchange old by new. For instance, an item which became obsolete or whose lifetime has come to an end is removed and replaced by a new one	RENOUVELLEMENT
RENOVATION	Action of putting the item into its original condition. The principal of renovation means a complete operation touching on all aspects of an item.	RENOVATION
REORDENABLE ITEM	Each component which is part of an item of equipment and subject to reordering	ARTICLE D'APPROVISIONNEMENT
RE-ORDERING BASED ON RE-ORDERING LEVEL	Each time the stock of spare parts reaches a level which equals the sum of the consumption during the internal reordering delay + the consumption during the delivery delay + the minimum stock, a certain quantity is reordered	REAPPROVISIONNEMENT SUR POINT DE COMMANDE
RE-ORDERING BY CONTRACT	Purchase technique which consists of a contract with a supplier of spare parts specifying the quantity to be supplied over a certain period of time. The contract details all the purchasing conditions, particularly price and delay	REAPPROVISIONNEMENT SUR CONTRAT
RE-ORDERING LEVEL	The level of spare parts which equals the sum of the consumption during the internal re-ordering delay + the consumption during the delivery delay + the minimum stocks	POINT DE COMMANDE
REPAIR	To restore an item in an acceptable condition by the renewal, replacement or reconditioning of worn, damaged or decayed parts	REPARATION
REPAIR BY REPLACEMENT	When repair of a failure on an item is done through removal and replacement of a component	REPARATION PAR REMPLACEMENT
REPAIRABILITY	The property of a component to be repaired and brought into its original condition	REPARABILITE
REPAIRABLE ITEM	A spare part which after removal can be reconditioned so that it can be used again under the same conditions as a new part	ARTICLE REPARABLE
REPOWERING	MAJOR OVERHAUL or REBUILT related to combustion engines	RECONSTRUCTION DE MOTEUR
RESTORATION	Maintenance actions intended to bring an item back to its original appearance or state	REMISE EN ETAT

ENGLISH	DEFINITION	FRENCH
RISK ITEM	See INSURANCE ITEM	PIECE DE SECURITE
ROCOF	Rate of occurrence of failures	ROCOF
ROM	Read-only memory (computer)	ROM
ROTABLE	See REPAIRABLE ITEM	PIECE DE ROTATION
ROUTINE MAINTENANCE	Is a form of first-level maintenance of very simple nature and with a high frequency such as greasing and cleaning. Often called DAILY MAINTENANCE	MAINTENANCE DE ROUTINE
ROUTINGS	See DATA FLOW	FLUX
RUNNING COSTS	The total costs at the charge of the material owner of the operation, maintenance and modification of an item of material	DEPENSES COURANTES
RUNNING FAILURE	Failure which occurs when the required function is in use (during its operation)	DEFAILLANCE EN FONCTIONNEMENT
RUNNING IN	Action during the period, immediately after first start up, which aims at progressively obtaining the requested performance of an item	RODAGE
RUNNING MAINTENANCE	Maintenance intervention carried out on an item during its operation	MAINTENANCE EN FONCTIONNEMENT
SAFETY ITEM	See INSURANCE ITEM	PIECE DE SECURITE
SAMPLE INSPECTION	A preventive maintenance intervention on a sample of identical items with the objective of defining a maintenance programme for the whole group of items	INSPECTION PAR ECHANTILLONAGE
SCANNER	Optical lecture equipment which recognises letters, figures, drawings and graphical symbols	SCANNER
SCHEDULED MAINTENANCE	See PLANNED MAINTENANCE	MAINTENANCE PLANIFIEE
SCHEDULED OUTAGE	Outage due to the programmed taking out of service of an item	MISE HORS D'USAGE PROGRAMMEE
SCHEDULED SHUT-DOWN	A stoppage of the equipment in order to execute a maintenance intervention according to a maintenance programme (see also SHUT-DOWN MAINTENANCE)	ARRET PROGRAMME
SCRAPPING	See DISPOSAL	MISE A LA MITRAILLE REFORME, DESAFFECTATION

ENGLISH	DEFINITION	FRENCH
SEASONAL SHUT-DOWN	Programmed shut-downs of an equipment or a plant in a certain season of the year. The reason for this seasonal shut-down can be holidays or raw-materials availability (for instance end of sugar-cane harvest). These shut-downs are generally used for major maintenance works	ARRET SAISONNIER
SECONDARY DAMAGE	Damage due to a secondary failure	DEGAT SECONDAIRE
SECURITY ITEM	See INSURANCE ITEM	PIECE DE SECURITE
SENSOR	Device which delivers, starting from a physical magnitude, another magnitude often electrical, which is related to the first and immediately capable of being used for measuring or command	SENSEUR
SHELF LIFE ITEM	Item with restricted storage life, for instance due to degradation, ageing or perishability	ARTICLE PERISSABLE
SHIFT	Personnel working 8 hours as part of a 3 x 8 hours timetable giving 24 hours cover	EQUIPE POSTEE
SHOCK PULSE METHOD	See SPM	ONDES DE SHOCK (METHODE D')
SHORTAGES TIME	The period of time during which the item is unable to perform due to shortages of labour, spares, facilities etc. See IDLE TIME	TEMPS MORT
SHUT-DOWN FAILURE	Failure which occurs when the required function is not in use (during its shut-down)	DEFAILLANCE A L'ARRET
SHUT-DOWN MAINTENANCE	Maintenance which is carried out during stoppage of an item.	MAINTENANCE A L'ARRET
SLEEPING ITEM	A spare part which has no movement, but the equipment in which it is built is still in use. As such it is a slow mover.	STOCK DORMANT
SOAP	Spectrometric oil analysis programme - a condition-based maintenance technique which measures the concentration and the nature of metallic parts in lubrication oil. The measurement is done by means of spectrometric analysis in a laboratory. This technique makes it possible to give an idea about the state of wear of certain components	SOAP
SOFTWARE	Computer programs, procedures, rules and any associated documentation concerned with the operation of a data processing system	LOGICIEL
SPARE PART	Item which is used to replace a worn-out or broken-down item	PIECE DE RECHANGE
SPC	Shock pulse control	SPC
SPECIFIC ITEM	See SPECIFIC PART	ARTICLE SPECIFIQUE

ENGLISH	DEFINITION	FRENCH
SPECIFIC PART	These parts are especially manufactured for a well-defined item of equipment and are not interchangeable with parts of another make (for instance, machine frames, valve-levers, spiral gears, switch contacts and connecting-rods)	PIECE SPECIFIQUE
SPECTRAL ANALYSIS	Frequency-based analysis in which the signal values in function of frequency is called spectrum.	ANALYSE SPECTRALE
SPM	A condition-based maintenance technique aimed at assessing the condition of ball- and roller-bearings. The basis of this technique is the measurement of a pulse-value which is generated by the rolling elements or by one of the rings subject to damage or wear. The magnitude of the value gives an idea about the degree of wear	SPM
SPRAY WELDING	A repair/reconditioning technique. See RECLAIMING BY WELDING	SOUDAGE PAR PROJECTION
STANDARD EXCHANGE	See EXCHANGE UNIT	ECHANGE STANDARD
STANDARDIZATION	Being in conformity with standards. Standardization of items allows setting up in-plant standards (see IN-PLANT STANDARDS)	NORMALISATION
STANDARDS	Rules or references which define the type and nature of an item. It is a criterium to which is related a specification or description	NORMES
STAND BY REDUNDANCY	See PASSIVE REDUNDANCY	REDONDANCE EN STAND BY
STOCK MOVEMENT	A movement of a spare part in the store is an entry, an issue or a return.	MOUVEMENT DU STOCK
STOCK-OUT	When the stock level is zero	RUPTURE DE STOCK
STORAGE LIFE ITEM	See SHELF-LIFE ITEM	ARTICLE PERISSABLE
SUB-ASSEMBLY	A machine is composed of assemblies and sub-assemblies which in turn are composed of parts. Subassemblies can generally be repaired or reconditioned	SOUS-ENSEMBLE
SUB-CONTRACTING	Manufacturing of a product or the execution of work or service by a specialized company for another company. In maintenance subcontracting, contracts are made for certain work in either specialized fields or because of the manpower needed	SOUS-TRAITANCE
SUDDEN FAILURE	See INSTANTANEOUS FAILURE	DEFAILLANCE SOUDAINE
SUITABILITY	See AVAILABILITY	DISPONIBILITE
SUPERFLUOUS FUNCTION	Items or components which serve no purpose in the context under consideration	FONCTION SUPERFLUE

ENGLISH	DEFINITION	FRENCH
SURPLUS ITEM	A spare part designed for equipment which has become obsolete or which does not exist anymore. Also called DEAD ITEM	STOCK MORT ROSSIGNOL
SURPLUS STOCK	Exists where too many spare parts are stored for certain equipment	STOCK EXCEDENTAIRE
SURVEY	An examination, the written report of which would include a recommendation for action. See also AUDIT	AUDIT
SYNOPTIC DISPLAY	Display representing in a graphical way the different components of an installation	SYNOPTIQUE
SYSTEMATIC MAINTENANCE	This consists in servicing the equipment at regular intervals, either according to a time schedule or on the basis of predetermined units of use (hours in operation or kilometres travelled), with a view to detecting failures or premature wear and eliminating them before a breakdown occurs. The servicing schedule is usually based on manufacturers' forecasts, revised and adjusted according to actual experience in previous servicing, and noted down in the machine files. This type of maintenance is also called periodic maintenance.	MAINTENANCE SYSTEMATIQUE
TARAN	Test and repair as necessary - see IRAN	ERSB
TELEMATIC	The use at distance of computers such as computer networks	TELEMATIQUE
TEROTECHNOLOGY	Comes from the Greek "TEREIN" which means "TO CURE". A combination of management, financial, engineering, building and other practices applied to physical assets in pursuit of economic life-cycle costs. Note : its practice is concerned with the specification and design for reliability and maintainability of plant, machinery, equipment, buildings and structures, with their installation, commissioning, operation, maintenance, modification and replacement, and with feedback of information on design, performance and costs	TEROTECHNOLOGIE
TEST	A critical trial or examination of one or more properties or characteristics of a material, product, set of observation, etc.	ESSAIS
THERMOGRAPHY	Control and supervising technique concerning the state of heating of an item. Infra-red thermography is a technique which allows to detect at a certain distance the surface temperature of an item based on the emission of infrared waves	THERMOGRAPHIE
THERMOVISION	Visual representation of heating effects. Technique which is used to represent variations in the state of heating of an equipment or part of it. It is used in condition-based maintenance to follow up the evolution of wear, for instance, of roller bearings	THERMOVISION
THROW-AWAY BITS (PARTS)	Parts which are thrown away when they are worn out	PIECES CONSOMMABLES PIECE CONSOMPTIBLE

ENGLISH	DEFINITION	FRENCH
TOTAL FAILURE	This results in a complete lack of ability of the product or service to perform the required function	DEFAILLANCE TOTALE
TOTAL PRODUCTIVE MAINTENANCE	See TPM	MAINTENANCE PRODUCTIVE TOTALE - TOPOMAINTENANCE
TPM	Total productive maintenance. The aim of TPM is to optimize the productivity of the equipment. Among the basic principles and ideas the following are worth mentioning : - Maintenance must always be considered as a productive function, to the same extent as production. - TPM must be the concern of every department in the plant. Not only maintenance but also production, planning etc. - Every level must have the will to cooperate in TPM - from the general management to the lowest echelon.	TPM TOPOMAINTENANCE
TRESHOLD SAMPLING	An analysis during a certain period of time on a sample of identical item aimed at increasing the prevailing maintenance interval	ECHANTILLONAGE TRESHOLD
TRIBOLOGY	The technology and service of lubrication (comes from the greek "TRIBEIN" which means "TO RUB")	TRIBOLOGIE
TROUBLE SHOOTING	An analysis of the failure process with the objective of detecting the origin of failure	RECHERCHE DE PANNES
TQC	Total quality control	TQC
TTT	Total time on test	TTT
UMS	Universal Maintenance standards - a time-allocation method based on a number of standard maintenance tasks for which an average time estimation has been done	UMS
UNAVAILABILITY	State of an item which is unable to fulfil a function under defined conditions. This unavailability can originate from a breakdown, a lack of spare parts or the absence of a certificate.	INDISPONIBILITE
UNSCHEDULED MAINTENANCE	Maintenance which is not subject to regular intervention, the latter being hardly predictable	MAINTENANCE NON-PLANIFIEE
UPTIME	Total duration during which an item is available for service	TEMPS UTILE
USE BASED MAINTENANCE	A form of maintenance which is based on a maintenance intervention after a period of use, independently of the condition at that moment. The periodicity is expressed either in time or in a use-based unity such as kilometres, running hours. See SYSTEMATIC MAINTENANCE.	MAINTENANCE SELON UTILISATION
UTILITIES	Installations for the production and distribution of energy and fluids in a plant (electricity, water, compressed air, oxygen, gaz, fuel etc.).	UTILITES

ENGLISH	DEFINITION	FRENCH
UTILIZATION	Time during which equipment is in operation	UTILISATION
UTILIZATION FACTOR	The ratio of the actual time in use to the availability over a stated interval of time	TAUX D'UTILISATION
VALUATION OF STOCK	The total value of stock, usually measured in monetary units	VALORISATION DU STOCK
VDU	Visual display unit - a device, visually similar to a television set, which is used to display data from a computer	VDU
WAIT AND SEE MAINTENANCE	A kind of corrective maintenance : this type of maintenance is used if insufficient transparency exists concerning an expected failure and its environment and consequences	MAINTENANCE EXPECTATIVE
WEAKNESS	Property is inherent in the product or service itself and, when subject to the normal stresses of use, results in one of the types of failure which occur. Weakness is usually introduced by poor or wrong design, materials, processes or operation	FAIBLESSE
WEAR DEBRIS MONITORING	Can be carried out through analysis of the wear debris in oil, using the following methods : magnetic plugs, ferrography, spectrometric oil analysis (SOAP)	CONTROLE DE DEPOTS
WILSON FORMULA	Formula used in spare parts management to calculate the economic reordering quantity	WILSON (FORMULE DE)
WORKMANSHIP	Error or default during the manufacturing process of an item	VICE DE FABRICATION
WORK ORDER	A written instruction detailing work to be carried out - see JOB ORDER	ORDRE DE TRAVAIL
WORK PROGRAMMING	The programming function is responsible for assembling the required material and human resources, drawing up a programme and setting time limits. The job includes, in particular : - Planning the overall programme to be tackled by the department (long-term planning); - Assessing work request priorities; - Making sure that orders for subcontracting and supplies required for programmed work are followed through, in liaison with the work preparation staff; - Seeing to it that instructions are obeyed and that time-lines are adhered to.	ORDONNANCEMENT
WORK REQUISITION	A document requesting work to be carried out	DEMANDE DE TRAVAIL
WORK SCHEDULING	The function closest to job execution (short-term planning). It deals with workload planning in accordance with the plan laid down in relation to team and machine workloads. In this context, it is a necessity if rational use is to be made of manpower.	LANCEMENT

ENGLISH	DEFINITION	FRENCH
WORK SPECIFICATION	A document describing the way in which the work is to be carried out. It may define the materials, tools, time and standards	PREPARATION DE TRAVAIL
WORK STUDY	See JOB PREPARATION See WORK SPECIFICATION	ETUDE DE TRAVAIL

```
┌─────────────────────────────────────────────────────┐
│         SELECTED LITERATURE ON MAINTENANCE            │
│      SELECTION DE LITTERATURE SUR LA MAINTENANCE      │
└─────────────────────────────────────────────────────┘
```

The present bibliography is a selection of interesting literature on maintenance edited in the English and French languages. It should be mentioned that very interesting litterature on the subject also exists in other languages, including German, Dutch and Swedish.

La présente bibliographie est une sélection de littérature éditée en anglais et en français. Il convient toutefois de signaler que des ouvrages très intéressants existent en d'autres langues, notamment en allemand, néerlandais et suédois.

AUTHOR/AUTEUR	PUBLISHER/EDITEUR	TITLE/TITRE
ACCT/UCL	UNIVERSITE CATHOLIQUE DE LOUVAIN, 1987	FAISABILITE DES PROJETS DANS L'INDUSTRIE DES PROCEDES
ACCT/UCL	UNIVERSITE CATHOLIQUE DE LOUVAIN-INSTITUT DE GENIE CHIMIQUE, 1991	MAINTENANCE ET POST-INVESTISSEMENT DANS L'INDUSTRIE DES PROCEDES
AFNOR	AFNOR-PARIS, 1986	COMMENT REUSSIR SA MAINTENANCE
AFNOR	AFNOR - PARIS, 1986	TENUE ET GESTION DES STOCKS
AFNOR	AFNOR - PARIS, 1984	DOCUMENTATION DE GESTION ET D'EXPLOITATION DES STOCKS
AFNOR	AFNOR - PARIS, 1989	MAINTENANCE INDUSTRIELLE
AFNOR	AFNOR - PARIS, 1988	GERER ET ASSURER LA QUALITE
AFNOR	AFNOR - PARIS, 1986	RATIOS DE MAINTENANCE ET GESTION DE BIENS DURABLES
AFNOR	AFNOR - PARIS, 1988	CONTRAT DE MAINTENANCE
ALCOUFFE	EYROLLES - PARIS, 1987	LA GESTION DES STOCKS

AUTHOR/AUTEUR	PUBLISHER/EDITEUR	TITLE/TITRE
ALLARD H.F.	PLANT ENGINEERING, 1968	WORK SAMPLING : VALUABLE MAINTENANCE MANAGEMENT AID
ANDERSON R.T. and L. NERI	ELSEVIER APPLIED SCIENCE, 1990	RELIABILITY - CENTERED MAINTENANCE : MANAGEMENT AND ENGINEERING METHODS
ANDRIEUX C.	EDITIONS LAVOISIER, 1983	NORMES DE TEMPS
APOSTOLAKIS G.E. and OTTERLOO R.W.	ELSEVIER APPLIED SCIENCE	RELIABILITY ENGINEERING AND SYSTEM SAFETY
ARMITAGE W.	M.U.P., 1970	MAINTENANCE EFFECTIVENESS. OPERATIONAL RESEARCH IN MAINTENANCE
ASSCHER H & FEINGOLD	MARCEL DEKKER INC. - NEW YORK, 1984	REPAIRABLE SYSTEMS RELIABILITY, MODELING INFERENCE, MISCONCEPTIONS AND THEIR CAUSES
AWS	AMERICAN WELDING SOCIETY	FLUORESCENT PENETRANT INSPECTION WELDING HANDBOOK
B.I.T.	B.I.T./I.L.O. GENEVE, 1983	LA GAMME DU STOCK
B.I.T. GENEVE	B.I.T./I.L.O. GENEVE, 1984	SECURITE ET HYGIENE DANS L'INDUSTRIE DU FER ET DE L'ACIER
B.I.T. GENEVE	B.I.T./I.L.O. GENEVE, 1984	CHOIX DE TECHNOLOGIES ET CREATION D'EMPLOIS PAR LES ENTREPRISES MULTI-NATIONALES DANS LES PAYS EN DEVELOPPEMENT
B.I.T. GENEVE	B.I.T./I.L.O. GENEVE, 1983	LES ASPECTS SOCIAUX DE L'INDUSTRIALISATION
B.I.T. GENEVE	B.I.T./I.L.O. GENEVE, 1981	INTRODUCTION A L'ETUDE DU TRAVAIL
B.I.T. GENEVE	B.I.T./I.L.O. GENEVE, 1987	AMELIORER LA MAINTENANCE DANS LES PAYS EN DEVELOPPEMENT : L'APPROCHE DE L'OIT
BALDIN A.	TEROTECHNICA, 1979	CONDITION BASED MAINTENANCE : A POWERFULL TOOL FOR MODERN PLANT MANAGEMENT
BANLY P.	CHAPMAN AND HILL, 1969	PURCHASING AND SUPPLY MANAGEMENT
BARREYRE P.Y.	REVUE FRANÇAISE DE GESTION, 1976	LA FONCTION APPROVISIONNEMENT DANS LA STRATEGIE DE L'ENTREPRISE
BASKER B. and HUSBAND T.	MAINTENANCE MANAGEMENT INTERNATIONAL, 1982	SIMULATING MULTI SKILL MAINTENANCE : A CASE STUDY

AUTHOR/AUTEUR	PUBLISHER/EDITEUR	TITLE/TITRE
BATTERSBY	DUNOD, 1967	METHODES MODERNES D'ORDONNANCEMENT
BCMA	DEPARTMENT OF INDUSTRY - COMMITTEE FOR TEROTECHNOLOGY - HMSO, 1978	MAINTENANCE ASPECTS OF TEROTECHNOLOGY 2. MANAGEMENT MAINTENANCE RATIOS
BEAUCLAIR	INDUSTRIES	MACHINES OUTILS. L'HEURE DE LA PREDICTIVE
BEAULIEU	UVIBERT, 1985	AUDIT ET GESTION DES STOCKS
BEMAS	MANAGENEMENT BEMAS, ANTWERP, 1991	MAINTENANCE 91 : SYMPOSIUM DE MAINTENANCE INDUSTRIELLE
BENNETT K.	PROCEEDINGS OF 6TH NAT. CONF. ON COMPUTERS FOR MAINTENANCE MANAGERS, 1985	EXPERT SYSTEMS IN MAINTENANCE
BERANGER	UVIBERT, 1987	GESTION DE LA PRODUCTION
BERANGER	DUNOD, 1987	LES NOUVELLES REGLES DE LA PRODUCTION
BERLIOU	EYROLLES	LE POSTE DE TRAVAIL INTELLIGENT
BERTHELOOT L.	MAINTENANCE 89 - SALON INTERNAT. DE LA MAINTENANCE	MAINTENANCE PREDICTIVE - EVOLUTION TECHNOLOGIQUE ET DEVELOPPEMENTS RECENTS DE L'APPAREILLAGE D'ANALYSE DE VIBRATIONS
BIGRET R.	TECHN. & DOC., 1980	VIBRATIONS DES MACHINES TOURNANTES ET DES STRUCTURES
BILLINGTON R. AND R.M. ALLAN	PITMAN ADVANCED PUBLISHING PROGRAM, 1983	RELIABILITY EVALUATION OF ENGINEERING SYSTEMS : CONCEPT AND TECHNIQUES
BLANCHARD B.	TEROTECHNICA, 1979	LIFE CYCLE COSTING : A REVIEW
BLANCHARD B.J.	M/A PRESS, PORTLAND, 1978	DESIGN AND MAINTENANCE TO LIFE CYCLE COST
BLANCHARD S.	PRENTICE HALL, 1974	LOGISTICS ENGINEERING AND MANAGEMENT
BLOCH H. AND GEITNER F.	VAN NOSTRAND REINHOLD, NEW YORK, 1990	MACHINERY RELIABILITY ASSESSMENT
BOITEL-HAZARD	NATHAN, 1987	GUIDE DE LA MAINTENANCE
BOLLIET T.	EYROLLES, 1976	L'ENTRETIEN : PREPARATION DU TRAVAIL ET PLANIFICATION

AUTHOR/AUTEUR	PUBLISHER/EDITEUR	TITLE/TITRE
BOTTECHIA	EDITIONS LAVOISIER - DOC. TEC. 81	ORGANISATION ET GESTION DE LA PRODUCTION
BOUCHE-PLANCHU-RETOUR	UNIVERSITE DES SCIENCES SOCIALES DE GRENOBLE 1988 EUROMAINTENANCE 88, HELSINKI	"INDUSTRIAL MAINTENANCE AND TROUBLE SHOOTING EXPERT SYSTEM SOME HUMAN, MANAGERIAL AND ORGANISATIONAL CONSIDERATIONS"
BOUCHE-PLANCHU-RETOUR	ACHATS ET ENTRETIEN, 1988	A LA RECHERCHE DU COUT GLOBAL
BOUCLY F.	ACHATS ET ENTRETIEN, 1988	LE COUT GLOBAL DE DUREE DE VIE
BOUCLY F.	AFNOR, 1988	LES COUTS DE LA NON-EFFICACITE DES EQUIPEMENTS
BOUCLY F.	ACHATS ET ENTRETIEN, 1987	L'EDUCATION, LA FORMATION, LA MOTIVATION DANS LA METHODE TPM
BOULENGER A.	AFNOR, 1988	VERS LE ZERO PANNE AVEC LA MAINTENANCE CONDITIONNELLE
BOULET A.	DUNOD - PARIS, 1970	LE PERT A LA PORTEE DE TOUS
BROCH J.	B & K LABORATORIES, 1972	MECHANICAL VIBRATION AND SHOCK MEASUREMENT
BRODIER	AFNOR, 1988	UNE AUTRE APPROCHE DE L'ENTREPRISE
BROWN P.	MAINTENANCE ENGINEERING 1976	PREVENTIVE MAINTENANCE OF MACHINERY BEARINGS
BROWN R.G.	WILEY, 1977	MATERIALS MANAGEMENT SYSTEMS
BROWN W.	UNIDO, 1970	HANDLING AND STORING OF SPARE PARTS AND MATERIALS FOR MAINTENANCE PURPOSES ON THE PLANT LEVEL
BRUEL	DUNOD 82	POLITIQUE D'ACHAT ET GESTION DES APPROVISIONNEMENTS
BSI	BSI, 1965	METHODS FOR NON-DESTRUCTIVE TESTING OF PIPES AND TUBES
BSI	BSI, 1974	MAINTENANCE TERMS IN TEROTECHNOLOGY
BSI	BSI, 1969	GLOSSARY OF TERMS IN WORK STUDY

AUTHOR/AUTEUR	PUBLISHER/EDITEUR	TITLE/TITRE
BUFFA E.	WILEY, 1983	MODERN PRODUCTION AND OPERATIONS MANAGEMENT
BULLOCK J. H.	NATIONAL ASSOCIATION OF ACCOUNTANTS, NEW YORK, 1979	MAINTENANCE PLANNING AND CONTROL
BUS	DUNOD	LE DICTIONNAIRE DE L'ENTREPRISE
CANNON A.G. and BENDELL A.	ELSEVIER APPLIED SCIENCE, 1991	RELIABILITY DATA BANKS
CARA	SINTEF - Safety and Reliability - NORWAY, 1989	COMPUTER AIDED RELIABILITY ANALYSIS
CARTER, A.D.S.	Mc MILLAN LONDON, 1972	MECHANICAL RELIABILITY
CARTIER R.	MAINTENANCE, 1986	CLAUSES CONTRACTUELLES DE FIABILITE, DE MAINTENABILITE, ET DE DISPONIBILITE
CATOLA S.G.	NAVAL SEA SYSTEMS - NEW YORK, 1983	RELIABILITY CENTERED MAINTENANCE HANDBOOK
CHEVALIER & LABURTE	DELAGRAVE, 1975	METROLOGIE DIMENSIONNELLE
CHONG K.P. and LIU S.C.	ELSEVIER APPLIED SCIENCE, 1990	INTELLIGENT STRUCTURES
CHRISTER A.H. and WHITELAW J.	OPERATIONAL RESEARCH AP Ltd. London, 1983	AN OPERATIONAL RESEARCH APPROACH TO BREAKDOWN MAINTENANCE : PROBLEM RECOGNITION
CLAESSENS C.	MOBIL PLASTICS EUROPE,Inc	LES MESURES DE VIBRATIONS DANS UNE STRATEGIE D'ENTRETIEN PREVISIONNEL
CLIFTON R.	EDWARD ARNOLD - LONDON, 1985	PRINCIPLE OF PLANNED MAINTENANCE
CNPP	CNPP - AFNOR, 1990	SECURITE INCENDIE, ENTRETIENS ET VERIFICATIONS DU MATERIEL
COLEMAN C.E.	ELSEVIER APPLIED SCIENCE, 1991	LEAK BEFORE BREAK IN WATER REACTOR PIPING AND VESSELS
COLLACOTT R. A.	CHAPMANN AND HALL LONDON, 1977	MECHANICAL FAULT DIAGNOSIS AND CONDITION MONITORING
COLORUB P.	EDITIONS EYROLLES - PARIS, 1978	GESTION DES STOCKS ET DES PIECES DE RECHANGE
COMMITTEE FOR TEROTECHNOLOGY	COMMITTEE FOR TEROTECHN. DEPARTMENT OF INDUSTRY - U.K.	TEROTECHNOLOGY, AN INTRODUCTION TO THE MANAGEMENT OF PHYSICAL RESOURCES

AUTHOR/AUTEUR	PUBLISHER/EDITEUR	TITLE/TITRE
CONFERENCE COMMUNICATION	CONFERENCE COMMUNICATION, 1990	MANAGING MAINTENANCE IN THE 1990S CONFERENCE PAPERS
CONFERENCE COMMUNICATION	CONFERENCE COMMUNICATION, 1991	3RD NATIONAL CONFERENCE ON CONDITION MONITORING CONFERENCE PAPERS
CORDER A.	McGRAW HILL, 1975	MAINTENANCE MANAGEMENT TECHNIQUES
CORDER G.	UNIDO, 1970	HUMAN RELATIONS IN INDUSTRY WITH SPECIAL REFERENCE TO THE MAINTENANCE/PRODUCTION RELATIONSHIP
CORDER G.	BRITISH COUNCIL OF PRODUCTIVITY - LONDON, 1972	MAINTENANCE TECHNIQUES AND OUTLOOKS
COSTE	USINE 87	LA GESTION DES STOCKS ASSISTEE PAR ORDINATEUR
CROSBY P.	McGRAW-HILL, 1984	QUALITY WITHOUT TEARS, THE ART OF HASSLE-FREE MANAGEMENT
CROSS M.	11TH NAT. CONF. ON MAINTENANCE ENG., 1986	MAINTENANCE MANPOWER, UTILISATION AND TRAINING
CZAJKIEWICZ Z.	SIMULATION, 1985	OPTIMIZATION OF THE MAINTENANCE PROCESS
DAUCHY	DUNOD, 1986	VERS LE ZERO PANNE DANS L'ENTREPRISE
DAVIES A.	INSTITUTION OF PRODUCTION ENGINEERS, 1990	MANAGEMENT GUIDE TO CONDITION MONITORING
DAVIS R.S.	MATERIALS EVALUATION 48 JUNE 1990	REMOTE VISUAL INSPECTION IN THE NUCLEAR, PIPELINE AND UNDER WATER INDUSTRIES
DE BONNIERES P. - BOUTES J.L. - CALAS M.A. - PARA S.	CONFERENCE AT WELDING INSTITUTE, CAMBRIDGE, UNITED KINGDOM, 1986	A KNOWLEDGE BASED SYSTEM FOR DIAGNOSIS N WELDING OPERATION
DE GROOTE-SCHELLENS	ACIER ARABE-ALGER, 1979	LA MAINTENANCE DANS UN ENVIRONNEMENT NON INDUSTRIEL
DE GROOTE P.	IFMI-PARIS, 1979	LA PREPARATION DE L'ORGANISATION ET DES MOYENS DE MAINTENANCE LORS DE LA FOURNITURE D'USINE "PRODUIT EN MAIN" EN TIERS-MONDE
DE GROOTE P.	ACHATS ET ENTRETIEN, 1988	LA GESTION DE LA MAINTENANCE DANS LES PAYS EN VOIE DE DEVELOPPEMENT

AUTHOR/AUTEUR	PUBLISHER/EDITEUR	TITLE/TITRE
DE GROOTE P.	MAINTENANCE MANAGEMENT INTERNATIONAL 1988 - ELSEVIER	MAINTENANCE PROBLEMS IN DEVELOPING COUNTRIES
DE GROOTE P.	ONUDI, 1989	PLAN D'ACTION POUR LA FORMATION DE LA MAIN-D'OEUVRE INDUSTRIELLE EN MAINTENANCE DANS LES PAYS EN VOIE DE DEVELOPPEMENT
DE GROOTE P.	UNIDO, 1989	PLAN OF ACTION FOR TRAINING OF INDUSTRIAL MANPOWER IN MAINTENANCE IN DEVELOPING COUNTRIES
DE GROOTE P.	ACHATS ET ENTRETIEN, 1990	MAINTENANCE DES STRUCTURES INDUSTRIELLES
DE GROOTE P.	UNIDO/ILO, 1991	MAINTENANCE MANAGEMENT MANUEL FOR DEVELOPPING COUNTRIES
DE GROOTE P.	ONUDI/BIT, 1991	MANUEL SUR LA GESTION DE LA MAINTENANCE POUR LES PAYS EN VOIE DE DEVELOPPEMENT
DELALANDE	ECONOMICA, 1987	GESTION DE L'ENTREPRISE INDUSTRIELLE EN AFRIQUE
DESCAMPS M.	ACHATS ET ENTRETIEN, 1986	ORGANISATION D'UN SERVICE DE TELE-MAINTENANCE
DGS	DGS INTERNATIONAL, 1991 GENT/BELGIQUE	LA GESTION MAINTENANCE
DGS	DGS INTERNATIONAL - SGS/LAGOS, 1991	SEMINAR ON MAINTENANCE MANAGEMENT
DGS	OADI - INMA - ALGER, 1987	GUIDE POUR L'APPLICATION DES RATIOS DE GESTION DE LA MAINTENANCE DANS L'INDUSTRIE
DHILLON, BALBIRS and REICHE, HANS	VAN NOSTRAND REINHOLD, 1985	RELIABILITY AND MAINTENANCE MANAGEMENT
DINZIA	AZOULAY, 1973	DECOUVRIR ET COMPRENDRE L'INDUSTRIE ESSAI DE METHODOLOGIE INDUSTRIELLE
DONARSKI J., HEATH R. and WALLACE J.	BIT/ILO - GENEVE, 1982	LA FORMATION PAR LE BIAIS DE LA CONSULTATION EN VUE D'AMELIORER LA GESTION DE LA MAINTENANCE
DUNLOP C.L.	BUTTERWORTHS, 1990	A PRACTICAL GUIDE TO MAINTENANCE ENGINEERING
DURAY M.	UCL - INSTITUT DE GENIE CHIMIQUE, 1978	ENTRETIEN - REGLEMENTATION - SECURITE : IMPORTANCE ET LIMITE

AUTHOR/AUTEUR	PUBLISHER/EDITEUR	TITLE/TITRE
EFNMS	AEM (SPAIN), 1986	CONFERENCE PAPERS - 8TH EUROPEAN MAINTENANCE CONGRESS
EFNMS	TEPA (FINLAND), 1988	CONFERENCE PAPERS - 9TH EUROPEAN MAINTENANCE CONGRESS
ELCHNER J.C.	IRON AND STEEL ENGINEER - NOV. 1981	TOTAL APPROACH TO COMPUTER DIRECTED PREVENTIVE MAINTENANCE
ESCANDE	L'USINE NOUVELLE, 1983	MAINTENANCE
FAA	FEDERAL AVIATION ADMINISTRATION - DEPARTMENT OF TRANSPORTATION - WASHINGTON DC, 1978	MAINTENANCE CONTROL BY RELIABILITY METHODS
FERNAU C.	BIT/ILO GENEVE, 1980	COMMENT ORGANISER UNE COLLECTION DE DOCUMENTATION : CONSERVATION ET CONSULTATION
FERRIER E.	UNIVERSITE CATHOLIQUE DE LOUVAIN - INSTITUT DE GENIE CHIMIQUE	LES CAUSES DE PANNES - L'ENTRETIEN DANS L'INDUSTRIE DES PROCEDES
FILE T.W.	BUTTERWORTH HEINEMANN, 1991	COST EFFECTIVE MAINTENANCE - DESIGN AND IMPLEMENTATION
FLEUROT	USINE, 1981	GMA : PRIORITE AU PREVENTIF
FOORD D.	6TH NAT. CONF. ON COMPUTERS FOR MAINT. MANAGEM., 1986	EXPERT SYSTEMS IN MAINTENANCE
FORD D. and FARMER D.	LONG RANGE PLANNING, VOL. 19, No. 5, 1986	MAKE OR BUY : A KEY STRATEGIC ISSUE
FRANCOIS A.R.	EDITION D'ORGANISATION, 1982	MANUEL D'ORGANISATION
FREEMAN R.	CONFERENCE COMMUNICATION - FARNHAM, 1986	THE USE OF COMPUTERS FOR REAL TIME MAINTENANCE MANATEMENT
GABRIEL M.	MASSON, 1987	MAINTENANCE ASSISTEE PAR ORDINATEUR
GABRIEL M.	ACHATS ET ENTRETIEN, 1987	LES SYSTEMES EXPERTS : NOTIONS DE BASE ET APPLICATIONS EN MAINTENANCE
J.R. GADD	CONFERENCE COMMUNICATION - 13TH NATIONAL MAINTENANCE MANAGEMENT SHOW - LONDON, 1990	THE NATIONAL MAINTENANCE MANAGEMENT AUDIT SERVICE

AUTHOR/AUTEUR	PUBLISHER/EDITEUR	TITLE/TITRE
GALLAND J.	ACHATS ET ENTRETIEN 06/1987	CORROSION ET MAINTENANCE
GALLET J.	MAINTENANCE, 1987	COMMENT INTRODUIRE LES ASPECTS MAINTENANCE DANS LES AUTOMATISMES
GANIER M.	CETIM	ANALYSE DES LUBRIFIANTS NDUSTRIELS APPLIQUEE A LA SURVEILLANCE DES MACHINES
GAVAULT L. and LAURET A.	MASSON, 1985	TECHNIQUE ET PRATIQUE DE LA GESTION DES STOCKS
GAZAY F.	MAINTENANCE, 1985	LES AUTOMATES PROGRAMMABLES AMELIORENT LA PRODUCTIVITE ET LA MAINTENANCE DES INSTALLATIONS INDUSTRIELLES
GELDERS L. and PINTELON L.	ENCYCLOPEDIA OF ROBOTICS, 1987	RELIABILITY AND MAINTENANCE
GELDERS L. and VAN LOOY P.	JOURNAL OF THE OPERATIONAL RESEARCH SOCIETY, 1978	AN INVENTORY POLICY FOR SLOW AND FAST MOVING ITEMS IN A PETROCHEMICAL PLANT : A CASE STUDY
GERAERDS W.	EINDHOVEN UNIVERSITY OF TECHNOLOGY, 1985	THE COST OF DOWNTIME FOR MAINTENANCE : PRELIMINARY CONSIDERATION
GERAERDS W.M.J.	THE ENGLISH UNIVERSITY PRESS, 1972	TOWARDS A THEORY OF MAINTENANCE
GERLING	EYROLLES	TECHNIQUES DE CONTROLE DIMENSIONNEL DANS L'USINAGE
GERTSBAKH I.	AMSTERDAM, 1977	MODELS OF PREVENTIVE MAINTENANCE
GEURTS J.H.J.	CONFERENCE TUE, EINDHOVEN, 1986	ON THE SELECTION OF ELEMENTARY MAINTENANCE RULES
GIBSON N. and WITTAKER J.	BIT/ILO - GENEVE, 1989	RESULTS-ORIENTED MANAGEMENT DEVELOPMENT : THE CASE OF THE ETHIOPIAN MANAGEMENT INSTITUTE
GITS C.W.	CONFERENCE TUE, EINDHOVEN, 1984	ON THE MAINTENANCE CONCEPT FOR A TECHNICAL SYSTEM. A FRAMEWORK FOR DESIGN
GONDRAN M.	EYROLLES	INTRODUCTION AUX SYSTEMES EXPERTS
GOTOH F.	PRODUCTIVITY PRESS - CAMBRIDGE, 1988	MAINTENANCE PREVENTION DESIGN
GOTOH F.	PRODUCTIVITY PRESS - CAMBRIDGE, 1989	EQUIPMENT PLANNING FOR TPM : MAINTENANCE PREVENTION DESIGN

AUTHOR/AUTEUR	PUBLISHER/EDITEUR	TITLE/TITRE
GRAM	GRAM - PARIS, 1989	GUIDE REPERTOIRE DE LA MAINTENANCE
GREEN, Dr. Malcolm F.	8th EUROPEAN MAINTENANCE CONGRESS EFNMS - BARCELONA, 1986	USING COMPUTERS IN MAINTENANCE - THE UK SCENE
GREENE E. and BOURNE J.	WILEY, 1972	RELIABILITY TECHNOLOGY
GROFF J.	TECHNIP, 1961	ABC DU GRAISSAGE
HAMELIN	EYROLLES, 1974	ENTRETIEN ET MAINTENANCE
HARRINGTON	EYROLLES	LE COUT DE LA NON-QUALITE
HARRIS M.	TEROTECHNICA, 1979	AN INTRODUCTION TO MAINTENANCE STORES ORGANISATION AND SPARES INVENTORY CONTROL
HARVEY G. and EASTBURN K.	TEROTECHNICA, 1979	TEROTECHNOLOGY : A CASE STUDY IN THE APPLICATION OF THE CONCEPT.
HAVILAND	EYROLLES, 1966	TECHNIQUE DE FIABILITE ET DUREE DE VIE DES EQUIPEMENTS
HEINTZELMAN, J.E.	ENGLEWOOD CLIFFS, PRENTICEHALL Inc., 1976	THE COMPLETE HANDBOOK OF MAINTENANCE MANAGEMENT
HEMOND	Mac GRAW, 1983	INITIATION AUX TECHNIQUES INDUSTRIELLES
HENRY T.	TEROTECHNICA ELSEVIER, 1979	A SIMPLE APPROACH TO CONDITION MONITORING
HERZBERG F.	HARVARD BUSINESS REVIEW, 1968	ONE MORE TIME : HOW DO YOU MOTIVATE EMPLOYEES ?
HIBI S.	ASIAN PRODUCTIVITY ORGANIZATION TOKYO, 1977	HOW TO MEASURE MAINTENANCE PERFORMANCE
HIRSCH A.	COMPUTER AND ELECTRONIC, 1984	ARTIFICIAL INTELLIGENCE IN COURSE OF AGES
HOLUB J.	UNIDO, 1970	CONSIDERATION OF PROBLEMS IN DESIGN OF INSTALLATIONS, MAINTENANCE AND REPAIR IN DEVELOPING COUNTRIES
HUSBAND T. M.	SAXON HOUSE - FARNBOROUGH, 1976	MAINTENANCE MANAGEMENT AND TEROTECHNOLOGY
IDHONNA C.	SALON INT. DE LA MAINT. IND. - PARIS, 1989	RESULT-ORIENTED MAINTENANCE MANAGEMENT : ITS PRINCIPLE AND IMPLEMENTATION

AUTHOR/AUTEUR	PUBLISHER/EDITEUR	TITLE/TITRE
ILO	GENEVA, 1967	TRAINING OF MAINTENANCE WORKERS
ILO	GENEVA, 1979	TRAINING CONSULTANCY ON REPAIR AND SERVICING OF DOMESTIC ELECTRONIC EQUIPMENT
ILO	GENEVA, 1980	MAINTENANCE SUPERVISION ; MODULAR PROGRAMME FOR SUPERVISORY DEVELOPMENT
ILO	GENEVA, 1982	GUIDELINES FOR THE IDENTIFICATION OF THE TECHNICAL AND TRAINING ACTIVITIES IN THE ELECTRICITY SUPPLY INDUSTRY
ILO	GENEVA, 1987	IMPROVING MAINTENANCE IN DEVELOPING COUNTRIES : THE ILO APPROACH
INPEC	IIPE (INDIA) / UNIDO, 1984	PAPERS OF 3RD INTERNATIONAL PLANT ENGINEERING CONFERENCE
INSTITUT FRANÇAIS DU PETROLE	TECHNIP, 1979	LA FIABILITE AU SERVICE DE L'ENTRETIEN ET DE L'INSPECTION DU MATERIEL
INTERNATIONAL LABOUR OFFICE	ILO/BIT, 1970	UPGRADING OF MAINTENANCE AND REPAIR PERSONNEL
ISHIHARA	AFNOR, 1986	MANUEL PRATIQUE DE GESTION DE LA QUALITE
JABOT R.	HOMMES & TECHNIQUES, 1966	LES TEMPS STANDARDS DE L'ENTRETIEN
JABOT R.	HOMMES & TECHNIQUES, 1969	ENTRETIEN ET TRAVAUX NEUFS
JABOT R.	NORMES ET TECHNIQUES, 1977	IMPLANTATIONS ET MANUTENTIONS DANS LES ATELIERS
JABOT R.	EDITIONS D'ORGANISATION, 1979	LES MAGASINS DE STOCKAGE : CONCEPTION ET ORGANISATION
JANSSENS	TRAV. ET METH., 1987	LES RATIOS DE GESTION DE LA MAINTENANCE INDUSTRIELLE
JARDINE A.	PITMAN, 1973	MAINTENANCE, REPLACEMENT AND RELIABILITY
JARDINE A.	MANCHESTER UNIVERSITY PRESS, 1970	OPERATIONS RESEARCH IN MAINTENANCE
JIPE-JMA	JIPE, 1977	INTERNATIONAL PLANT ENGINEERING CONFERENCE

AUTHOR/AUTEUR	PUBLISHER/EDITEUR	TITLE/TITRE
JMA	JAPANESE MANAGEMENT ASSOCIATION, TOKIO, 1989	TOTAL PRODUCTIVE MAINTENANCE : MAXIMIZING PRODUCTIVITY AND QUALITY
JONES R.	CONFERENCE COMMUNICATION - FARNHAM, 1986	CONDITION MONITORING AND CONTROL OF AIR COMPRESSORS
JURAN	AFNOR, 1988	PLANIFIER LA QUALITE
JURAN	AFNOR, 1985	GESTION DE LA QUALITE
KANAWATY G.	KANAWATY G., 1981	MANAGING AND DEVELOPING NEW FORMS OF WORK ORGANIZATION
KELLY A. and HARRIS M.	THE PLANT ENGINEER, 1971	SIMULATION, AND AID TO MAINTENANCE DECISIONS
KELLY A.	FACTORY, 1972	WORK MEASUREMENT FOR MAINTENANCE MANAGER
KELLY A. and HARRIS M.	BUTTERWORTHS, 1978	THE MANAGEMENT OF INDUSTRIAL MAINTENANCE
KELLY A.	BUTTERWORTHS, 1984	MAINTENANCE PLANNING AND CONTROL
KELLY A.	CONFERENCE COMMUNICATION, 1989	MAINTENANCE AND ITS MANAGEMENT
KILLEEN L.	BORDAS, 1971	TECHNIQUES DE GESTION DES STOCKS
KLOECKNER E.	ACHATS ET ENTRETIEN, 1986	CHOIX D'UN PROGICIEL DE MAINTENANCE : REFLEXIONS PREALABLES
KUBR M.	BIT/ILO - GENEVE, 1983	LE CONSEIL EN MANAGEMENT : GUIDE POUR LA PROFESSION
KUBR M. and PROKOPENKO J.	BIT/ILO - GENEVE, 1989	DIAGNOSING MANAGEMENT TRAINING AND DEVELOPMENT NEEDS : CONCEPTS AND TECHNIQUES
LAMBERT P.	LES EDITIONS D'ORGANISATION, 1975	LA FONCTION MAINTENANCE
LAMBERT P. and LABOURIER R.	LES ED. D'ORGANISATION, 1984	LA FONCTION ORDONNANCEMENT
LANGHAM-BROWN J.B.	B.A.C.I.E. JOURNAL - LONDON, 1971	TRAINING FOR FAULT DIAGNOSIS
LARIDAN	EYROLLES	CERCLES DE QUALITE
LAURENT C.	IRD MECHANALYSIS, 1985	EVOLUTION DE L'ENTRETIEN SYSTEMATIQUE VERS L'ENTRETIEN PREDICTIF

AUTHOR/AUTEUR	PUBLISHER/EDITEUR	TITLE/TITRE
LAVAU	DUNOD, 1989	LES RATIOS ET LA GESTION DE L'ENTREPRISE
LAVINA Y.	ACHATS ET ENTRETIEN, 1986	METHODOLOGIE DE CHOIX D'UN PROGICIEL DE GESTION DE LA MAINTENANCE
LECOEUR	DELAGRAVE	ASSEMBLAGE & MONTAGE
LIE C.H. e.a.	AIIE TRANSACTIONS, SEPT 1987	AVAILABILITY OF MAINTAINED SYSTEMS : A STATE OF THE ART SURVEY
LIGERON	TEC DO, 1984	LA FIABILITE EN EXPLOITATION
LIGERON J.	MAINTENANCE, 1985	L'AMDEC, UN OUTIL INDISPENSABLE DE CONSTRUCTION DE LA FIABILITE
LISSARAGUE J.	DUNOD - PARIS, 1987	QU'EST-CE QUE LE PERT
LUANCO E.	DUNEGAN FRANCE, 1984	LA MAINTENANCE CONDITIONNELLE
LUANCO E.	MAINTENANCE, 1986	MAINTENANCE DES MACHINES TOURNANTES PAR LA SURVEILLANCE VIBRATOIRE
LUCK W.	ASIAN PRODUCTIVITY ORGANIZATION, 1977	NOW YOU CAN REALLY MEASURE MAINTENANCE
LYNN F.	MIDWEST INST. FOR RESEARCH AND TRAINING, CHICAGO, 1967	AN INVESTIGATION OF THE TRAINING AND SKILL REQUIREMENTS OF INDUSTRIAL MACHINERY MAINTENANCE WORKERS
LYONNET P.	LAVOISIER - PARIS, 1987	LA MAINTENANCE, MATHEMATIQUES ET METHODES
MACLEOD R., FLEGG D. and PROUT R.	TEROTECHNICA, 1981	MINIMISING THE COST OF MAINTENANCE IN A LARGE INTEGRATED STEELWORKS
MANN L.	LEXINGTON BOOKS, 1983	MAINTENANCE MANAGEMENT
MAUREL E., ROUX D., DUPONT D.	EDITIONS EYROLLES, 1977	TECHNIQUES OPERATIONNELLES D'ORDONNANCEMENT
Mc. CORMICK N.J.	ACADEMIC PRESS, 1981	RELIABILITY AND RISK ANALYSIS
MICHEL J.	INSTITUT FRANCAIS DU PETROLE	LA MAINTENANCE DES MACHINES PAR L'ETUDE DES VIBRATIONS
MILLS P.	CONFERENCE COMMUNICATION 13TH NATIONAL MAINTENANCE MANAGEMENT SHOW - LONDON, 1990	THE STRATEGIC LINK - MAINTENANCE COSTS VS RISKS

AUTHOR/AUTEUR	PUBLISHER/EDITEUR	TITLE/TITRE
MOBLEY K.	VAN NOSTRAND REINHOLD - NEW YORK, 1988	INTRODUCTION TO PREDICTIVE MAINTENANCE
MONCHY F.	MASSON, 1987	LA FONCTION MAINTENANCE
MOORE L.S.	BIT/ILO - GENEVE, 1983	HOW TO DESIGN INTERVENTIONS FOR IMPROVED MAINTENANCE MANAGEMENT
MORIN	ORGANISATION, 1983	COMPRENDRE LA MECANIQUE D'ETANCHEITE
MORROW L.C.	MC GRAW HILL - NEW YORK, 1957	MAINTENANCE ENGINEERING HANDBOOK
MOSS M.	MARCEL DEKKER INC. - NEW YORK, 1985	DESIGNING FOR MINIMAL MAINTENANCE EXPENSE
MOUBRAY J.	BUTTERWORTH-HEINEMANN, 1991	RCM : RELIABILITY-CENTRED MAINTENANCE
NACHI-FUJIKOSHI	PRODUCTIVITY PUBLISHING - CAMBRIDGE, 1990	TRAINING FOR TPM : A MANUFACTURING SUCCESS STORY
NAKAJIMA S.	7th EFNMS CONGRESS VENEZIA 9 - 11 MAY 1984	TPM = CHALLENGE TO THE IMPROVEMENT OF PRODUCTIVITY BY SMALL GROUP ACTIVITES
NAKAJIMA S.	AFNOR, 1987	LA TPM : NOUVELLE VAGUE DE PRODUCTION INDUSTRIELLE
NAKAJIMA S.	AFNOR, 1989	LA MAINTENANCE PRODUCTIVE TOTALE TPM TOTAL PRODUCTIVE MAINTENANCE TPM
NAKAJIMA S.	SALON INT. DE LA MAINT. IND. - PARIS, 1989	TPM UPDATE AND ITS DEVELOPMENT PROGRAM
NAKAJIMA S.	PRODUCTIVITY PRESS - CAMBRIDGE, 1988	INTRODUCTION TO TPM : TOTAL PRODUCTIVE MAINTENANCE
NAKAJIMA S.	PRODUCTIVITY PRESS - CAMBRIDGE, 1989	TPM DEVELOPMENT PROGRAM : IMPLEMENTING TOTAL PRODUCTIVE MAINTENANCE
NEALE J.	UNIDO, 1987	CONDITION MONITORING TECHNIQUES IN MAINTENANCE
NEALE M. and ASSOCIATES	HMSO, 1978	A GUIDE TO THE CONDITION MONITORING OF MACHINERY
NEUBERT M.	APAVE	LES MESURES DE VIBRATIONS, UNE ECONOMIE SUR LE COUT DE L'ENTRETIEN

AUTHOR/AUTEUR	PUBLISHER/EDITEUR	TITLE/TITRE
NEWBROUGH E. T.	Mc GRAW HILL - NEW YORK, 1967	EFFECTIVE MAINTENANCE MANAGEMENT
NEYRET G.	ACHATS ET ENTRETIEN 04/1989	EVOLUTION DE LA MAINTENANCE A L'APPROCHE DE L'AN 2000
NEYRET G.	PARIS, 1976	REFLEXIONS SUR LA METHODE DE PROJETER, CONSTRUIRE, CONSTITUER L'EQUIPE, ORGANISER ET METTRE EN ROUTE UNE USINE SIDERURGIQUE AU TIERS-MONDE
NEYRET G.	IFMI, 1979	LES PIECES DE RECHANGE DANS LA MAINTENANCE DES ENTREPRISES IMPLANTEES DANS LES PAYS EN DEVELOPPEMENT
NICHOLLS C.	THE PLANT ENGR., 1974	VIBRATION MONITORING AND ANALYSIS OF CRITICAL MACHINERY
NICOLET	MASSON, 1985	FIABILITE HUMAINE DANS L'ENTREPRISE
NIEBEL B.	MARCEL DEKKER - NEW YORK, 1985	ENGINEERING MAINTENANCE MANAGEMENT
O'CONNOR P.	JOHN WILEY & SONS - CHICHESTER, 1991	PRACTICAL RELIABILITY ENGINEERING
OGUS	TRAVAIL ET METHODES, 1979	LA MAINTENANCE INDUSTRIELLE: SES IMPLICATIONS ECONOMIQUES
OGUS	TRAVAIL ET METHODES, 1979	L'APPLICATION DE QUELQUES RATIOS A LA MAINTENANCE INDUSTRIELLE
OGUS - BOUCLY	AFNOR, 1989	LE MANAGEMENT DE LA MAINTENANCE
ONUDI et BIT	ONUDI/BIT - DEUXIEME CONSULTATION SUR LA FONCTION DE LA MAIN-D'OEUVRE INDUSTRIELLE - PARIS, 1987	TEXTES DES CONFERENCES ET ETUDES DE CAS
ONUDI et VDMA	ONUDI, 1970	L'ENTRETIEN ET LES REPARATIONS DANS LES PAYS EN VOIE DE DEVELOPPEMENT, RAPPORT DU COLLOQUE TENU A DUISBURG (RFA)
ONUDI	NATIONS UNIES, ONUDI NEW YORK, 1973	DIRECTIVES POUR L'AQUISITION DE TECHNIQUES ETRANGERES POUR LES PAYS EN VOIE DE DEVELOPPEMENT
ONUDI	NATIONS UNIES, NEW YORK, 1976	"INTRODUCTION A LA PLANIFICATION DE L'ENTRETIEN DANS L'INDUSTRIE

AUTHOR/AUTEUR	PUBLISHER/EDITEUR	TITLE/TITRE
OREDA	OREDA Participants - NORWAY, 1984	OFFSHORE RELIABILITY DATA HANDBOOK
ORLICKY J.	MCGRAW HILL, NEW YORK, 1975	MATERIAL REQUIREMENTS PLANNING
PAGES A. et M. GONDRAN	EYROLLES - PARIS, 1980	FIABILITE DES SYSTEMES
PAPELEUX ET VIATOUR	ACCT - UCL, 1991 - MAINTENANCE ET POST-INVESTISSEMENT DANS L'INDUSTRIE DES PROCEDES	GESTION DE LA MAINTENANCE ASSISTEE PAR ORDINATEUR
PARKES D.	MAINTENANCE ENGINEERING, 1971	MAINTENANCE COST COMPARISONS
PARKS R./WIREMANT	INDUSTRIAL PRESS INC. - NEW YORK, 1986	MAINTAINING AND TROUBLE SHOOTING ELECTRICAL EQUIPMENT
PAU	CEPAUDE EDITIONS - TOULOUSE, 1975	DIAGNOSTIC DES PANNES DANS LES SYSTEMES INDUSTRIELS
PELLETIER	COMMUNICATION, 1980	LA PRATIQUE DU CONTROLE PAR ULTRASON
PNUD	EDITIONS DE PNUD - RABAT, 1985	SEMINAIRE SUR LE POST-INVESTISSEMENT
POGGIOLI P.	LES ED. D'ORGANISATION, 1986	PRATIQUE DE LA METHODE P.E.R.T
PRIEL V.	EME, 1976	LA MAINTENANCE, TECHNIQUES MODERNES DE GESTION
PRIEL V.	MAC DONALDS AND EVIANS LTD - LONDON, 1974	MAINTENANCE
PROKOPENKO J.	ILO/BIT - GENEVE, 1987	PRODUCTIVITY MANAGEMENT : A PRACTICAL HANDBOOK
PROUVOST	DUNOD	INNOVER DANS L'ENTREPRISE
REYNOLDS R.P.	8th EUROPEAN MAINTENANCE CONGRESS-EFNMS - BARCELONA, 1986	USE OF COMPUTER TO CONTROL ECONOMICAL ASPECTS OF MAINTENANCE
RIDDELL, H.S.	TEROTECHNICA 2, 1981	LIFE CYCLE COSTING IN THE CHEMICAL INDUSTRY : TWO CASE STUDIES
RIDDELL H.	ENGINEERING LABS, UNIVERSITY OF MANCHESTER, 1987	LECTURE NOTES FOR COURSE ON ENGINEERING MANAGEMENT

AUTHOR/AUTEUR	PUBLISHER/EDITEUR	TITLE/TITRE
RIEUSSET A.	MAINTENANCE, 1990	LA MAINTENANCE CONDITIONNELLE
ROBERT AA.	EDITIONS DE L'USINE NOUVELLE - PARIS, 1985	COMMENT INFORMATISER SA MAINTENANCE
ROCOF	SINTEF - Safety and Reliability - NORWAY, 1990	COMPUTER PROGRAM TO ANALYSE REPAIR PROCESSES MODELLED BY A NON-HOMOGENEOUS POISSON PROCESS, FOR IBM AT AND PS/2
ROOK P.	ELSEVIER SCIENCE PUBLISHING, 1990	SOFTWARE RELIABILITY HANDBOOK
SAKAKIBARA S.	UNIDO, 1973	APPLICATION OF MODERN PRODUCTION MANAGEMENT TECHNIQUE TO MAINTENANCE FROM THE DEVELOPING COUNTRIES POINT OF VIEW
SALIN	ORGANSATION, 1986	LA GESTION DES STOCKS
SCHELLENS H.	DGS INTERNATIONAL, 1984	GESTION DES COUTS ET BUDGETS DE MAINTENANCE
SCHOFIELD CH. G.	SYDNEY - IES, 1984	COMPUTERS IN MAINTENANCE MANAGEMENT
SCHULLER W.M.	EYROLLES, 1981	CONTROLE DU BRUIT DU MILIEU INDUSTRIEL
SCOTT D.	TRIBOLOGY, 1970	FAILURE DIAGNOSIS AND INVESTIGATION
SHINGO S.	LES ED. D'ORGANISATION, 1986	MAITRISE DE LA PRODUCTION : LE CAS TOYOTA
SHIROSE K.	PRODUCTIVITY PRESS INC. - CAMBRIDGE, 1992	TPM FOR WORKSHOP LEADERS
SILVER E. and PETERSON R.	WILEY, 1985	DECISION SYSTEMS FOR INVENTORY MANAGEMENT AND PRODUCTION PLANNING
SMITH A.R.	ILO/BIT - GENEVE, 1988	TECHNIQUES FOR MANAGERIAL MANPOWER PLANNING
SMITH D. J.	Mc MILLAN, 1985	RELIABILITY AND MAINTAINABILITY & PERSPECTIVE
SMITH R.	CONFERENCE COMMUNICATION 13TH NATIONAL MAINTENANCE MANAGEMENT SHOW - LONDON, 1990	THE EFFECTIVE INTEGRATION OF CONDITION MONITORING INTO MAINTENANCE MANAGEMENT
SNOW D. A.	BUTTERWORTH/HEINEMANN	PLANT ENGINEER'S REFERENCE BOOK

AUTHOR/AUTEUR	PUBLISHER/EDITEUR	TITLE/TITRE
STEWART H.	BUSINESS BOOK LTD, 1969	EFFICIENT MAINTENANCE MANAGEMENT
SULZER	DUNOD 85	COMMENT CONSTRUIRE UN TABLEAU DE BORD
SWARD K.	UNIDO, 1970	MAINTENANCE GUIDELINES AT A TENDERING STAGE
SWARD K.	UNIDO, 1973	PRACTICAL ASPECTS OF MAINTAINABILITY
TAKAHASHI Y.	TEROTECHNICA, 1981	MAINTENANCE-ORIENTED MANAGEMENT VIA TOTAL PARTICIPATION
TAKAHASHI Y.	UNIDO, 1973	PRACTICAL ASPECTS OF APPLICATION OF MODERN PRODUCTION MANAGEMENT TECHNIQUES TO MAINTENANCE
THIBAULT	CHOTARD, 1981	PRATIQUE DE L'ORGANISATION INDUSTRIELLE
TIXIER J.	ACHATS ET ENTRETIEN, 1986	LA COMMUNICATION DANS L'ENTREPRISE : FACTEUR DE PRODUCTIVITE
TRAMOND M.	TRAVAIL ET METHODES, 1986	OPTIMISATION DE L'ORDONNANCEMENT
TSIKURIN N.	UNIDO, 1973	STANDARDIZATION AND MATERIAL SAVING IN MECHANICAL ENGINEERING
U.C.L. - INSTITUT DU GENIE CHIMIQUE	UNIVERSITE CATHOLIQUE DE LOUVAIN, 1978	SYMPOSIUM SUR L'ENTRETIEN DANS L'INDUSTRIE DES PROCEDES
U.C.L. - INSTITUT DU GENIE CHIMIQUE	UNIVERSITE CATHOLIQUE DE LOUVAIN-LA-NEUVE, 1990	LA MAINTENANCE ET SA GESTION ASSISTEES PAR ORDINATEUR
UNIDO and VDMA	UNIDO	MAINTENANCE AND REPAIR IN DEVELOPING COUNTRIES, REPORT OF CONFERENCE HELD IN DUISBURG (GFR), 1970
UNIDO and ILO	UNIDO/ILO - 2nd CONSULTATION ON TRAINING OF INDUSTRIAL MANPOWER - PARIS, 1987	CONFERENCE PAPERS AND CASE STUDIES
UNIDO	UNIDO - UNITED NATIONS - NEW YORK, 1971	MAINTENANCE AND REPAIR IN DEVELOPING COUNTRIES
UNIDO	UNIDO - UNITED NATIONS NEW YORK, 1973	MAINTENANCE PLANNING, ITS REQUIREMENT AND IMPLICATIONS

AUTHOR/AUTEUR	PUBLISHER/EDITEUR	TITLE/TITRE
UNIDO	UNIDO - UNITED NATIONS NEW YORK, 1976	INTRODUCTION TO MAINTENANCE PLANNING IN INDUSTRY
VAN SANTEN GW	DUNOD	VIBRATIONS MECANIQUES
VAUDEVILLE	AFNOR, 1985	GESTION ET CONTROLE DE QUALITE
VILLEMEUR A.	EYROLLES - PARIS, 1988	SURETE DE FONCTIONNEMENT DES SYSTEMES INDUSTRIELS, FIABILITE
VISINTINI G.	Ed. l'USINE NOUVELLE	COMMENT AUGMENTER SA PRODUCTIVITE PAR LA MAINTENANCE
WALZ D.	THE A.I. MAGAZINE, 1983	ARTIFICIAL INTELLIGENCE
WARNECKE M.	EDIREP, 1983	TECHNIQUES DE MONTAGES ET D'ASSEMBLAGES
WASSERMAN R.	INSTITUT CASTOLLIN, 1971	COMMENT ECONOMISER DES MILLIONS EN REDUISANT LES STOCKS DE PIECES DE RECHANGE
WEIGEL H.	PROC. CONF. ISI,1972	FUNCTIONAL MAINTENANCE SYSTEMS APPROACH
WHITE E. N.	GOWER PRESS - EPPING, 1973	MAINTENANCE PLANNING, CONTROL AND DOCUMENTATION
WIIG K.	ILO/BIT - GENEVE, 1990	EXPERT SYSTEMS : A MANAGER'S GUIDE
WILKINSON J. J.	HARVARD BUSINESS REVIEW, 1968	HOW TO MANAGE MAINTENANCE
WILSON A.	CONFERENCE COMMUNICATION, 1984	PLANNING FOR COMPUTERIZED MAINTENANCE
WILSON, Dr. A.	8th EUROPEAN MAINTENANCE CONGRESS EFNMS - BARCELONA, 1986	SELECTION OF THE BEST COMPUTER SYSTEM BY USERS
WILSON B.	MAINTENANCE MANAGEMENT INTERNATIONAL, 1982	ENGINEERING RESOURCE PLANNING
WINTER J. and ZAKREWSKI R.	SOC. MFG. ENG., 1984	MAINTENANCE MANAGEMENT FOR QUALITY PRODUCTION
WIREMANT T.	INDUSTRIAL PRESS INC. - NEW YORK, 1990	WORLD CLASS MAINTENANCE MANAGEMENT
WIREMANT T.	INDUSTRIAL PRESS INC. - NEW YORK, 1988	COMPUTERIZED MAINTENANCE MANAGEMENT SYSTEMS

AUTHOR/AUTEUR	PUBLISHER/EDITEUR	TITLE/TITRE
WOLF T.	IN. COM. TEC., 1967	IMPROVING THE EFFICIENCY OF MAINTENANCE STORES
WYNNE R.	CONFERENCE COMMUNICATION 13TH NATIONAL MAINTENANCE MANAGEMENT SHOW - LONDON, 1990	INTRODUCTION TO THE USES AND CHARACTERISTICS OF INDUSTRIAL CONTROL SYSTEMS
ZERMATI P. and GISSEROT P.	DUNOD, 1985	LA PRATIQUE DE LA GESTION DES STOCKS

APPENDICES 1)

---

1) All forms in these appendices are made available by courtesy of DGS International S.A.

Remark :   For common abbreviations used in the forms, refer to the list of principal abbreviations.

APPENDIX 1

STANDARD ORGANIZATION CHART OF
CENTRAL MAINTENANCE PLANNING (CMPO)

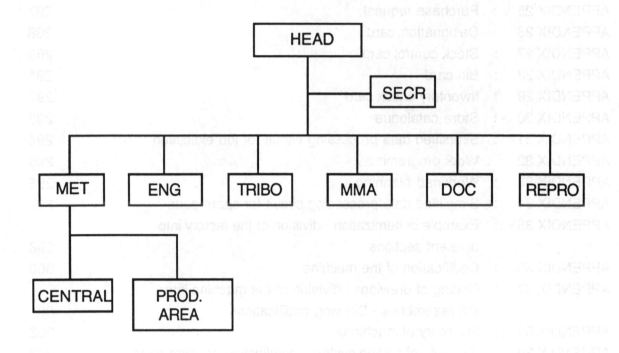

SECR	:	Secretariat
MET	:	Maintenance Methods
ENG	:	Maintenance Engineering and Construction, incl. drawing office
TRIBO	:	Tribology
MMA	:	Maintenance Management Section
DOC	:	Central Technical Documentation
REPRO	:	Reprography

STANDARD ORGANIZATION CHART OF
MECHANICAL AND ELECTRICAL SERVICES (MS AND ES)

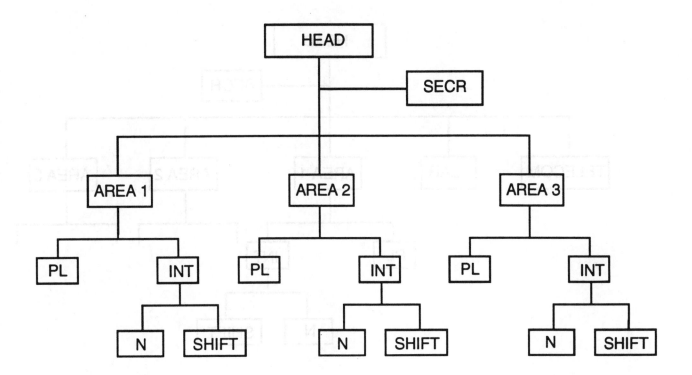

SECR : Secretariat
PL : Planning section : Programming - work specifications
(job preparation) - work scheduling
INT : Intervention
N : Normal day-crew (8 hours/day)
SHIFT : 3 shifts (3 x 8 hours giving 24 hours cover)

APPENDIX 3

STANDARD ORGANIZATION CHART OF
INSTRUMENTATION SERVICE (INS)

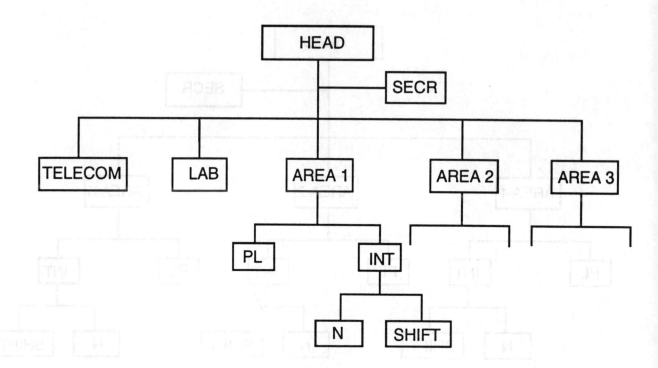

SECR	:	Secretariat
TELECOM	:	Maintenance of telecommunication system
LAB	:	Laboratory / Workshop for instrumentation and electronics
PL	:	Planning section : maintenance programming - work specifications
		(job preparation) - work scheduling
INT	:	Intervention
N	:	Normal day-crew (8 hours/day)
SHIFT	:	3 shifts (3 x 8 hours giving 24 hours cover)

STANDARD ORGANIZATION CHART OF
CENTRAL MAINTENANCE WORKSHOPS (CMWS)

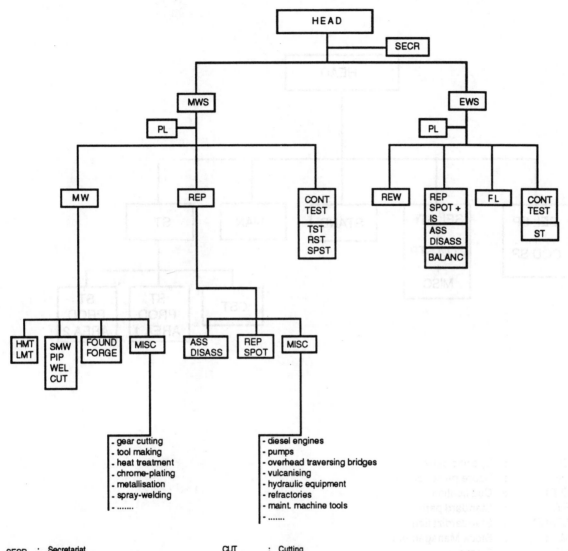

SECR	:	Secretariat
PL	:	Planning (programming - preparation - scheduling)
MWS	:	Mechanical Workshop
EWS	:	Electrical Workshop
MW	:	Metal-working
REP	:	Repair
CONT	:	Control
HMT	:	Heavy machine-tools
LMT	:	Light machine-tools
SMW	:	Sheet metalworking
PIP	:	Piping
WEL	:	Welding
TST	:	Toolstore
RST	:	Store for raw material
SPST	:	Spare parts store

CUT	:	Cutting
FOUND	:	Foundry
MISC	:	Miscellaneous
ASS	:	Assembling
DISASS	:	Disassembling
REP SPOT	:	Repair on the spot
REW	:	Rewinding
REP IS	:	Repair in the shop
BALANC	:	Balancing
FL	:	Factory lighting
ST	:	Store
TEST	:	Testbenches

APPENDIX 5

STANDARD ORGANIZATION CHART OF
SPARE PARTS MANAGEMENT AND STORES (SPMS)

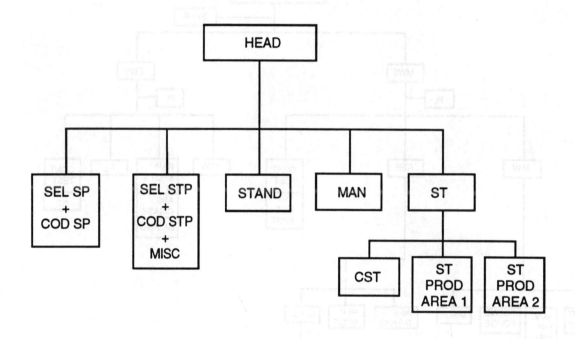

SP	:	Specific parts
SEL	:	Spare parts selection
COD	:	Codification
STP	:	Standard parts
STAND	:	Standardization
MAN	:	Stock Management
ST	:	Stores
MISC	:	Miscellaneous store items
CST	:	Central Store

STANDARD ORGANIZATION CHART OF
GENERAL MAINTENANCE SERVICE (GM)

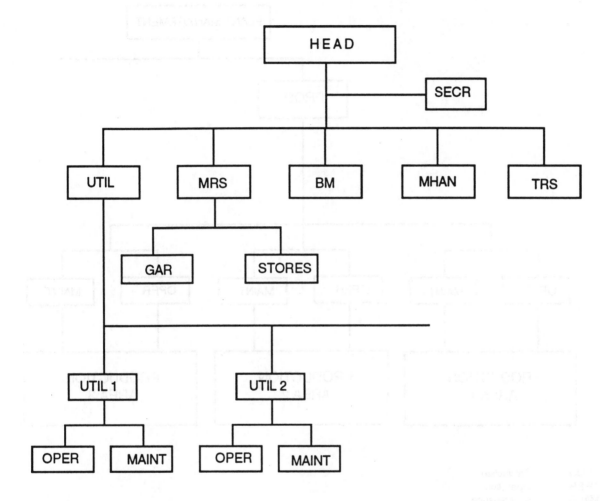

SECR : Secretariat
UTIL   : Utilities
OPER : Operation
MAINT : Maintenance
MRS   : Maintenance of rolling stock
GAR   : Garage
BM   : Maintenance of buildings and infrastructure
MAHN : Materials handling
TRS   : Tracks, roads, sewerage

APPENDIX 7

DECENTRALIZED MAINTENANCE STRUCTURE

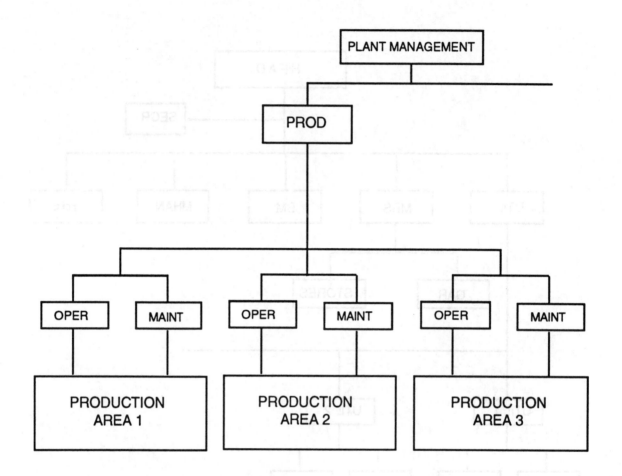

PROD : Production
OPER : Operation
MAINT : Maintenance

MIXED MAINTENANCE STRUCTURE

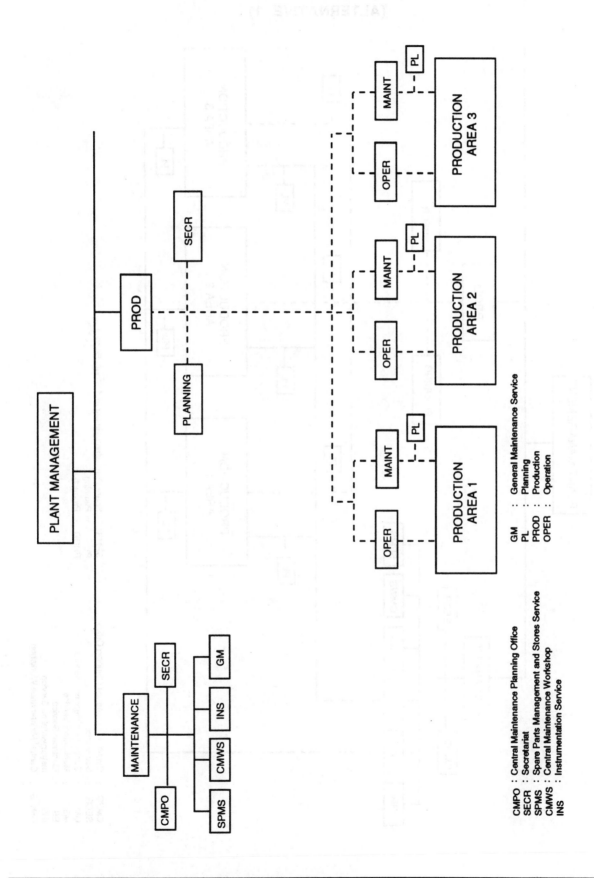

CMPO : Central Maintenance Planning Office
SECR : Secretariat
SPMS : Spare Parts Management and Stores Service
CMWS : Central Maintenance Workshop
INS : Instrumentation Service

GM : General Maintenance Service
PL : Planning
PROD : Production
OPER : Operation

APPENDIX 9/1

CENTRALIZED MAINTENANCE STRUCTURE
(ALTERNATIVE 1)

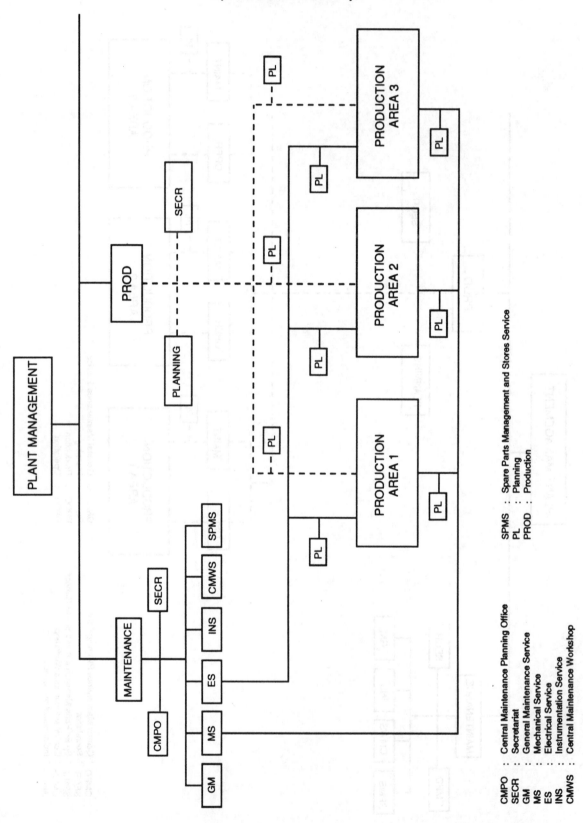

SPMS : Spare Parts Management and Stores Service
PL : Planning
PROD : Production

CMPO : Central Maintenance Planning Office
SECR : Secretariat
GM : General Maintenance Service
MS : Mechanical Service
ES : Electrical Service
INS : Instrumentation Service
CMWS : Central Maintenance Workshop

CENTRALIZED MAINTENANCE STRUCTURE
(ALTERNATIVE 2)

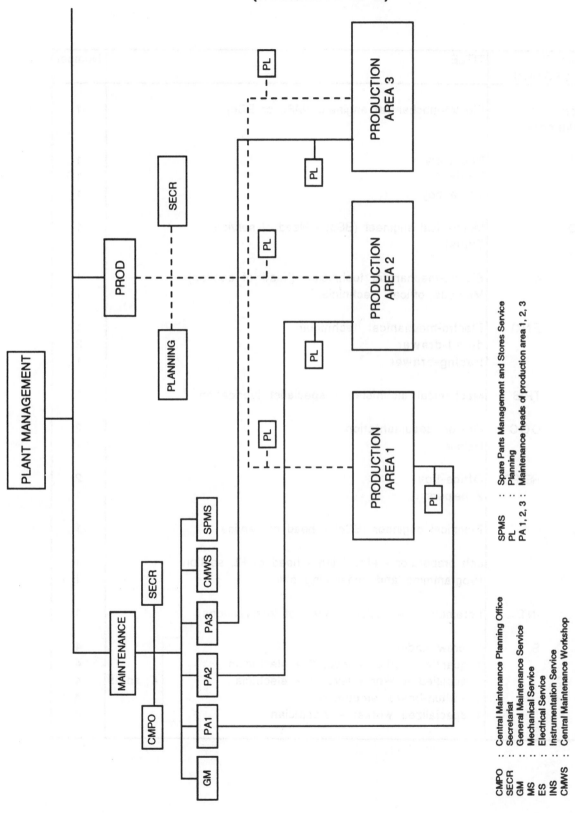

SPMS : Spare Parts Management and Stores Service
PL : Planning
PA 1, 2, 3 : Maintenance heads of production area 1, 2, 3

CMPO : Central Maintenance Planning Office
SECR : Secretariat
GM : General Maintenance Service
MS : Mechanical Service
ES : Electrical Service
INS : Instrumentation Service
CMWS : Central Maintenance Workshop

APPENDIX 10/1

EXAMPLE OF MANNING TABLE (PLANT WITH WORKFORCE OF 900)

SERVICE/ SECTION		TITLE	Number
Director of Maintenance		Electro-mechanical engineer (MSc or BSc)	1
SECR		Secretary	1
		Typist	1
		Office boy	1
CMPO		Mechanical engineer (BSc) - Head of service	1
		Typist	1
	M	Electro-mechanical technician (head of section)	1
		Methods officer (technician)	1
	ENG	Electro-mechanical technician	1
		detail-drawer	3
		tracing-drawer	1
	TRIB	Mechanical technician - specialist lubrication	1
	DOC	Officer documentation	2
		Helper	1
	REPRO	Office-boy	2
		2 helpers	1
ES		Electrical engineer (BSc) - head of service	1
	PL	Job preparator - electrician - head of PL section	1
		Programming and scheduling officer	1
	INT	Foreman - electrician - head of interventions	1
	S	1 crew-leader	4
		1 qualified worker - level 2 - electrician	4
		1 qualified worker - level 1 - electrician 4 shifts	4
		1 switch-board electrician	4
		1 specialized worker - electrician	4

SERVICE/ SECTION		TITLE	Number
	N	Qualified worker - electrician	3
		Specialized worker - electrician	3
	EWS	Qualified workers - level 2 - rewinder	1
		Qualified workers - level 1 - electrician	2
		Qualified workers - level 1 - electro-mechanic	2
		Specialized worker - electrician	2
		Helper	1
MS		Mechanical Engineer (BSc) - head of Service	1
	PL	Job preparator - mechanic - head of PL section	1
		Qualified worker - level 3 - sheetmetal working - piping for job preparation, welding and metalworking	1
		Programming officer	1
		Scheduling officer	1
	INT	Foreman - mechanic - head of interventions	1
	S	1 crew-leader	4
		1 qualified worker - level 2 - mechanic } 4 shifts	4
		2 qualified workers - level 1 - mechanic	8
		1 specialized worker mechanic	4
	N	Qualified worker - level 3 - mechanic	1
		Qualified worker - level 2 - mechanic	2
		Qualified worker - level 1 - mechanic	1
		Specialized worker - mechanic	2
		Qualified worker - level 3 - lubricator	1
		Qualified worker - level 1 - lubricator	2
		Specialized worker - lubricator	2
MWS		Foreman - Head of workshop	1
	MT	Highly qualified worker - lathe operator/miller	1
		Qualified worker - level 2 - lathe operator	1
		Qualified worker - level 3 - fitter	2
		Qualified worker - level 2 - tool grinder	1
		Specialized worker - mechanic	3
		Specialized worker - level 2 - carpenter	1
		Carpenter - helper	1
	TST	Store-keeper	1
	REP	Crew-leader	1
		Highly qualified worker - hydraulics	1
		Qualified worker - level 3 - mechanics	3
		Qualified worker - level 2 - mechanics	3
		Specialized worker - mechanic	1

APPENDIX 10/3

SERVICE/ SECTION		TITLE	Number
SMW		Crew-leader	
	PIP/W/CUT	Qualified worker - level 3 - sheet metalworking - piping	1
		Qualified worker - level 2 - sheet metalworking - piping	2
		Specialized worker - sheet metalworking	1
		Highly qualified welder (HP-welding)	1
		Qualified worker - level 2 - welding	2
		Specialized worker - welding	2
		Helper	2
INS		Electronical engineer (BSC) - head of Service	1
	PL	Job preparator - head of PL section	1
		Programming / Scheduling officer	1
	INT	Technician - instrumentation - head of intervention	1
		Qualified worker - level 3 - instrumentation	3
		Qualified worker - level 2 - instrumentation	2
		Technician automation	1
		Highly qualified worker - electronics	1
	LAB	Technician instrumentation	1
		Qualified worker - level 3 - instrumentation	1
		Specialized worker - Instrumentation	1
		Qualified worker - level 3 - Telecommunication	1
SPMS		High-level technician - head of service	1
		Typist	1
		Office-boy	1
	SP + STP	Technician - mechanic	1
		Technician - electrician / instrumentation / automation	1
		Qualified worker - level 3 - mechanics	2
		Qualified worker - level 3 - electrician	1
	SM	Spare parts management officer	3

APPENDIX 10/4

SERVICE/ SECTION	TITLE	Number
ST	Qualified worker - Level 3 - electro-mechanic in charge of reception/entering	1
	Store-keeper - qualified worker - level 2	2
	Store-keeper - qualified worker - level 1	2
	Store-keeper	2
	Helper	2
GM	Chief foreman - head of service	1
UTIL	1 qualified worker - level 3 - electro mechanics ⎤ 4 shifts	4
	1 qualified worker - level 1 - electro mechanics ⎦	4
MRS	Qualified worker - level 2 - vehicle mechanics	3
	Specialized worker - vehicle mechanics	2
	Qualified worker - level 3 - vehicle electricity	1
	Store-keeper	1
	Helper	1
BM	Crew leader	1
	Qualified worker - level 2 - Building electricity	1
	Aid-electrician	1
	Mason	4
	Aid-mason	4
	Plumber	1
	Painter	2
	2 workers for shuttering and wiring	2
MHAN	Material handling - planner	1
	Material handling - driver	4
	TOTAL	**199**

APPENDIX 11/1

MACHINE RECORD CARD

	IDENTITY (ID) OR FILE N°	
	27.333	

MACHINE / UNIT **POWDER MIXER**						

TYPE **MPH 1500**					CARD N° **MR 001**	PAGE **1/1**

MANUFACTURER **COLLETTE**						

SERIAL N° **86MPH150031**	PLANT **1**	DEPARTMENT **B**	SECTION **05**			

YEAR OF CONSTRUCTION **1986**	ORDER N° **247729**		INVENTORY N° **21.307**		COST CENTRE **21**	

START-UP DATE **Sept. 1986**	ORDER DATE **1986**					

SUPPLIER **ALFA COMPANY Ltd.**
Cross Road 22
KERBY - U.K.

TECHNICAL SPECIFICATIONS

Powder mixer with planetary gear drive :

- Capacity : gross capacity 1500 l
  net capacity min. 375 l/max. 1200 l
- Speed selection : mixing arm 10/18/51 rpm
  plateau 5/8/14/24 rpm
- Material : frame cast iron
  bowl, cover, outlet diam. 400 S.S. AISI 304
  mixing arm, scraper S.S. AISI 304

Equipped with :

- V-drive belt (7 V-belts SpA 12,5 x 2582 Lw)
- Main motor 18,5 kW 1500 rpm
- Hydraulic unit with motor 5,5 kW 1500 rpm
- Helical mixing arm and scraper
- Hydraulic unit and two hydraulic cylinders for bowl lifting
- Electrical switch cabinet with control panel

ACCESSORIES

- 1 light fitting on bowl cover MAX MULLER-CHEMLUX
  type 20H-D-Sch 220 V, 20 VA (see technical literature chapter 7)
- 1 timer for selection of mixing time SCHLEICHER
  type DZA52-SL (60h) 220 VAC (see technical literature, chapter 7)
- 2 bowls (see drawing 224.284, chapter 5.1)
- 1 standard bowl cover (see drawing 224.470, chapter 5.1)
- 1 bowl cover with two lids (see drawing 224.469, chapter 5.1)
- 2 trolleys for bowls (see drawing 224.478, chapter 1.2)
- 1 installation device for mixing arm (see drawing 224.471, chapter 1.2)

DG8 SYSTEM

DG8 30 / 90 / 132

APPENDIX 11/2

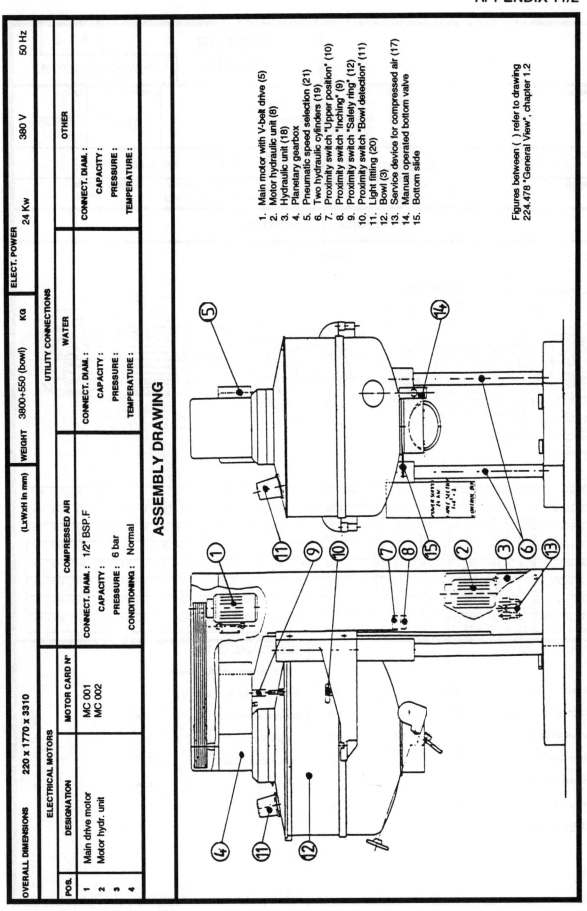

ASSEMBLY DRAWING

| OVERALL DIMENSIONS | 220 x 1770 x 3310 | (LxWxH in mm) | WEIGHT | 3800+550 (bowl) | Kg | ELECT. POWER | 24 Kw | 380 V | 50 Hz |

ELECTRICAL MOTORS

POS.	DESIGNATION	MOTOR CARD N°
1	Main drive motor	MC 001
2	Motor hydr. unit	MC 002
3		
4		

UTILITY CONNECTIONS

COMPRESSED AIR	WATER	OTHER
CONNECT. DIAM. : 1/2" BSP.F	CONNECT. DIAM. :	CONNECT. DIAM. :
CAPACITY :	CAPACITY :	CAPACITY :
PRESSURE : 6 bar	PRESSURE :	PRESSURE :
CONDITIONING : Normal	TEMPERATURE :	TEMPERATURE :

1. Main motor with V-belt drive (5)
2. Motor hydraulic unit (8)
3. Hydraulic unit (18)
4. Planetary gearbox
5. Pneumatic speed selection (21)
6. Two hydraulic cylinders (19)
7. Proximity switch "Upper position" (10)
8. Proximity switch "Inching" (9)
9. Proximity switch "Safety ring" (12)
10. Proximity switch "Bowl detection" (11)
11. Light fitting (20)
12. Bowl (3)
13. Service device for compressed air (17)
14. Manual operated bottom valve
15. Bottom slide

Figures between ( ) refer to drawing
224.478 "General View", chapter 1.2

APPENDIX 12/1

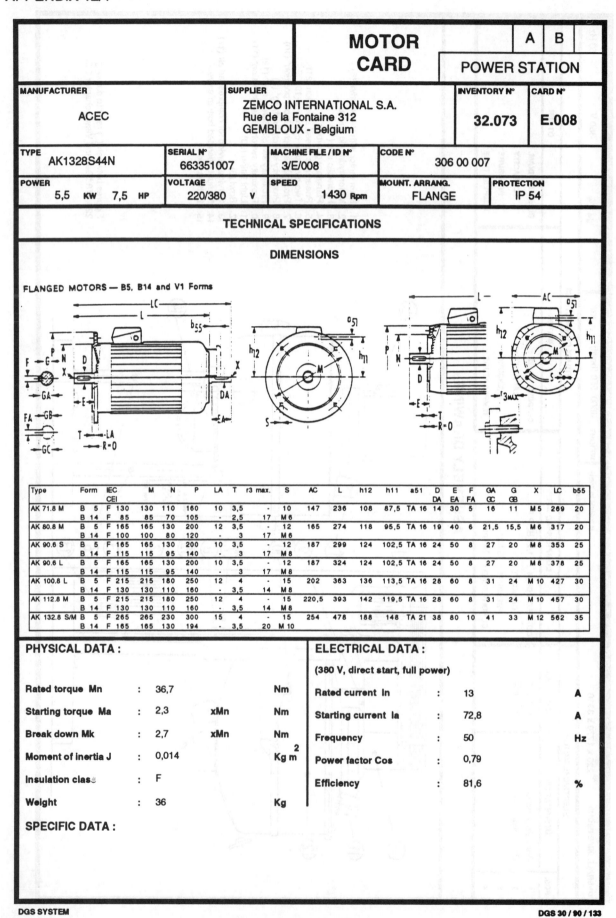

		MOTOR CARD		A	B
			POWER STATION		

MANUFACTURER	SUPPLIER		INVENTORY N°	CARD N°
ACEC	ZEMCO INTERNATIONAL S.A. Rue de la Fontaine 312 GEMBLOUX - Belgium		32.073	E.008

TYPE	SERIAL N°	MACHINE FILE / ID N°	CODE N°
AK1328S44N	663351007	3/E/008	306 00 007

POWER			VOLTAGE		SPEED	MOUNT. ARRANG.	PROTECTION
5,5	KW	7,5 HP	220/380	V	1430 Rpm	FLANGE	IP 54

TECHNICAL SPECIFICATIONS

DIMENSIONS

FLANGED MOTORS — B5, B14 and V1 Forms

Type	Form	IEC CEI	M	N	P	LA	T	r3 max.	S	AC	L	h12	h11	a51	D DA	E EA	F FA	GA GC	G GB	X	LC	b55
AK 71.8 M	B 5	F 130	130	110	160	10	3,5	-	10	147	236	108	87,5	TA 16	14	30	5	16	11	M 5	269	20
	B 14	F 85	85	70	105	-	2,5	17	M 6													
AK 80.8 M	B 5	F 165	165	130	200	12	3,5	-	12	165	274	118	95,5	TA 16	19	40	6	21,5	15,5	M 6	317	20
	B 14	F 100	100	80	120	-	3	17	M 6													
AK 90.6 S	B 5	F 165	165	130	200	10	3,5	-	12	187	299	124	102,5	TA 16	24	50	8	27	20	M 8	353	25
	B 14	F 115	115	95	140	-	3	17	M 8													
AK 90.6 L	B 5	F 165	165	130	200	10	3,5	-	12	187	324	124	102,5	TA 16	24	50	8	27	20	M 8	378	25
	B 14	F 115	115	95	140	-	3	17	M 8													
AK 100.8 L	B 5	F 215	215	180	250	12	4	-	15	202	363	136	113,5	TA 16	28	60	8	31	24	M 10	427	30
	B 14	F 130	130	110	160	-	3,5	14	M 8													
AK 112.8 M	B 5	F 215	215	180	250	12	4	-	15	220,5	393	142	119,5	TA 16	28	60	8	31	24	M 10	457	30
	B 14	F 130	130	110	160	-	3,5	14	M 8													
AK 132.8 S/M	B 5	F 265	265	230	300	15	4	-	15	254	478	188	148	TA 21	38	80	10	41	33	M 12	562	35
	B 14	F 165	165	130	194	-	3,5	20	M 10													

PHYSICAL DATA :

Rated torque Mn	:	36,7		Nm
Starting torque Ma	:	2,3	xMn	Nm
Break down Mk	:	2,7	xMn	Nm
Moment of inertia J	:	0,014		Kg m²
Insulation class	:	F		
Weight	:	36		Kg

ELECTRICAL DATA :

(380 V, direct start, full power)

Rated current In	:	13	A
Starting current Ia	:	72,8	A
Frequency	:	50	Hz
Power factor Cos	:	0,79	
Efficiency	:	81,6	%

SPECIFIC DATA :

DGS SYSTEM   DGS 30 / 90 / 133

INSTALLED ON :		IDENTICAL MOTORS ON :		
1. B. 005		3. E. 803		
7. D. 016		4. D. 002		
3. E. 702		8.H. 039		
		9. I. 702		

CODE OF EQUIVALENT MOTORS

306 00 103
306 00 721
306 00 302

SPARE PARTS

NUMBER	CODE	DESCRIPTION	REF. MANUFACTURER
1		Driving end endshield	54 (19)
2		Non-driving end endshield	52 (19)
3		Fan cover	55 (22)
4		Metallic fan	58 (21)
5		Driving end ball bearing 6308 2Z	62 (5)
		Non-driving end ball bearing 6308 2Z	62 (5)
6		Metallic teminal box complete	64 (29)
7		Stator	- (2)
8		Shaft with die cast rotor	- (3,4)

REMARKS

When ordering spare parts, always mention type, serial number and mounting
arrangements of the motor
* Figures between ( ) refer to drawing A-66-A3-2298 "Motor AK 132-8",
Chapter 7.

APPENDIX 13

JOB REQUEST	②

③ N°	⑤ DATE OF REQUEST	⑥ JOB TO BE READY BY (DATE)	⑦	⑧ DEGREE OF URGENCY

④ N° REQUESTING SERVICE   DRAFTER   PHONE N°

A   B   C

NAME SUPERVISOR - CHECK

⑨ COST CENTRE	⑩ MACHINE ALLOCATION	⑪	⑫ REPETITIVE WORK	⑬ WORK-FILE N°

YES | NO

DESIGNATION OF WORK

⑭	⑮ N° ENCLOSED DRAWINGS AND INSTRUCTIONS

⑯ EXECUTING SECTION	⑰ NUMBER OF JO	⑱ NUMBER OF SECONDARY JO	OTHER TRADES OR SUB-CONTRACTOR	⑲	⑳ PREPARED BY

㉑ REMARKS	JR RECEIVED ON	㉒	㉓ JR COMPLETED AT

DGS SYSTEM

DGS 30/90/068

APPENDIX 14

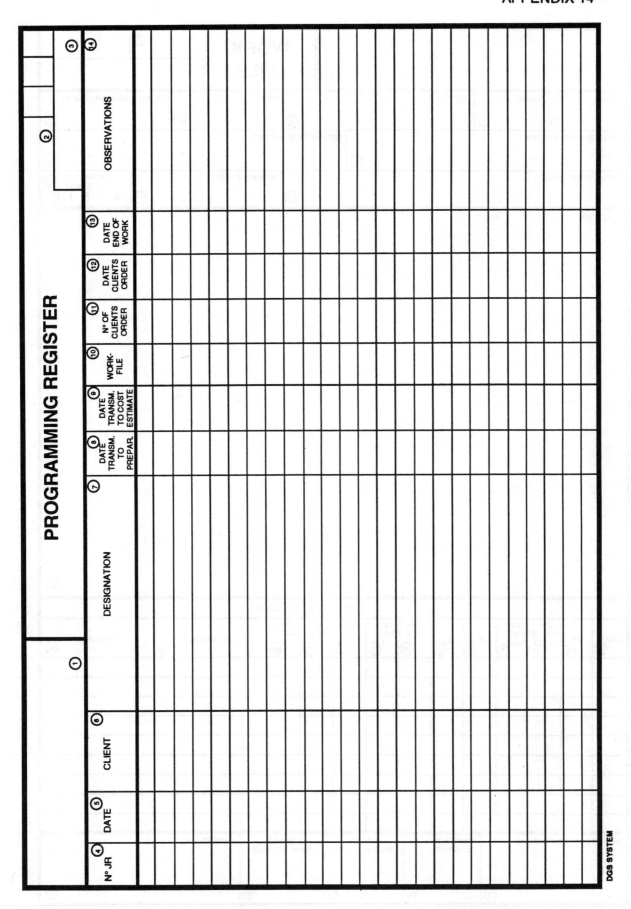

APPENDIX 15

		WORK-FILE		②		

① ②

WORK-FILE NUMBER	NUMBER JR	DRAFTER	DATE	C/C ALLOCATION MACHINE N°
③	④		⑤	⑥	⑦

PRODUCTION AREA/MACHINE	REQUESTED BY/SERVICE
⑧	⑨

DESIGNATION OF WORK	REQUESTED DATE	DEGREE OF URGENCY ⑫
⑩	⑪	A B C

REMARKS

⑬

CONTENT OF FILE/DATA

DATE	JR	JOB PHASING SHEET	JOB SPEC. SHEET	IS	JO	ESTI-MATE 1	ESTI-MATE 2	ESTI-MATE 3	ESTI-MATE 4	ESTI-MATE 5	DRAWINGS	MANUALS
⑭	⑮	⑯	⑰	⑱	⑲	⑳	㉑	㉒	㉓	㉔	㉕	㉖

PREPARED BY - TELEPHONE N°	TRANSM. DATE TO PREPAR.	VISA OF JOB PREPARATOR	VISA OF HEAD METHODS	REMARKS
㉗	㉘	㉙	㉚	㉛

DGS SYSTEM

DGS 30/90/097

APPENDIX 16/1

JOB ORDER

ORIGIN AND NUMBER JR	REQUESTED BY	PREPARED BY	DATE OF SCHEDULING	WORK-FILE N°	N°	PAGE
	TEL.	TEL.				

MACHINE ALLOCATION	C.C.	DESIGNATION OF WORK ORDER

EXECUTING MACHINE OR DIVISION	SPECIALITY	CHECK SUPERVIS.-PREPARATION	DESIGNATION OF JOB PHASE	SECONDARY JOB-ORDERS
		DATE		

WORK DESCRIPTION

N°. OF DRAWINGS AND INSTRUCTIONS

JOB INSTRUCTIONS

REMARKS	CHECK REQUESTING PERSON	DATE HOUR OF MACHINE STOP	DATE HOUR OF START-UP
	DATE	CHECK PROD. DPT.	CHECK PROD. DPT.

DGS SYSTEM

DGS 30/90/062

APPENDIX 16/2

CLOCKED HOURS OF JOB-ORDER									VALUATION		REMARKS
			ON-JOB HOURS RECORD						HOURLY RATE (43)	TOTAL (44)	(45)
DATE (37)	TRADESMAN (38)	NUMBER (39)	FROM (40)		TO (41)		TIME USED (42)				
			HOUR	MIN.	HOUR	MIN.	HOUR	MIN.			

CHECK CREW-LEADER	CHECK FOREMAN	CHECK PL	CHECK COST -ACCOUNT.	TOT.	TOTAL (50)
DATE (46)	DATE (47)	DATE (48)	DATE (49)	REMARKS (51)	

DGS SYSTEM

DGS 30/90/064

APPENDIX 17/1

WORK SPECIFICATION SHEET						PAGE 1/3
		JOB ORDER N° 83.592	**DRAFTER** PVDB/DGS	**DATE** 24.11.83	**MACHINE FILE / ID N°** 810-012-603	**SPECIALITY** MEC
MACHINE / DEVICE MOTOPUMP	**TYPE** MPG-160					**SHEET N°** 0006/A
SUB-ASSEMBLY ENGINE LISTER	**TYPE** HR-3	**VISA SUPERVISOR**	**NAME** HARDOUIN	**DATE** 24.11.83	**INVENTORY N°** 27.832	**COST CENTRE** 10.201

SERVICE ITEMS

- Adjust valve tappet clearances

TOOLS AND DEVICES

- 1 screw driver 1,2 x 8
- open-end spanner 5/8 x 3/4
- thickness-gauge
- ring spanner 5/8 x 3/4

SAFETY PROCEDURES

- Before dismantling make sure that the MPG cannot be started by accident

SPARE PARTS

NBR.	DESIGNATION	CODE N°
1	Seal ring C3K40702	403.20.087

REMARKS

- Before removing cylinder head cover, clean properly
- Valve clearance for inlet and exhaust valve
  inlet : 0,05 mm
  exhaust : 0,10 mm

DRAWING AND MANUAL N°

DGS SYSTEM

APPENDIX 17/2

WORK SPECIFICATION SHEET	DESCRIPTION OF PROCEDURES		SHEET N°	PAGE 2/3
POS.	**PROCEDURES**	**EST. TIME h**	**REMARKS**	
1	Remove cylinder head covers - 1 - - disconnect decompressor levers - 2 - - (longer studs - 4 - are used holding lifting eye - 5 - - remove joints (- 6 - and - 7 -)	0,25		

2	Valve clearance adjusting of cylinder 1
	- turn fley-wheel to the T.D.C. position
	  (both valves closed)
	- hold adjusting screw - 8 - with screwdriver - 9 - and slacken locknut - 10 - with twelve-point ring spanner - 11 -
	- adjust clearance with screwdriver - 9 - and check with thickness-gauge - 12 -
	  inlet : 0,05 mm
	  exhaust : 0,10 mm
	- after adjusting, tighten locknut - 10 - with twelve-point ring spanner - 11 - and re-check to make sure that clearance is correct
		0,25		

3	For cylinder 2 see point 2	0,25		
4	For cylinder 3 see point 2	0,25		
5	Refitting cylinder head cover - 1 - - clean cylinder head surface - 13 - (scratch rests of joint when necessary - clean inside of head covers and cover jointing faces - replace joints - 6 - and - 7 - (apply a tightness paste) - tighten bolts - 3 - - refit decompressor coupling rods - 2 -	0,5		

DGS SYSTEM

APPENDIX 17/3

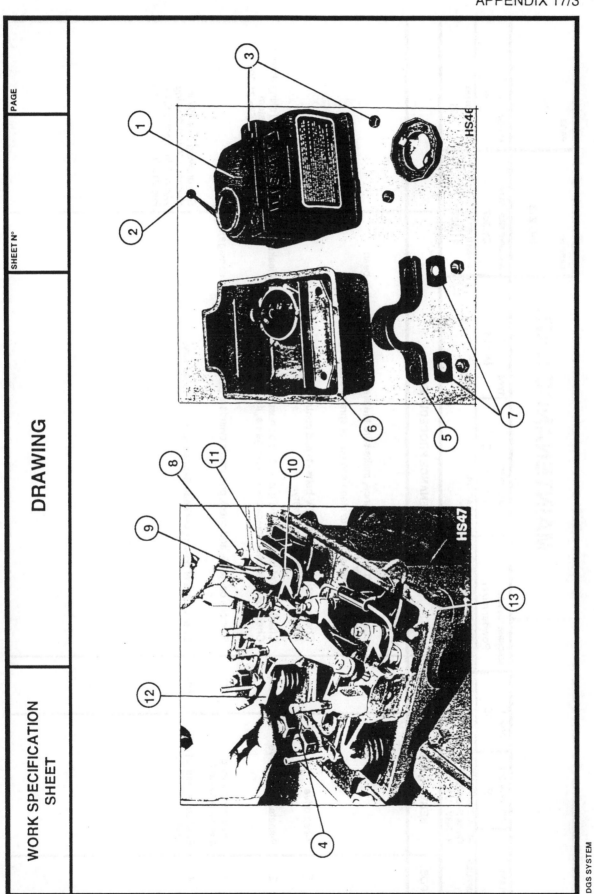

PAGE

SHEET N°

DRAWING

WORK SPECIFICATION
SHEET

DGS SYSTEM

APPENDIX 18/1

MAINTENANCE CARD

CARD No.	PAGE
MC 213	1/1

MACHINE FILE / ID No.	SPECIALITY
21.307	M

INVENTORY No.	COST CENTRE
21.307	21

PLANT	DEPARTMENT	ROOM N°
1	B	05

MACHINE / DEVICE	TYPE	MANUFACTURER
Powder mixer	MPH 1500	COLLETTE

SUB-ASSEMBLY	TYPE	MANUFACTURER

SUPPLIER ALFA COMPANY Ltd. Cross Road 22 KERBY - U.K.

MAINTENANCE PROCEDURES

POS.	SERVICE ITEM	PERIOD. (*)	MAINTENANCE PROCEDURES	
			ATTENTION : - Before doing any maintenance, make sure the electrical control box has been switched off and secured. - Do not use detergents to clean and do not spray water on the machine.	
1	V-belt drive	3m	Check tension and state of V-belts -1- and control alignment of pulleys -2-. Adjust or replace, if necessary.	
2	Planetary gear drive	3m	Check state of bearings and gears -3- (no unusual noices, vibrations or oil leaks). Check oil level and replace bearings or gears, if necessary.	See instructions "Taking down of planetary gear system" Chapter 4.1.2.3 - File 21.307
3	Pneumatic speed selection system	6m	Remove cover -5- and check pneumatic cylinders (fixing, no air leaks, no damage).	
4	Bowl cover seal of both bowls	6m	Check state of bowl cover seal -6- and replace, if necessary.	See drawing 224.497 in chapter 1.2 and drawing 224.469 in chapter 5.1 - File 21.307

* h = every hour ; d = daily ; w = weekly ; m = monthly ; a = annually ; an = according to needs

DGS SYSTEM   DGS 30 / 90 / 134

ASSEMBLY DRAWING

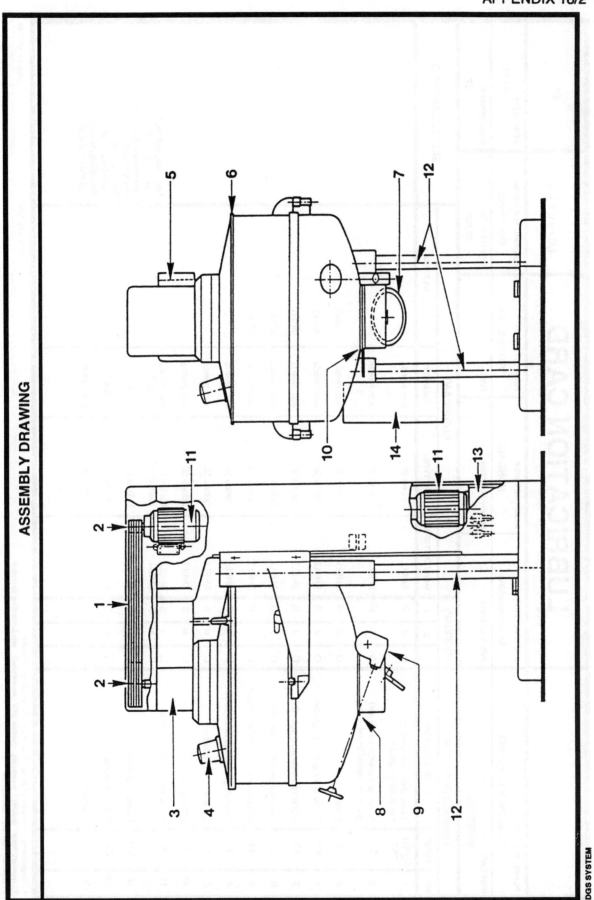

APPENDIX 19/1

LUBRICATION CARD

PLANT / SECTOR	MACHINE / DEVICE	MANUFACTURER	TYPE	CARD No.	PAGE
WORKSHOP 2 - MILLING	Milling machine	MONDIALE	VIKING 3 - MA	LC/0007 C	1/1

SUPPLIER	SUB-ASSEMBLY	MANUFACTURER	TYPE	MACHINE FILE / ID No.	SPECIALITY
MONDIALE				810-012-603	LUB
				INVENTORY N° 27.832	COST CENTRE 27

POS.	MARK	DESCRIPTION	1	2	3	MANUFACTURER	TYPE	QUANTITY	METHOD	MISCELLANEOUS
1	2/12/ 15/17	Table slide and bearing of longitudinal spindle	O	d	R	SHELL	Talona 30	acc. needs	oilcan	
2	3/7	Slides of traverse travel and gears of vertical travel	O	d	R	SHELL	Talona 30	acc. needs	oilcan	
3	4/5	Slides	O	d	R	SHELL	Talona 30	acc. needs	oilcan	
4	9/13	Pillow of longitudinal spindle	O	d	R	SHELL	Talona 30	acc. needs	oilcan	
5	10	Pillow of transversal spindle	O	d	R	SHELL	Talona 30	acc. needs	oilcan	
6	11	Transversal spindle and nut	O	d	R	SHELL	Talona 30	acc. needs	oilcan	
7	14	Mecanism of longitudinal travel	O	d	R	SHELL	Talona 30	acc. needs	oilcan	
8	B	Oil level gearbox of headstock	L	w	S	SHELL	Talona 30	acc. needs		
9	C	Oil level travel gearbox	L	w	S	SHELL	Talona 30	acc. needs		
10	F	Oil level overarm	L	w	S	SHELL	Talona 30	acc. needs		
11	6	Oil bath of vertical spindle	L / C	w / a	S / S	SHELL / SHELL	Tona oil 27 / Tona oil 27	acc. needs / 1,5 l		See oiling instructions - File 810-012-603 / See oiling instructions - File 810-012-603
12	A/16	Gearbox of headstock	C	A	S	SHELL	Talona 30	4 l		See oiling instructions - File 810-012-603
13	D/8	Travel gearbox	C	a	S	SHELL	Talona 30	5,4 l		See oiling instructions - File 810-012-603
14	1	Overarm	R	a	S	SHELL	Talona 30	acc. needs		See oiling instructions - File 810-012-603

1 : G=greasing - L=check oil level - C=change oil - O=oiling - R=refill
2 : h=every hour - d=daily - w=weekly - m=monthly - a=annually - an=according to needs
3 : R=when running - S=stopped

DGS SYSTEM

DGS 30 /90 /135

APPENDIX 19/2

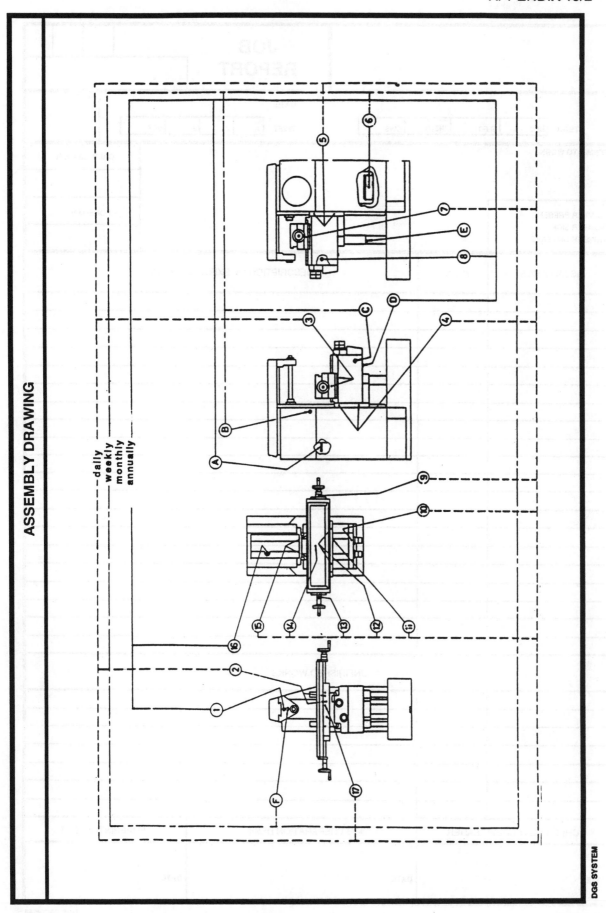

ASSEMBLY DRAWING

daily
weekly
monthly
annually

DGS SYSTEM

APPENDIX 20

	JOB REPORT		

TEAM	MEC	ELEC	INSTR	CWS		DATE				PAGE
					SHIFT	1	2	3	DAY	

PERMIT TO WORK

CREW-LEADER

NUMBER PRESENT
NUMBER SICK
NUMBER ON LEAVE

FOREMAN

INSTALLATION	N°. JO	DESCRIPTION OF EXECUTED WORK

UNFINISHED WORKS

CHECK NEXT CREW-LEADER	JOB-PREPARATION DESK	SUPERINTENDENT
DATE	DATE	DATE

DGS SYSTEM   **DGS 30/90/058**

APPENDIX 21

HISTORY RECORD CARD

NAME OF MANUFACTURER		GARANTEE	INVENTORY Nr.
SALMSON		1 year on parts	37.204

DESIGNAT. MACHINE / APPAREIL	MACHINE/DEVICE TYPE	START UP DATE	MACHINE FILE / ID Nr.
NO-200-250 D3	CENTRIFUGAL PUMP	15.01.84	802.073

SERIAL N°	DATE OUT OF SERVICE
NO. 5377.83	

YEAR OF CONSTRUCTION	DRAFTER	DATE
1983	PVDB/DGS	24.11.83

RUNNING TIME

YEAR	JAN.	FEB.	MAR.	APR.	MAY	JUN.	JUL.	AUG.	SEPT.	OCT.	NOV.	DEC.
1992												
1993												
1994												
1995												
1996												
1997												

JOB ORDER N°.	NATURE (*)	DATE AND HOUR OF SHUT DOWN	DATE AND HOUR OF START UP	TOT. DOWNTIME	TYPE OF MAINTENANCE INTERVENTION	CAUSES OF FAILURES
106.24	B	14.02.84/14h	15.02.84/15h	25h	Replacement of packed gland	Shaft lightly damaged
137.84	B	15.03.84/19h	16.03.84/13h	18h	Renewing transmission blocks of coupling	Wrong alignement of pump and engine
145.84	R	23.05.84/15h	23.05.84/18h	3h	Rewelding motopump frame	
159.84	P	14.06.84/13h	14.06.84/19h	6h	Renewing ball bearings	

* P = Preventive maintenance ; B = Break down maintenance ; O = Overhaul ; R = Repair

DGS SYSTEM

DGS 30 / 90 / 017

APPENDIX 22

SPARE PARTS LIST

MACHINE/DEVICE AND TYPE BRIDGE DEMAG GP 204	**INVENTORY No.** 2.1.168 — **MACHINE FILE / ID No.** 810.009.500
NAME AND ADDRESS OF SUPPLIER MANNESMANN DEMAG FORDERTECHNIK Karl Wilhelmstrasse 33B - DUISBURG / B.R.D. Tel.: 0241/44561 - Telex: 22846	**SUBASSEMBLY AND TYPE** ELECTRIC ROPE HOIST PK1N-2F
	NAME AND ADDRESS OF MANUFACTURER MANNESMANN DEMAG FORDERTECHNIK Karl Wilhelmstrasse 33B - DUISBURG / B.R.D. Tel.: 0241/44561 - Telex: 22846
PLANT/SECTION CRANES AND OVERHEAD TRAVELLING BRIDGES	**PAGE** 1/1 — **SPECIALITY** MEC
DRAFTER PVDB/DGS — **DATE** 20.06.1983	

POS.	DESIGNATION OF SPARE PART	CODE No.	DRAWING No.	ITEM	INST. TOT.	MANUF.	REF. FOR ORDERING	U.P.	NETT WEIGHT IN KG	ORIGIN	CUSTOM CODE	DEL. IN M.	MONTH. ESTIM. CONS.	PROP. Q.	REMARKS
1	Brake ring Ref. DEMAG 560 29 044	265 00 721	DEMAG 206 056 44	2	1	DEMAG	560 29 044	220	0,500	D	8444	2	0,75	9	
2	Deep grove ball bearing 6003 DIN 625	281 19 022	DEMAG 206 056 44	3	4	SKF	6003	385	0,285	B	7302	3	0,10	4	
3	Slotted cheese head screw M4 x 16 - DIN 84-5.8	263 07 923	DEMAG 206 056 44	26	2	BSK		2	0,004	B	5201	1	0,10	2	Minimum ordering quantity: 100 parts
4	Spring 3 kg. for 13/3 PKF4 DEMAG 563 79 344	278 07 928	DEMAG 206 056 44	29	1	DEMAG	563 79 344	24	0,03	D	6304	1	0,10	1	
5	Spherical roller bearing 22218 CK ISO 15	281 21 015	DEMAG 206 056 44	31	2	SKF	22218 CK	3200	4,5	B	8444	6	0,10	2	
6	Grease nipple R 1/4" model H1, form A, DIN 71412	353 02 027	DEMAG 206 056 44	39	1	TECALAMIT	RH1A	12	0,03	F	8201	1	0,10	1	Minimum ordering quantity: 50 parts
7	Hexagon head screw plug M22 x 1,5 - DIN 910-5.6	352 03 520	DEMAG 206 056 44	40	1	BSK	-	4	0,004	B	5303	1	0,10	1	
8	Fitting key B 5x5x11,5 DIN 6885 - C 45 K	262 09 421	DEMAG 206 056 44	41	1	BSK	-	3	0,003	B	5201	1	0,25	3	
9	Male union fitting DS-16 DIN 2363-St-GT	254 08 203	DEMAG 206 056 44	48	3	ERMETO	GE 16 SR	29	0,019	B	5206	4	0,10	3	
10	Hexagon head screw M 12 x 35 DIN 601-4.6	263 09 708	DEMAG 206 056 44	2	4	BSK	-	27	0,004	B	5201	1	0,10	4	Minimum ordering quantity: 100 parts

DGS SYSTEM

INST. TOT. : TOTAL INSTALLED
MANUF : MANUFACTURER
U.P. : UNIT PRICES
DEL. IN M. : DELAY IN MONTHS

MONTH. ESTIM. CONS. : MONTHLY ESTIMATED CONSUMPTION
PROP. Q. : PROPOSED QUANTITY

APPENDIX 23

ISSUING SHEET

N°

DRAFTER :	①
PHONE NO. :	②
SECTION	③
CHECK HEAD	④
DATE OF ISSUE	⑤
DES. DELIVERY DATE	⑥
DES. DELIVERY LOC.	⑦
	⑧
	⑨

REQUESTED QUANTITY ⑩	COMPLETE DESIGNATION ⑪	MU ⑫	CODE REQUESTE ITEM ⑬	STOR. POS. ⑭	CODE ISSUED ITEM ⑮	QUANTITY ISSUED ⑯	MU ⑰	STOCK BALANCE ⑱	MVT. No. ⑲	CC ⑳	UP ㉑	TP ㉒

TOTAL ㉚

No. WORK-FILE OF JR ㉔	REAL DELIVERY DATE ㉕	RECEIVED BY ㉖	ISSUED BY ㉗	CHECK STOCK SUPERVISOR ㉘	CHECK SPMS ㉙	REMARKS
㉓				DATE	DATE	

UNIT CODES
- 0 : PART, BOOK
- 1 : SET, PAIR
- 2 : CAN, BARREL, BOX, PACKET
- 3 : KILO
- 4 : LITRE
- 5 : METRE
- 6 : M2
- 7 : M3
- 8 : GR
- 9 : TON
- A : 100 P
- B : 1000 P
- C : 1000 KG
- D : 100 L
- E : 1000 L
- F : CM
- G : MM

- MU : MANAGEMENT UNIT
- DES. DELIV. LOC. : DESIRED DELIVERY LOCATION
- DES. DELIV. DATE : DESIRED DELIVERY DATE
- STOR. POS. : STORAGE POSITION
- SPMS : SPARE PARTS MANAGEMENT AND STORES
- CC : COST CENTRE
- UP : UTILITARIAN PRICE
- TP : TOTAL PRICE

DGS SYSTEM

DGS 30/90/053

APPENDIX 24

ENTERING SHEET

DATE | DRAFTER | No.

PHONE No.

DGS 30/90/051

REASON FOR ENTERING: PURCH. | RET. | MANUF. | REP.

SUPPLIER

PURCHASE ORDER — No. | DATE

DELIVERY BILL — No. | DATE

INVOICE — No. | DATE

Column headers:
ORD. QUANT. | REC. QUANT. | ITEM CODE | PU | COMPLETE DESIGNATION | ENTERING ITEM CODE | ENTERING QUANTITY | MU | STOR. POS. | STOCK BALANCE | MVT No. | C.C. | UTIL. PRICE | TOTAL PRICE

REMARKS

TOTAL

No. OF JO | CHECK QUALITY CONTROL | CHECK STORE-KEEPER | ENTERING DATE | CHECK STORE SUPERVISOR | CHECK SPMS

UNIT CODES
0 : PART, BOOK
1 : SET, PAIR
2 : CAN BARREL, BOX, PACKET
3 : KILO
4 : LITRE
5 : METRE
6 : M2
7 : M3
8 : GR

9 : TON
A : 100 P
B : 1000 P
C : 100 KG
D : 100 L
E : 1000 L
F : CM
G : MM

DGS SYSTEM

APPENDIX 25

DGS 30/90/056

PURCHASE REQUEST

REQUESTED BY	DIVISION	DATE OF ISSUE	FIRST ORDERING	REORDERING	No.
PHONE No.			EXT. MANUF.	EXT. REP.	

CHECK SUPERINTENDANT	C.C. DESTIN.	ALLOCATION MACHINE	BUDGET No.	PURCHASER - PHONE	REMARKS OF PURCHASE DEPARTMENT
DATE					

REQUESTED DELAY

POS.	ITEM CODE	QUANTITY	FULL DESIGNATION OF ITEM	MU	DEL	ORDER No.	UP	TP	POSSIBLE SUPPLIER

UNIT CODES

0 : PART, BOOK	9 : TON
1 : SET, PAIR	A : 100 P
2 : CAN, BARREL, BOX, PACKET	B : 1000 P
3 : KILO	C : 10000 KG
4 : LITRE	D : 100 L
5 : METRE	E : 1000 L
6 : M2	F : CM
7 : M3	G : MM
8 : GR	

CHECK SPMS	CHECK BUDGET. CONTR.	CHECK PURCHASE SUPERINTENDANT	CONTR.	REC.	PHONE
DATE	DATE	DATE		DATE	

DGS SYSTEM

APPENDIX 26

DESIGNATION CARD

DGS 30/90/042

DESIGNATION OF SUB-GROUP

CODE

REMARKS :

ITEM CODE	DESIGNATION	MU	No. PR/DATE	REMARKS

DGS SYSTEM

APPENDIX 27/1

STOCK CONTROL CARD

ITEM CODE

COMPLETE DESIGNATION

PU	SUV	TYPE	REP	CUSTOMS CODE	AVERAGE MONTHLY CONSUMPT.	DELIVERY DELAY	ISSUE RESTRICTION

SUPPLIER	ITEM REF./SUPPLIER	MINIM. PURCHASING QUANTITY

PR AND ORDERS							EXPECTED		
	DATE	QUANTITY	U	DELAYS	SUPPLIER	NUMBER	DATE	QUANT.	DELAYS
PR									
PO									
PR									
PO									
PR									
PO									
PR									
PO									
PR									
PO									
PR									
PO									
PR									
PO									
PR									
PO									
PR									
PO									

NORMAL STOCK
REORD. LEVEL
MINIM. STOCK
STOCK ZERO
PR IN PROGRESS
PO IN PROGRESS
DELAY EXCEEDED

REMARKS

PU : PURCHASE UNIT
SUV : STANDARD UNIT VALUE
UP : UTILITARIAN PRICE
REP : REPARABILITY

MU : MANAGEMENT UNIT
MAN.MODE : MANAGEMENT MODE
CC : COST CENTER
PO : PURCHASE ORDER
PR : PURCHASE REQUEST

KALAMAZOO SYSTEM

APPENDIX 27/2

	STOR. POS.	MU	MAN. MODE	REORD. LEVEL	MINIM. STOCK	MAXIM. STOCK
ITEM CODE						

STOCK LEVEL

MVT No.	DATE	No. SHEET	SUPPLIER C.C. CLIENT	REQUIRED QUANTITY	QUANTITY IN	QUANTITY RETURN	QUANTITY OUT	STOCK BALANCE	REMARKS
		TRANSFER							
									TO BE CARRIED FORWARD

	BIN CARD					
STORAGE POSITION PRINCIPAL						
SECONDARY						
DESIGNATION						
ISSUE RESTRICTION						
MU	CODE					

MVT No.	DATE	SHEET No.	SUPPLIER C.C. CLIENT	MOVEMENT			STOCK BALANCE
				IN	RE-TURN	OUT	

DGS SYSTEM   DGS 30/90/050

MU   :   MANAGEMENT UNIT
MVT N° :   MOVEMENT NUMBER
CC   :   COST CENTER

APPENDIX 29

| ITEM CODE | INVENTORY | | | MVT No. | STOR. POS. | ACTUAL PHYSICAL STOCK | VARIANCE | UP | VALUE OF VARIANCE | REMARKS |
	DATE	MU	STOCK BALANCE				MAN		ACCOUNT	DATE

INVENTORY CHECK CARD N°

NAME OF CONTROLLER

CHECK CONTROLLER   CHECK SPMS   REMARKS

DGS 30/90/046

UNIT CODES :

0: PIECE, BOOK	6: M2	C: 100 KG
1: SET, PAIR	7: M3	D: 100 L
2: CAN, BARREL, BOX, PACKET	8: GR	E: 1000 L
3: KILO	9: TON	F: CM
4: LITRE	A: 100 P	G: MM
5: METRE	B: 1000 P	

DGS SYSTEM

MU   : MANAGEMENT UNIT
MVT N°   : MOVEMENT NUMBER
STOR. POS. : STORAGE POSITION
UP   : UTILITARIAN PRICE
MAN   : SPARE PARTS MANAGEMENT SECTION

APPENDIX 30

STORE CATALOGUE

DGS 30/90/044

ITEM CODE	DESIGNATION OF ITEM	STOR. POS.	SUPPLIER	UP	MU	REMARKS

DATE

PAGE

DGS SYSTEM

APPENDIX 31

SIMPLIFIED DATA PROCESSING CIRCUIT FOR JOB EXECUTION

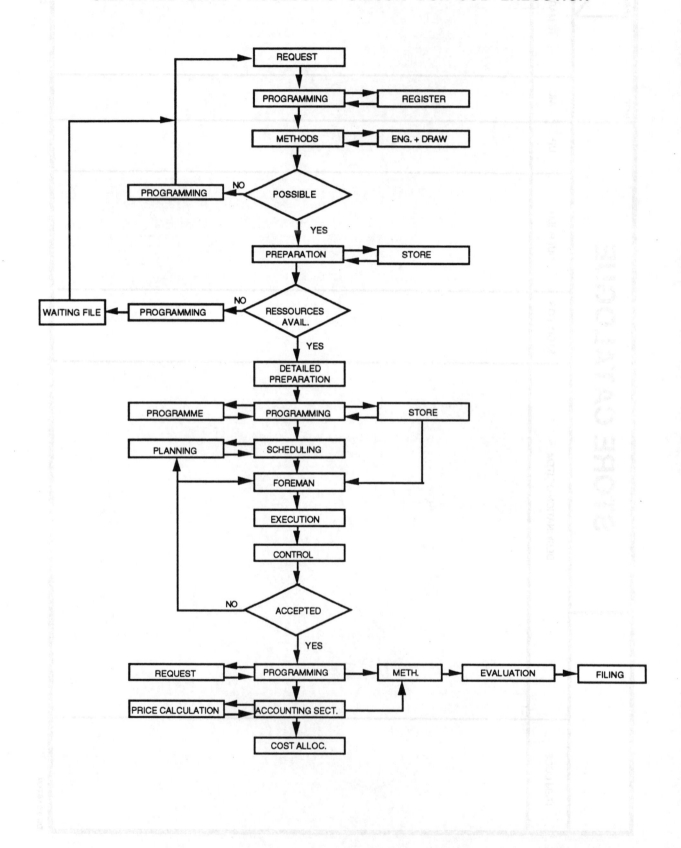

APPENDIX 32

WORK PROGRAMME

PAGE 1
NUMBER OF PAGES 2

YEAR : 1988

TIME IN WEEKS

MACHINE	N° JO	1	2	3	4	5	6	7	8	9	10	11	12	13	14	15	16	17	18	19	20	21	22	23	24	25	26	27	28	29	30	31	32	33	34	35	36	37	38	39	40	41	42	43	44	45	46	47	48	49	50	51	52
Steam generator Wanson N° 1	MEC	M				M					M				M				M				M					A	A	A	A				M				M				M				M				M		
	ELEC	M				M					M				M				M				M					A	A	A	A				M				M				M				M				M		
	INSTR	M				M					M				M				M				M					A	A	A	A				M				M				M				M				M		
	LUB										4M																				4M																4M						
	0321					X																																															
	0386		X																																																		
	0422	X																																																			
	0427									X	X																																										
	Overhaul																												X	X	X																						
Steam generator Wanson N° 2	MEC						M				M				M				M				M					A	A	A	A					M				M				M				M				M	
	ELEC						M				M				M				M				M					A	A	A	A					M				M				M				M				M	
	INSTR						M				M				M				M				M					A	A	A	A					M				M				M				M				M	
	LUB										4M																				4M																	4M					
	0337				X																																																
	Overhaul																												X	X	X																						

DGS SYSTEM

M : monthly
4M : 4-monthly
A : annually
X : during the indicated week

APPENDIX 33

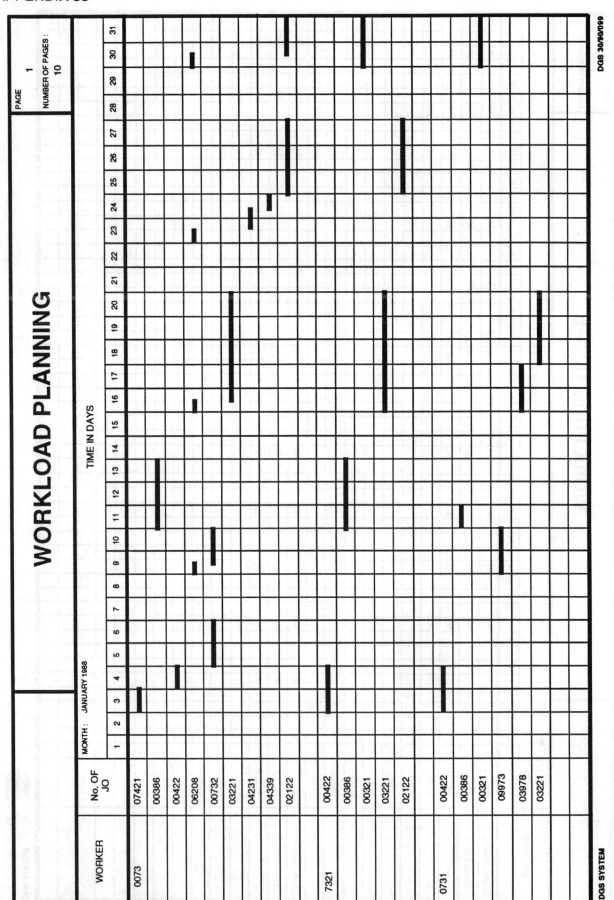

APPENDIX 34

SIMPLIFIED DATA PROCESSING CIRCUIT FOR SPARE PARTS

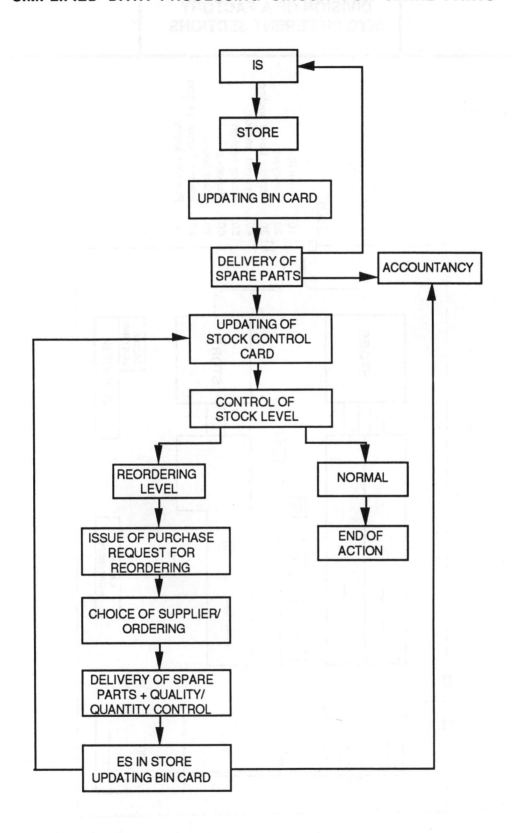

APPENDIX 35/1

	DIVISION OF A FACTORY INTO DIFFERENT SECTIONS	

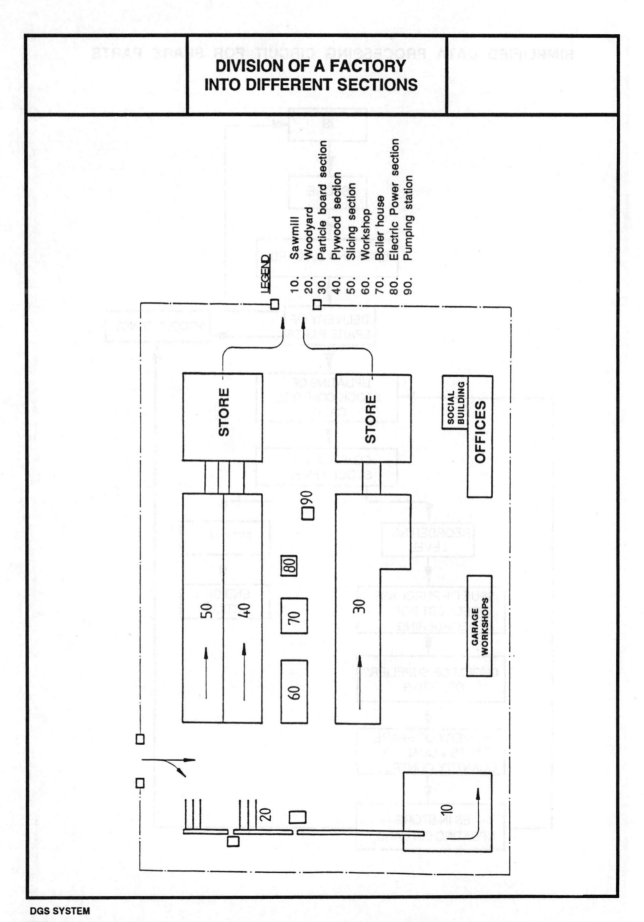

LEGEND

10. Sawmill
20. Woodyard
30. Particle board section
40. Plywood section
50. Slicing section
60. Workshop
70. Boiler house
80. Electric Power section
90. Pumping station

STORE

STORE

SOCIAL BUILDING

OFFICES

GARAGE WORKSHOPS

50

40

30

70

60

10

20

80

90

DGS SYSTEM

APPENDIX 35/2

| | DIVISION OF THE SECTION
OF A FACTORY INTO
SUB-SECTIONS | |

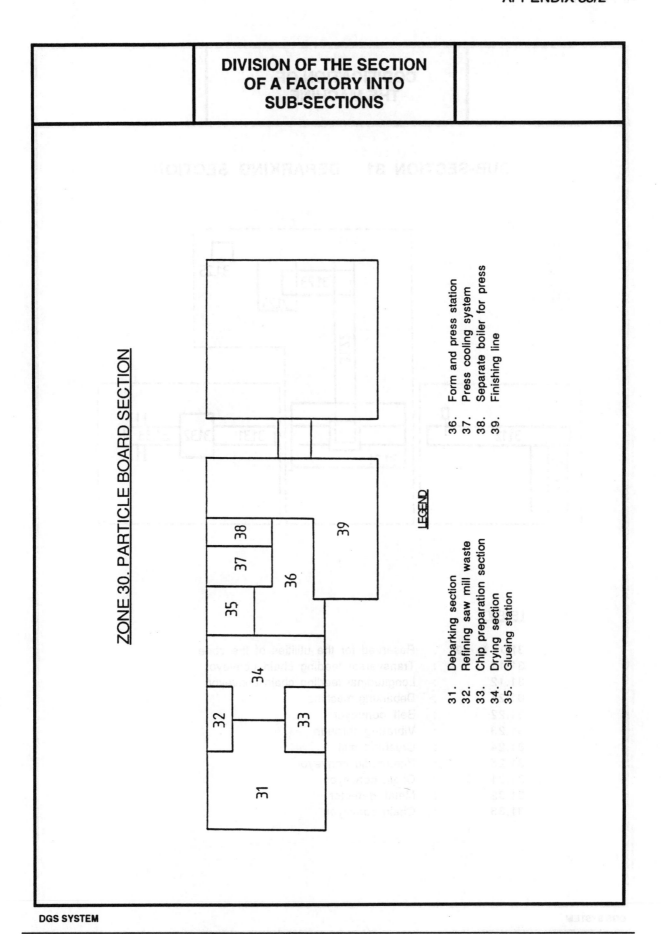

ZONE 30. PARTICLE BOARD SECTION

LEGEND

31. Debarking section
32. Refining saw mill waste
33. Chip preparation section
34. Drying section
35. Glueing station
36. Form and press station
37. Press cooling system
38. Separate boiler for press
39. Finishing line

APPENDIX 36

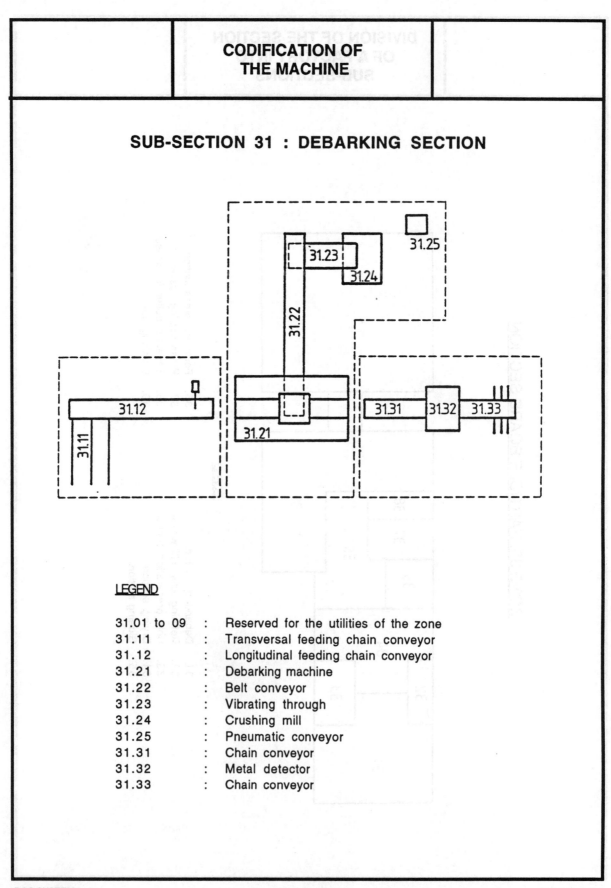

| | CODIFICATION OF THE MACHINE | |

SUB-SECTION 31 : DEBARKING SECTION

LEGEND

31.01 to 09	:	Reserved for the utilities of the zone
31.11	:	Transversal feeding chain conveyor
31.12	:	Longitudinal feeding chain conveyor
31.21	:	Debarking machine
31.22	:	Belt conveyor
31.23	:	Vibrating through
31.24	:	Crushing mill
31.25	:	Pneumatic conveyor
31.31	:	Chain conveyor
31.32	:	Metal detector
31.33	:	Chain conveyor

	DIVISION OF THE MACHINE INTO SUB-ASSEMBLIES - DRAWING CODIFICATIONS	

DIVISION OF DEBARKING MACHINE No. 31.21

31.21.00   :   Debarking machine
31.21.10   :   Feeding conveyor of debarking machine
31.21.11   :   Frame of feeding conveyor
31.21.12   :   Drive of feeding conveyor
31.21.13   :   Lifting cylinder of feeding conveyor
    .
    .
    .
31.21.20   :   Debarking ring
    .
    .
    .
31.21.30   :   Evacuating conveyor

CODIFICATION OF THE DRAWINGS

No. (2) 31.21.11 M 001/A   :   Debarking machine : frame of feeding conveyor

No. (3) 31.21.11 M 002/C   :   Debarking machine : detail of rear bearing block

The figures between brackets refer to the size of the drawing (according to DIN standards).

M refers to a mechanical drawing (E = electric, R = regulation and control, H = hydraulic, P = pneumatic).

A and C at the end of the drawing No. refer to the updating index.

APPENDIX 38

INVENTORY OF MACHINES

		ZONE NO./DEPARTMENT	PAGE
		320.00	1/1

DESCRIPTION OF THE ZONE/DEPARTMENT

PREPARATION RAW MATERIALS

DRAWING NO.
(1) 320.00.00.M 001

ITEM	MACHINE No.	DESIGNATION	MANUFACTURER	TYPE/ REFERENCE	MAIN CHARACTERISTICS	No. MACHINE FILE	OBSERVATIONS
1.	350.10.00	Blower (inlet)	ALVI	DB31-3DL-M1	Flow 4.000 m3/h Pressure 800 Pa Rpm 2650 Orientation 1	350.11	
2.	350.10.05	Electric motor for blower	ASEA	MT 100LA	Power 2,2 Kw Rpm 1.500 Form B3 Voltage 220/380 V	A10.012	
3.	350.20.00	Filter	A.A.F.	DRI-PACK-F95 N° 4-1-08-925		A01.002	Dimensions, see drawing (0) 350.20.00M002/C
4.	350.11.02	Pressure controller	HONEYWELL	C6045D-1043	Diff. pressure 0,2-3 mbar Max. pressure 100 mbar Contact 10 A (220 V)	H03.003	
5.	350.30.00	Register	FLAKT	SRDB.0504		F02.005	
6.	350.30.01	Servomotor	HONEYWELL	MG44G1028	Angle 160° Power 5 VA Voltage 24 V= Rpm 1.600	H03.025	Dimensions, see drawing (1) 350.30.00M001/D
7.	350.40.00	Blower	ALVI	DB31-3DL-M1	Flow 3.500 m3/h Pressure 600 Pa Rpm 2.300 Orientation 7	350.11	

DGS SYSTEM

CODIFICATION OF SPARE PARTS

1. INTRODUCTION

Designating a spare part means defining its physical, dimensional, electrical or other characteristics. Parts codification can only be efficient if its designation has been correctly done.

An example is given below of a hexagon socket head cap screw M20 x 100. This designation is incomplete : the exact form of the head is missing (thick, flat), and also the physical characteristics (i.e. tensile strength) and thread (fine, normal). Obviously a description which would include all that information would be too long and unusable. In the case of standardized parts all information can be expressed by referring to a national or international standard which gives the correct identification of the part.

In the example, the head of the screw is a thick head, of normal metric thread, completely threaded, with a minimum breaking strength of 80 Kgf/mm2 and elasticity of elongation limit of 64 Kgf/mm2, hardened and tempered. Complete information is included in the following standardized designation :

hexagon socket head cap screw M20 x 100 DIN 912-8.8

2. ATTRIBUTION OF A CODE NUMBER

This example belongs for instance to class 1 : assembling elements and mechanical transmission parts.

To define the family and the subfamily, the codification grid of class 1 should be analysed (appendix 39/3). The number of the family is obtained by reading the grid horizontally (family : assembling elements - number 0).

The subfamily is obtained by reading the grid vertically (bolts and screws - number 2).

This gives the first 3 numbers of the code : 102.

APPENDIX 39/2

The same process is applied for the group and subgroup with the grid of appendix 39/4. The number of the group is 2 (hexagon socket head cap screw), that of the subgroup (according to DIN 912) is 1.

This gives the first numbers of the code 102.21.

The last 3 numbers define the dimensions. In the case of screws it is possible to attribute a pre-coded number to the dimensions defined in the standard DIN 912 (appendix 39/5). For instance a screw M20 x 100 has 164 as its 3 last numbers. This method can be used for all standardized items of which a certain variety is stored.

The complete designation with code number for the example is :

102 21 164 Hexagon socket head cap screw M20 x 100 DIN 912-8.8.

1 STANDARD PARTS : FASTENERS AND MECHANIC TRANSMISSIONS

FAMILY \ SUB-FAMILY	0	1	2	3	4	5	6	7	8	9
0 FASTENERS			SCREWS, BOLTS AND NUTS	SCREWS, BOLTS AND NUTS ACCESSORIES		NAILS AND BRADS	SUPPORTS AND HOLDERS			
1										
2 PARTS FOR TRANSMISSION	CHAINS AND CHAIN-WHEELS	BELTS AND PULLEYS	PARTS OF CONVEYOR BELTS	VARIOUS PULLEYS	GEAR-WHEELS AND PINIONS	COUPLINGS	ARTICULA-TIONS			
3 PARTS FOR TRANSMISSION	TIN TAPPER KEYS	CLUTCHES	EXTREMITY PARTS							
4 AUXILIARY PARTS FOR TRANSMISSION	BEARINGS	BEARING-BLOCKS	PLAIN BEARINGS	ROLLERS AND WHEELS		LUBRICATION DEVICES				
5										
6 OPERATION DEVICES		BRAKES	SPRINGS	SHOCK ABSORBERS		MECHANICAL OPERATION ELEMENTS				
7										
8 MOTOR AND GEAR BOXES	ROTATING ENGINES	JACKS	GEAR-BOXES VARIATORS							
9										

APPENDIX 39/4

102 — BOLTS, SCREWS AND STUDS

GROUP	SUB GROUP 0	1	2	3	4	5	6	7	8	9
0										
1 HEXAGON AND BOLTS		Hexagon Head Bolts DIN 601	Hex. fitting bolts with long threaded portion DIN 609	Hex. bolts finish M and MG metric coarse Thread 5.6 DIN 931	Hex. bolts finish M and MG metric coarse Thread 8.8 DIN 931	Hex. screws finish M and MG 5.6 DIN 933	Hex. screws finish M and MG 8.8 DIN 933	Hex. set screws with full dog point DIN 561	Hexagon screws DIN 558	Hexagon head bolts Withworth series
2 HEXAGON SOCKET HEAD CAP SCREWS		Hexagon socket head cap screws DIN 912-8.8	Hexagon socket head cap screws DIN 6912		Hexagon Head pipe plugs DIN 910	Hexagon socket pipe plugs DIN 906				
3 SLOTTED CHEESE HEAD SCREWS COUNTERSUNK HEAD SCREWS		Slotted cheese head screw DIN 84		Slotted countersunk Head screws DIN 963		Hexagon socket counter-sunk head screw DIN 7991				Slotted pan and countersunk head screws Withworth series
4 WOOD SCREWS		Hexagon wood screws DIN 571		Slotted countersunk Head wood screws DIN 97		Slotted round head wood screws DIN 96				
5										
6 THREADED RODS, STUDS HEADLES SCREWS		Slotted headless screws DIN 525	Hexagon socket set screws DIN 914		Studs DIN 438	Threaded rods DIN 975				Studs, rods and set screws Withworth series
7 VARIOUS SCREWS		Studs for welding DIN 525	Lifting eye bolts DIN 580		Thread forming screws DIN 7513	Slotted pan head tapping screws DIN 7971			Screws various forms metric series	Screws various forms Withworth series
8 NUTS		Hexagon nuts DIN 555	Hexagon nuts DIN 934	Hexagon thin nuts DIN 439			Self-locking hexagon nuts DIN 980	Hexagon domed cap nuts DIN 1587		Nuts Withworth
9 NUTS		Wing nuts DIN 315				Castle nuts DIN 935		Nuts various forms		Nuts Withworth

PRECODIFCATION OF A HEXAGON SOCKET HEAD CAP SCREW
M20 X 100 ACCORDING TO DIN 912
IN STEEL OF 80 KGf/mm2

102 21 001	Hexagon socket head cap screw M 4 x 6	DIN 912-8.8
102 21 002	Hexagon socket head cap screw M 4 x 8	DIN 912-8.8
102 21 003	Hexagon socket head cap screw M 4 x 10	DIN 912-8.8
102 21 004	Hexagon socket head cap screw M 4 x 12	DIN 912-8.8
"		
"		
"		
102 21 097	Hexagon socket head cap screw M 12 x 140	DIN 912-8.8
102 21 098	Hexagon socket head cap screw M 14 x 30	DIN 912-8.8
102 21 099	Hexagon socket head cap screw M 14 x 35	DIN 912-8.8
102 21 100	Hexagon socket head cap screw M 14 x 40	DIN 912-8.8
"		
"		
"		
102 21 151	Hexagon socket head cap screw M 18 x 180	DIN 912-8.8
102 21 152	Hexagon socket head cap screw M 18 x 190	DIN 912-8.8
102 21 153	Hexagon socket head cap screw M 18 x 200	DIN 912-8.8
102 21 154	Hexagon socket head cap screw M 20 x 40	DIN 912-8.8
102 21 155	Hexagon socket head cap screw M 20 x 45	DIN 912-8.8
102 21 156	Hexagon socket head cap screw M 20 x 50	DIN 912-8.8
102 21 157	Hexagon socket head cap screw M 20 x 55	DIN 912-8.8
102 21 158	Hexagon socket head cap screw M 20 x 60	DIN 912-8.8
102 21 159	Hexagon socket head cap screw M 20 x 65	DIN 912-8.8
102 21 160	Hexagon socket head cap screw M 20 x 70	DIN 912-8.8
102 21 161	Hexagon socket head cap screw M 20 x 75	DIN 912-8.8
102 21 162	Hexagon socket head cap screw M 20 x 80	DIN 012-8.8
102 21 163	Hexagon socket head cap screw M 20 x 90	DIN 912-8.8
102 21 164	Hexagon socket head cap screw M 20 x 100	DIN 912-8.8
102 21 165	Hexagon socket head cap screw M 20 x 110	DIN 912-8.8

APPENDIX 40/1

<table>
<tr>
<td colspan="2" rowspan="2"></td>
<td colspan="3" style="text-align:center">EXAMPLE</td>
<td>1/3</td>
</tr>
</table>

		EXAMPLE	1/3

FUNCTION AND JOB DESCRIPTION SHEET

DESIGNATION OF POST	NUMBER	MALE/ FEM.	AGE	PROFESSIONAL QUALIFICATION
FITTER (Mechanical workshop)	3	M	21	Qualified worker

GENERAL DEFINITION OF FUNCTION	- adjustments and/or repair of spare parts and accessoires - manufacturing of new parts

SITUATION IN ORGANIZATION CHART

POSITION OF POST	DEPARTEMENT	SECTION	CREW	
	Maintenance	Mechanical Workshop	Equipe de jour	WORKTIME
HIERARCHICAL DIRECT SUPERIOR	DESIGNATION	PROF. QUAL.	SUPERIOR	
	Foreman Workshop	Foreman level	Day crew	

SYSTEMATIC FUNCTIONAL RELATIONS

IN PRODUCTION UNIT	With : - Foreman mechanical workshop - Colleagues
WITH HEADQUARTER	None
OUTSIDE COMPANY	None

DIMENSIONS OF POST

IN CHARGE OF FOLLOWING STAFF			GLOBAL BUDGET
N°	FUNCTION	PROF. QUAL.	OPERATION
			OTHER
			RESPONS.-VALUES-MATERIAL-TOOLS-PRODUCTS
			Tools

DGS SYSTEM

EXAMPLE

2/3

REQUIRED COMPETENCES

EDUCATION				TECHNICAL EDUCATION	MINIMUM EXPERIENCE
MINIMUM	CAP.	**ENGLISH**		General mechanics	Must have done mechanical work before
		Read	X		
		Write	X		
		Understand	X		
		Calculate	X		
MAXIMUM					**FELLOWSHIP TO FORESEE**
					Duration
					Period

ACTIVITIES AND RESPONSABILITIES

	PRINCIPAL	%	OCCASIONALS
DESIGN STUDIES			- Assist intervention crews during trouble shooting
	TOTAL	0	
EXECUTION OF WORK	- Clean and prepare parts before welding - Adjust welded parts - Do various adjustments acc. to instructions of foreman - Repair parts or accessoires acc. to instructions of foreman - Order and cleanliness on workpost		
			MISCELLANEOUS
	TOTAL	95	
CONTROL MATERIAL PERSONNEL	- State of tools		
	TOTAL	5	

DGS SYSTEM

APPENDIX 40/3

		EXAMPLE	
			3/3
		CONDITIONS OF WORK	

PHYSICAL CONDITIONS	**WORKING HOURS**	Day crew
	EFFORT	Can be important
	POSITION AT WORK	Straight
	SIZE	Average
	MANUAL DEXTERITY	Good
	TENSION / ATTENTION / MONOTONIY	Good
	MOVEMENT	Mechanical Workshop Occasionally in the plant
	VISION	Very good
AMBIENT CONDITIONS	**NOICES**	Variable
	RESPIRATION / SKIN	None
	LIGHT	600 Lux
	FILTHINESS	Oil, grease and solvents
	ODOURS	Negligeable
	CLIMATIC CONDITIONS	Variable
ACCID. RISKS	**FOR HIMSELF**	Imprudence in use of certain tools Neglection of safety instructions
	FOR OTHERS	Idem

OBSERVATIONS

Principal activity area : mechanical workshop

DGS SYSTEM

APPENDIX 41

RESULTS OF STUDY OF PERFORMANCE RATIOS

	RATIOS	RESULTS OF SURVEYS IN EUROPE AND ANALYSIS OF WORLD LITTERATURE			ALGERIA		
		MEC	CEM	PETROCHEM	MEC	CEM	PETROCHEM
1.	Direct cost of maintenance / Added value of production	10,44	12,9	11,87	15-25	20-30	10-15
2.	Direct maintenance cost / Replacement value of assets	12,7	16,4	7,98	10-15	10-15	5-12
3.	Cost of maintenance personnel / Direct cost of maintenance	58,35	41,75	52,90	35-45	35-45	45-50
4.	Cost of spare parts and current maintenance items / Direct maintenance cost	22,79	44,64	17,02	40-50	45-60	25-35
5.	Average stock value / Replacement value of production equipment	13,06	9,8	3,49	5-10	7-12	8-12
6.	Cumulated value of issued spares over 12 months / Average stock value over 12 months	120,8	71,15	n.a.	50-60	40-50	50-60
7.	Maintenance workforce / Total plant workforce	5,6	28,4	65,70	10-15	15-20	30-40
8.	Downtime due to breakdown / Hours theoretically available for prouction on yearly basis	10,42	5,94	n.a.	10-15	8-12	3-10
9.	Number of stock items satisfied on IS / Total number of requested items on IS	95,83	98,07	100	75-85	75-85	75-85
10	Number of stock-outs / Total items in stock	3	6,99	0	2-5	5-10	5-10

MEC : mechanical construction
CEM : cement
PETROCHEM : petrochemicals
n.a. : data non available

1/ Guide for the application of management ratios for maintenance in industry - by DGS INTERNATIONAL for AODI and INMA/Algeria (Institut National d'Etudes et Recherches en Maintenance)

APPENDIX 42/1

TECHNICAL DOCUMENTATION

CONTENT OF MACHINE FILE

1. Technical information

   1.1. *Machine record card*

   Each machine has its own card comprising the principal technical specifications, a photo or an outline (see example in appendix 11). In case of important sub-assemblies or devices, a separate card is made (e.g. electric motor card in appendix 12).

   1.2. *Layout drawings*

   - The general layout and, if necessary, the layout for the subassemblies indicating any cumbersome obstructions, the free areas for dismantling and handling, connection points for earthing circuits of the machines and the utilities with their related connection data (electricity, compressed air, cooling circuit etc.);

   - The layout also indicates the static weight and the centre of gravity of the machines.

   1.3. *Description of functioning*

   A description is given of the different modes of operation, the aim of the components and accessories for manoeuvring and the applied principles of operation.

2. Installation and start-up

   2.1. *Foundations and installation*

   - The data relative to the foundations, such as dynamic and static loads, and the principle drawings of foundations;
   - Installation drawings and physical characteristics of circuits of fluids, the electrical network and other circuits which are necessary for functioning.

2.2. Transport and handling

This heading comprises all the information relative to transport and handling of the machine (handling diagrams, protection, choice of slings, weight of the heaviest parts and sizes of the most cumbersome parts etc.).

The description also mentions the safety measures (mechanical and electrical, precautions regarding the products used etc.) which must be taken when dismantling and moving the machine.

2.3. Instructions for assembling

This chapter describes the order in which the different subassemblies of the machine or installation must be mounted, if necessary with the help of sketches, as well as data on tuning and adjustments.

If need be, the manufacturing drawings for the framework, metallic constructions or any other device to be supplied locally can be added.

2.4. Commissioning

- A list of the various checks to be carried out and actions to be undertaken before initial start-up (filling-up of oil, greasing, cleaning, removal of the safety packaging used during transport etc.);
- Safety measures to be taken before start-up (checking the correct sense of rotation of the motors, testing the safety elements and interlocking);
- An elementary description of the procedure for a test run, together with a sketch of the synoptic display.

3. Instructions for operation

3.1. Safety instructions

- Precautions during normal operation;
- Actions in case of breakdowns or power cuts and shortage of fluids or raw materials;
- Safety measures during maintenance and repairs;

APPENDIX 42/3

- Precautions and the special equipment and clothing needed during the handling of materials for the production and maintenance of the installations;
- A detailed list of raw materials and cleaning products together with their chemical features.

3.2. Operation

- A check list of controls must be implemented by the operators at each start-up and while the machine or installation is in service (cleaning of air filters, checking of oil levels, checking of pressure gauges and thermometers);
- Start-up procedure for the machine or installation;
- Procedures for the different operational modes (manual, automatic etc.);
- Means of intervention and safety systems which have been foreseen in case of accidents or danger;
- Procedure for the shut-down of the machine or installation.

3.3. Instructions for tuning

With the help of sketches, figures or photos, detailed descriptions of tuning and adjusting operations are given, which must be carried out during the dismantling of a machine for maintenance. A list of instruments, measuring devices, tools and other accessories is also added.

3.4. Troubleshooting

This procedure is presented in three columns:"symptoms"; "possible causes"; and "remedies".

4. Service instructions

4.1. Maintenance

- Maintenance cards (see example in appendix 18) containing the sub-assemblies of the machine or installation which have to be checked or maintained regularly with the indications of work to be done and the periodicity;
- The list of maintenance products with their chemical characteristics, so that they can be purchased;
- Check cards with tolerances for assembling and tuning;

- Check-lists for control and verification after assembling;
- Test programmes;
- Fault diagnosis instructions.

4.2. Lubrication

The lubrification files (see example in appendix 19) indicate the points on the machine, subassemblies or installation which must be lubricated or where lubrification must be checked. They also state the periodicity with which the work must be carried out and the type and quantity of lubricant to be used.

At the back of the files there is a drawing showing the points for lubrication or checking.

5. Drawings and nomenclature

5.1. Mechanical

- Assembly drawings of machines and installations;
- Drawings of subassemblies (mechanical assemblies, transmissions, special hydraulic components etc.) for gear boxes, with a diagram of the kinematic chain and all technical data;
- The workshop drawings with the data the customer needs to manufacture the parts (dimensions, tolerances, finishing, quality of material);
- A maximum of section drawings and/or exploded views of the machine and its components;
- The complete nomenclatures of parts on different drawings.

5.2. Electrical and automation

5.2.1. Electrotechnical diagrams

- Electrotechnical drawings (power, control, signalization, diagrams, time and cycles);
- Connection drawings;
- List of electrical components.

5.2.2. Automation file (documented programs, logic schemes, PLC, Grafcets, operation manual, saving programs on separate disks)

APPENDIX 42/5

5.3. Instrumentation

- Drawings of circuits of various fluids with all devices for measuring, controlling and regulation;
- Nomenclature of all equipment.

5.4. Hydraulic

- Hydraulic schemes (power, diagram of phases);
- Nomenclature of components.

5.5. Pneumatic

- Pneumatic diagrams (conditioning, power, logic, control and diagram of phases);
- Nomenclature of components.

5.6. Other fluids

- Fluids schemes;
- Nomenclature of components and equipment.

6. Recommended spare parts

The list of recommended spare parts consists of safety parts (important parts that could be accidentally damaged or broken, but which do not normally show any significant signs of wear) and replacement parts (consumables) which have to be kept in stock to replace those subject to wear and tear. All the data for an exact identification of all these parts should be presented on a special form (appendix 22).

7. Prospectuses and catalogues

This heading covers the complete technical documentation for each component or accessory (motors, instruments, regulators, registers, special relays, level detectors, pumps, pneumatic and hydraulic components, electrical and electronic apparatus, gear boxes, variators, transmissions, couplings, brakes, exchangers, transport and handling chains etc.).

8. Control certificates and commissioning reports

   -   Commissioning reports for test run;
   -   A control certificate for various apparatus or subassemblies subject to official controls, such as pressure vessels, crane cables etc.

APPENDIX 43/1

TABULAR SUMMARY OF RESULTS OF A MAINTENANCE AUDIT

TOPICS SUBJECT OF SURVEY	RESULT	TOPICS SUBJECT OF SURVEY	RESULT

GENERAL DATA
 	
- manufactured products
- year of start up
- type of construction contract
- management
- total workforce of the plant
- process profile
- location (+ nearest industrial centre)
 	
PRODUCTION EQUIPMENT
 	
- *Mechanical equipment*
  - variety of suppliers
  - standardization of equipment
  - complexity
  - maintainability
  - state of machinery of main production equipment
  - state of utilities
 	
- *Electrical equipment*
  - variety of suppliers
  - standardization of equipment
  - complexity
  - maintainability
  - state of machinery and equipment
		- *Instrumentation equipment*
		  - variety of suppliers
		  - standardization of equipment
		  - complexity
		  - maintainability
		  - state of equipment
		
		ORGANIZATION AND SERVICES OF THE MAINTENANCE DEPARTMENT
		
		- Organization chart of the plant
		- Organization chart of the maintenance department
		
		- *Central Maintenance Planning Office*
		  - organization chart
		  - existence of sections :
		    methods
		    engineering/drawing office
		    inspection
		    programming
		    job-preparation
		    scheduling
		    central documentation
		    photocopying facilities
		  - location of the various sections
		  - manning tables	

APPENDIX 43/2

RESULT	TOPICS SUBJECT OF SURVEY	RESULT	TOPICS SUBJECT OF SURVEY

	- lubricating
	  - scheduling
	  - execution
	  - efficiency
	  - standardization of lubricants
	
	- preventive maintenance
	  - scheduling
	  - execution
	  - efficiency
	
	- maintenance management system
	  - manual/computerized
	  - if computerized, which software
	  - which ratios are gathered
	  - management monitoring chart
	
	- *Mechanical Service (MS)*
	
	- Organization chart
	
	- Planning section
	
	- Interventions :
	  - organization
	  - quality of work
	  - specialized teams
	  - tools
			- efficiency of :
			  methods
			  engineering
			  programming/scheduling
			
			- technical documentation
			- drawings, manuals, instructions
			- lubrication programmes, preventive programmes
			- uniform codification of drawings
			- itemisation of machines
			- % completed (estimation)
			- updating
			- efficiency
			
			- forms/design/efficiency
			- work execution (JR, JO, work specification sheet)
			- machine-file
			- machine history record
			- machine record card
			- preventive maintenance card
			- permit to work
			
			- information flows

APPENDIX 43/3

TOPICS SUBJECT OF SURVEY	RESULT	TOPICS SUBJECT OF SURVEY	RESULT
- mechanical workshop (MWS) - hierarchical dependence - workshop centralized or not - machine-tools section - sheet metal working section - repair section - other sections - organization/information flows - job preparation/efficiency - capacity - location - equipment - orderliness and cleanliness - quality of work - cleaning and maintenance of machine-tools - manning tables - *Electrical Service (ES)* - Organization chart - Planning section - Interventions - organization - quality of work - specialized teams - tools		- Electrical workshop (EWS) - hierarchical dependence - workshop centralized or not - rewinding section - organization/information flow - job preparation/efficiency - capacity - location - design - equipment - orderliness and cleanliness - quality of work - Manning tables - *Instrumentation Service (INS)* - Organization chart - Planning section - Interventions : - organization - quality of work - specialized teams - equipments/tools - manning tables - workshop for instrumentation (LAB)	

APPENDIX 43/4

TOPICS SUBJECT OF SURVEY	RESULT	TOPICS SUBJECT OF SURVEY	RESULT

- *Spare parts management and stores Service (SPMS)*
 	
- hierarchical dependence
- organization chart
- study and selection of spare parts
- codification and designation :
  - codification grid
  - uniform codification
  - % of codified stock (estimation)
  - efficiency
 	
- stock management :
  - location
  - data collection + flow
  - efficiency
 	
- stores
  - central stores
  - storage capacity
  - store catalogue
  - orderliness and cleanliness
  - conservation of parts
  - storage facilities/systems
  - information flow
  - number of stock items (estimation)
  - stock value
  - standardization of parts
		- sufficient quantity of stocks (estimation)
		  - specific parts
		  - standard parts
		  - consumables
		
		- % of stock-outs (estimation)
		- number of movements per month
		- satisfaction of requested items
		- reordering
		  - in-plant delays
		  - organization
		  - efficiency
		- % of imported parts
		- manning table
		
		- *General Maintenance Service*
		
		- Organization chart
		- Production and distribution of energy and fluids
		- Transport and handling
		- Maintenance of rolling Stock (MRS)
		  - hierarchical dependence
		  - garage/equipment
		  - tools
		  - quality of work
		  - manning tables
		  - orderliness and cleanliness
		  - technical documentation
		  - data collection
		  - spare-parts	

APPENDIX 43/5

TOPICS SUBJECT OF SURVEY	RESULT	TOPICS SUBJECT OF SURVEY	RESULT

- Building Maintenance (BM)
  - various trades
  - manning tables
  - quality of work
 	
COMPLEXITY OF MAINTENANCE WORK
 	
- % of routine work (estimation)
- % of specialized work (estimation)
- % of very specialized work (estimation)
 	
MAINTENANCE PERSONNEL
 	
- Manning tables for whole maintenance department
- Detailed account of qualifications
- Total for each qualification group :
  - cadres
  - foremen level
  - qualified workers
  - unqualified workers
- Vocational training
  - manning tables training section
  - training equipment, buildings, etc.
  - training on-the-job
  - training outside the plant
  - forecast
  - in progress
- complementary training
		- results of training actions
		  - discipline
		  - turn-over of personnel
		  - respect of internal procedures and rules
		
		MAINTENANCE COST AND BUDGET
		
		Adequacy of cost-accounting system
		
		- systematic collection of maintenance costs
		- systematic processing of maintenance costs
		
		Assessment of maintenance investments
		
		Management ratios in relation to cost	

TOPICS SUBJECT OF SURVEY	RESULT	TOPICS SUBJECT OF SURVEY	RESULT

MAINTENANCE MANAGEMENT
 	
Corporate Maintenance Management
Master Plan - YES/NO
If yes, does it include/explain :
- HPD
  - general strategy
  - methods for implementation
  - problems
- acquisition/renewal of equipment
  - corporate policy
  - implementation
  - problems
- computer aided maintenance
  - corporate policy
  - links with other computerized systems
- subcontracting
  - corporate policy
  - which fields
  - how is it managed
- maintenance concept
  - definition
  - based on which principles
  - implementation
  - problems
- describe relations with or concerning
  - production
  - QC
  - safety department
  - protection of environment
		- Reliability-centered maintenance
		  - does the principle exist ?
		  - list all technical analysis
		    - FMECA
		    - system reliability
		    - FTA
		    - HAZOP
		    - ABC (Pareto)
		    - MTBF
		    - MTTR
		    - others
		  - condition monitoring techniques
		  - computer assistance for condition monitoring
		  - implementation
		  - results
		  - problems
		- Ratios and other management topics
		(complementary to questions asked under CMPO/Personnel and Cost Control)
		  - list other ratios (technical/ economical)
		  - use of steering chart in relation to strategical decisions
		  - give correct figures of last 6 months
		  - relation to CMMS	

APPENDIX 44/1

MAJOR NEEDED MAINTENANCE TRADES

	FIELD	QW	F/S/T	E
1	*Mechanic*			
	Head of section		X	X
	Fitting	X	X	
	Vehicle-mechanic	X	X	
	Diesel engine	X		
	Pumps, compressors	X		
	Pneumatics	X		
	Hydraulics	X		
	Job preparation	X		
2	*Metalworking*			
	Head of workshop		X	X
	Lathe operator	X	X	
	Universal miller	X	X	
	Various machine-tools operators	X	X	
	Metalsheet-working	X	X	
	Special welding	X		
	Forge	X		
	Mold-making	X		
	Wood modelling	X		
	Modelling (mechanic)	X		
	Universal hardener	X		
	Heat treatment	X		
	Job preparator machine tools		X	
	Job preparator metalsheet-working		X	
3	*Electricity*			
	Head of section/workshop		X	X
	Electricity HT	X		
	Electricity (installation)	X	X	
	Motor rewinding	X		
	Electro-mechanic	X	X	
	Vehicle electricity	X		
	Job preparation		X	

APPENDIX 44/2

FIELD	QW	F/S/T	E
4 *Instrumentation*			
Head of section		X	X
Instrumentist	X	X	
Telecommunications	X	X	
Electronics	X	X	X
Automatisation		X	X
Job preparation		X	X
5 *Civil works*			
Buildings and infrastructures		X	
Drawers	X		
6 *Energy-fluids*			
Thermician	X	X	
Cold technician	X	X	
7 *Various specialities*			
Technical documentation		X	X
Methods officer		X	
Planning man		X	
Engineering (mechanic, electric)		X	X
Industrial drawer	X		
Drawer-designer		X	
Drawer engineering studies		X	
Spare parts management	X	X	
Coding-filing (spare parts)	X	X	
Refractories	X	X	
Tribology		X	
Condition monitoring		X	X
Maintenance management			X
Computer aided maintenance		X	X

QW   : Qualified worker
F/S/T : Foreman/Supervisor/Technician
E   : Engineer

APPENDIX 45/1

MASTER CHART FOR TRADE-RELATED TRAINING

TRAINING FOR MAINTENANCE

MAINTENANCE TRADE-RELATED MASTER CHART

TRADE : INDUSTRIAL MAINTENANCE MECHANIC

NUMBER OF TRADES : 4

NUMBER OF LEVELS : 6

HEAD :
UP-DATING
1. 14/05/91
2. 16/05/91
3. ../../..
4. ../../..
5. ../../..
6. ../../..
7. ../../..
8. ../../..
9. ../../..
10. ../../..

LEGEND

- ▨ on training
- ▦ career progress
- ■ normal career limit
- ▨ valuation exceptional agents

Lev 1 : Level 1
Lev 2 : Level 2
Lev 3 : Level 3

O.D.M.P. : Organisation and Development of manpower

TRADES				ACCES			TRAINING				
NAME	DESCRIPTION	LEV	KEY-POINTS	CAP 1 2	T	TS	ON-THE-JOB	RETRAINING UPGRADING	MODULES	MANAGEMENT	HUMAN
AID	- knows the current tools - dismantles simple equipment - lubricates - stores the tools		- works under supervision				- tools - safety - modes of work execution		- oils and greases level 1	- job order	
MAINTENANCE MECHANIC	- can read and interprete drawings - can execute all lubrication operations - can make dimensioned sketches - can dismantle, reassemble and adjust mechanical equipment - can adjust the parts of a machine on a bench - can execute machine-tooling of simple parts (lathe, milling-machine, shaping-machine) - inspects equipment in operation - detects failures - executes and controls his own work - executes operation tests - tunes and adjusts cinematic chains - can do cold and hot vulcanizing - can make use of mechanical clamping	1	- reads, interpretes drawings - clamping and vulcanizing - makes sketches - executes simple dismantling and reassembling - adjusts parts on bench - simple machine-tooling				- modes of work execution	- handling - rope slings - mechanical clamping - vulcanising	- bearings		
		2	- executes dismantling and re-assembling of machines on site - tunes and adjusts cinematic chains - controls and tunes mechanical automation systems				- modes of work execution	- metrology	- failure diagnostic - tribology level 2		

DGS SYSTEM

DGS 30/90/062

APPENDIX 45/2

NAME	DESCRIPTION	LEV	KEY-POINTS	CAP 1 2	T	TS	JOB	RETRAINING UPGRADING	MODULES	MANAGEMENT	HUMAN
		3	- executes operational tests and tuning of equipment - inspects the equipment in operation - executes in the workshop dismantling, reassembling and adjusting of mechanical assemblies	2				- mechanical automation	- inspection techniques - monitoring techniques	- activity reports	
CREW-LEADER	- prepares, organises and distributes the work to his crew - launches spare parts reordering - is informed about new equipment - follows-up the training of his crew - assists during complex trouble-shooting - inspects the work of his crew - participates in the evaluation of his crew-members - makes activity reports and reports to his supervisors		- prepairs - organises - plans - controls - trains - supervises - inspects					- technical documentation	- maintenance methods - workstudy (job specification)	- organisation - preparation - activity reports	- O.D.M.P. - Management personnel - training curricula
FOREMAN	- organises, coordinates and controls the work of his crews - analyses and solves practical problems - makes workload planning and time schedules - makes sure that safety rules are respected - controls the training of crew-members		- organises - analyses - imposes respect of safety rules - controls					- technology		- stock - planning - quality circles - integrated safety - activity reports	- communication - training techniques - leadership - training curricula

CAP : certificate of professional aptitude
T : technician
TS : high level technician

Remark: This form has been developped at INMA (Institut National d'etudes et de recherche en Maintenance) in Algeria

APPENDIX 46

FRAMEWORK OF PLAN OF ACTION
FOR IMPROVEMENT OF MAINTENANCE

FIELD	ACTIONS WILL DEAL WITH FOLLOWING TOPICS
1 PRODUCTION EQUIPMENT	- state (cleanliness, order, housekeeping, ...) - operation - standardization - design and technology - acquisition of new equipment
2 ORGANIZATION AND MANAGEMENT	- Corporate Maintenance Management Master Plan - Maintenance concept - hierarchical position of maintenance - maintenance organization chart - organization chart of all services - function and job descriptions - maintenance management information system (MMIS) - maintenance planning - management tools - computerization
3 MATERIAL RESOURCES	- technical documentation - spare parts - maintenance workshop - tools, measuring instruments - maintenance cost and budget (incl. accountancy system)
4 HUMAN RESOURCES	- manning table - qualifications - recruitment - career development policy - motivation/incentive policy - training - subcontracting - technical assistance - safety
5 ENVIRONMENT	- lodging - transport - medical care

RESTRUCTURING OF A MAINTENANCE DEPARTMENT

PROPOSED ACTIONS ON THE LEVEL OF INDUSTRIAL PLANTS

Ghent, March 1994

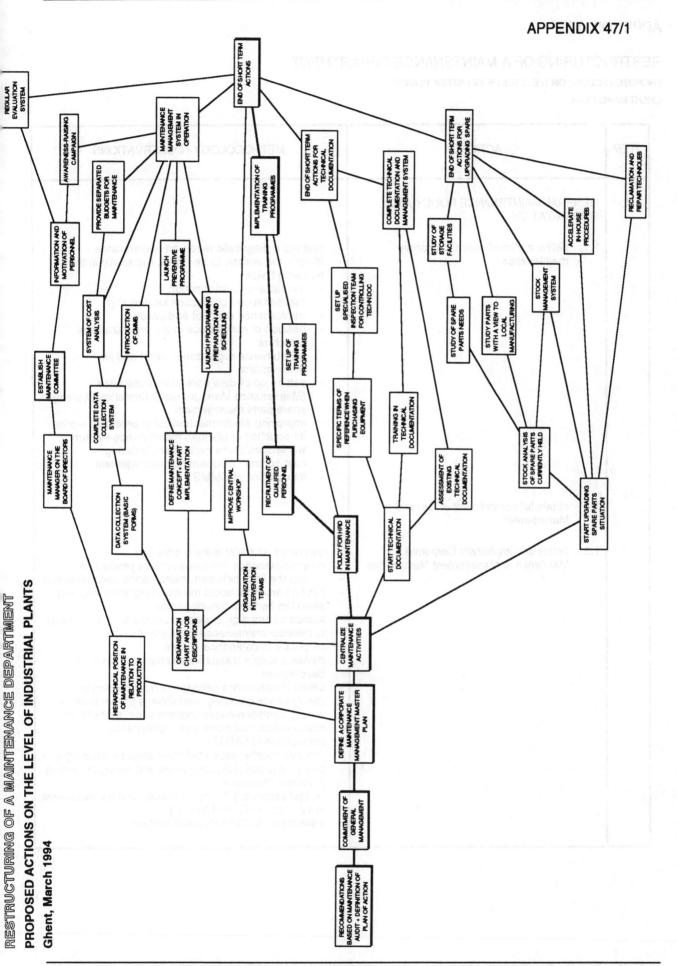

APPENDIX 47/2

RESTRUCTURING OF A MAINTENANCE DEPARTMENT
PROPOSED ACTIONS ON THE LEVEL OF INDUSTRIAL PLANTS

GHENT MARCH 1994

ITEM	ACTIONS	METHODOLOGY / OBSERVATIONS
1.	**GENERAL MAINTENANCE POLICY AND ORGANIZATION**	
	1.1. define a plan of action to improve maintenance	- prepare a diagnostic report on maintenance - identify the actions to be taken, especially in the following fields : - sensitization / information - maintenance / production relationship - maintenance concept and policy - position of maintenace in the organizational structure - maintenance organization chart and job descriptions - setting up of data collection procedures (Maintenance Management Information System) - spare parts management - improving electromechanical intervention works - introduction of planned maintenance system - workshops/spare parts manufacturing - cost control / maintenance management - introduction of CMMS
	1.2 obtain full commitment of General Management	
	1.3 define and implement Corporate Maintenance Management Master Plan	- centralize all maintenance activities - give maintenance the same rank as production - tighten the links between maintenance and production - inform personnel about the maintenance policy and show the benefits resulting from it - launch a campaign of awareness creation at all levels to develop maintenance-mindedness - develop corporate maintenance culture - devise a simple maintenance chart and clear job descriptions - define maintenance concept - introduce planned maintenance gradually, and strike a proper balance among condition-based maintenance, systematic maintenance and corrective maintenance - introduction of CMMS - improve maintenance staff motivation by devising a policy on productivity incentives and on implementing guidance measures - budget separately for maintenance and for investment in systems, skills and training - implement regular evaluation system

ITEM		ACTIONS	METHODOLOGY / OBSERVATIONS
	1.4	include maintenance managers on the executive board of directors	
	1.5	establish a maintenance committee within the company, with the job of observing the implementation of actions for maintenance improvement and evaluating their results	
2		TRAINING	
	2.1	devise a policy of human resources development for maintenance	
	2.2	recruit highly qualified staff for maintenance - provide for additional training if need be	
	2.3	establish training courses in maintenance, coordinated with production needs	- of practical type - of specific type * by apprenticeship * vocational training * at polytechnics or universities - on-the-job
3.		TECHNICAL DOCUMENTATION	
	3.1	draw up specific terms of reference on technical documentation	The following points must be incorporated in it : - itemized contents - language of user - presentation (illustrated with samples, perhaps even standard forms) - delivery conditions (time schedule, amount, packing, place etc.) - conditions of acceptance - penalties
	3.2	set up a team of specialists (methods officers) to do the acceptance of/inspect the technical documentation at the time of the equipment acquisition	
	3.3	start training programmes on technical documentation	subject matter : - drawing up terms of reference - checking documentation sent in connection with equipment supply - setting up machine-files - updating documentation - filing documentation - providing user service

APPENDIX 47/4

ITEM		ACTIONS	METHODOLOGY / OBSERVATIONS
	3.4	make an assessment of existing technical documentation at the factory - gather all documentation in one central place - make copies for the users	
	3.5	complete technical documentation	- make ABC analysis of most important works in relation to safety, production, quality and environment - launch requests to machine manufacturers or colleagues
4.		SPARE PARTS	

	4.1	make analysis of stocks currently held in the plant	- classify and valuate on spare parts in three categories:
			  - consumables
			  - standard parts
			  - specific parts
			  - identify dead stock

	4.2	make a study of spare parts needs / make sure that designations are accurante	- study of technical documentation and investigation among users according to priority machines - bring stock up to required levels
	4.3	set up a stock management department	- code all spare parts - define stock management parameters - set up a data collection system - institute a computerised stock management system based on a preceding feasibility study

	4.4	study the parts with a view to local manufacturing or repair	- classify parts as
			  - to be imported
			  - available on the market
			  - can be manufactured
			  - can be repaired

	4.5	design warehouses of ample size, with adequate facilities for the storage, handling and protection of the spare parts	
	4.6	speed up the enterprise's in-house procedures for parts reordering	
	4.7	develop parts reclamation / repair techniques	

ABACUS FOR THE CALCULATION OF THE ECONOMIC ORDERING QUANTITY

Economic Ordering Quantity

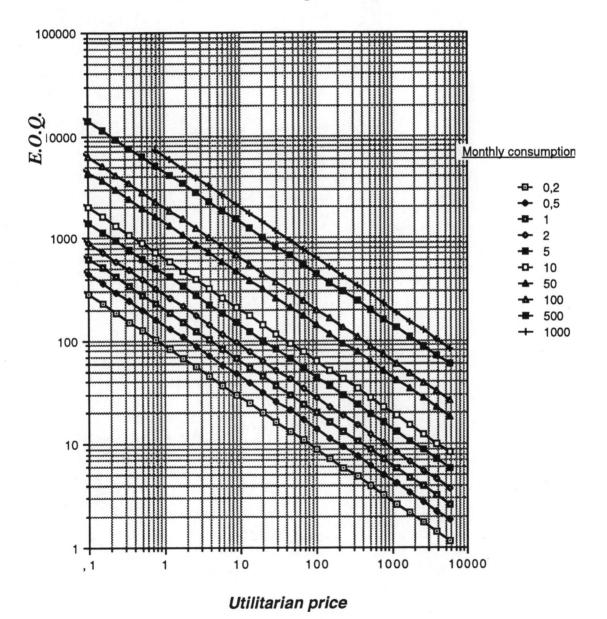

Utilitarian price

ABACUS FOR THE CALCULATION OF THE ECONOMIC ORDERING QUANTITY

Economic Ordering Quantity

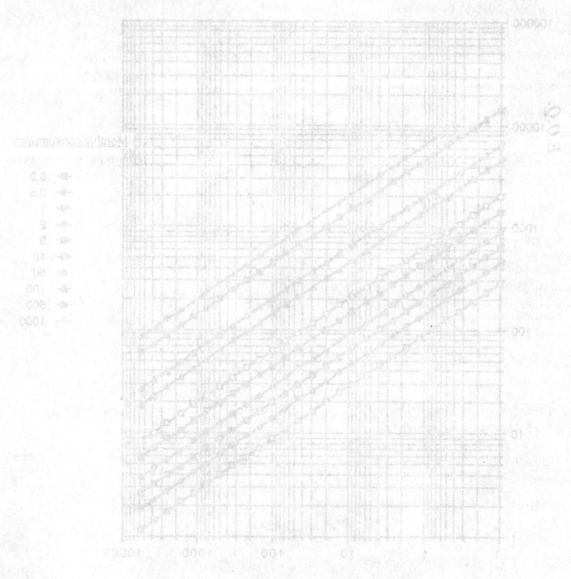

Utilisation price

UNIDO GENERAL STUDIES SERIES

The following publications are available in this series:

Title	Symbol	Price (US$)
Planning and Programming the Introduction of CAD/CAM Systems A reference guide for developing countries	ID/SER.O/1	25.00
Value Analysis in the Furniture Industry	ID/SER.O/2	7.00
Production Management for Small- and Medium-Scale Furniture Manufacturers A manual for developing countries	ID/SER.O/3	10.00
Documentation and Information Systems for Furniture and Joinery Plants A manual for developing countries	ID/SER.O/4	20.00
Low-cost Prefabricated Wooden Houses A manual for developing countries	ID/SER.O/5	6.00
Technical Criteria for the Selection of Woodworking Machines	ID/SER.O/11	25.00
Issues in the Commercialization of Biotechnology	ID/SER.O/13	45.00
Software Industry Current trends and implications for developing countries	ID/SER.O/14	25.00
Maintenance Management Manual With special reference to developing countries	ID/SER.O/15	35.00

Forthcoming titles include:

Title	Symbol	Price (US$)
Timber Construction for Developing Countries Introduction to wood and timber engineering	ID/SER.O/6	10.00
Timber Construction for Developing Countries Structural timber and related products	ID/SER.O/7	20.00
Timber Construction for Developing Countries Durability and fire resistance	ID/SER.O/8	11.00
Timber Construction for Developing Countries Strength characteristics and design	ID/SER.O/9	16.00
Timber Construction for Developing Countries Applications and examples	ID/SER.O/10	10.00
Design and Manufacture of Bamboo and Rattan Furniture	ID/SER.O/12	25.00

Please add US$ 2.50 per copy to cover postage and packing. Allow 4-6 weeks for delivery.

UNIDO GENERAL STUDIES SERIES

The following publications are available in this series:

Title	Symbol	Price (US$)
Planning and Programming the Introduction of CAD/CAM Systems: A reference guide for developing countries.	ID/SER.O/1	25.00
Value Analysis in the Furniture Industry	ID/SER.O/2	7.00
Production Management for Small- and Medium-Scale Furniture Manufacturers: A manual for developing countries	ID/SER.O/3	10.00
Documentation and Information Systems for Furniture and Joinery Plants: A manual for developing countries	ID/SER.O/4	20.00
Low-cost Prefabricated Wooden Houses: A manual for developing countries	ID/SER.O/5	6.00
Technical Criteria for the Selection of Woodworking Machines	ID/SER.O/11	25.00
Issues in the Commercialization of Biotechnology	ID/SER.O/13	45.00
Software Industry: Current trends and implications for developing countries	ID/SER.O/14	25.00
Maintenance Management Manual: With special reference to developing countries	ID/SER.O/15	35.00

Forthcoming titles include:

Title	Symbol	Price (US$)
Timber Construction for Developing Countries: Introduction to wood and timber engineering	ID/SER.O/6	18.00
Timber Construction for Developing Countries: Structural timber and related products	ID/SER.O/7	20.00
Timber Construction for Developing Countries: Durability and fire resistance	ID/SER.O/8	11.00
Timber Construction for Developing Countries: Strength characteristics and design	ID/SER.O/9	16.00
Timber Construction for Developing Countries: Applications and examples	ID/SER.O/10	14.00
Design and Manufacture of Bamboo and Rattan Furniture	ID/SER.O/12	25.00

Please add US$ 2.50 per copy to cover postage and packing. Allow 4-6 weeks for delivery.

ORDER FORM

Please complete this form and return it to:

UNIDO Documents Unit (F-355)
Vienna International Centre
P.O. Box 300, A-1400 Vienna, Austria

Send me _____ copy/copies of _____

_____ (ID/SER.O/_____) at US$ _____/copy plus postage.

PAYMENT

☐ I enclose a cheque, money order or UNESCO coupon (obtainable from UNESCO offices worldwide) made payable to "UNIDO".

☐ I have made payment through the following UNIDO bank account: CA-BV, No. 29-05115 (ref. RB-7310000), Schottengasse 6, A-1010 Vienna, Austria.

Name _____

Address _____

Telephone _____ Telex _____ Cable _____ Fax _____

Note: Publications in this series may also be obtained from:

Sales Section
United Nations
Room DC2-0853
New York, N.Y. 10017, U.S.A.
Tel.: (212) 963-8302

Sales Unit
United Nations
Palais des Nations
CH-1211 Geneva 10, Switzerland
Tel.: (22) 34-60-11, ext. Bookshop

✂--✂